DOES MANKIND HAVE A FUTURE?

In this brilliant and controversial book, a famous biologist explores the crucial social, political and ethical problems of man in terms of evolution and heredity.

Beginning with the debate on evolution that flared around Darwin's *The Origin of Species* one hundred years ago, Professor Hardin goes on to explore the thinking of Mendel and the contemporary biologists Haldane and Muller. He gives the biologist's view of sterility and artificial insemination, the effect of atomic radiation on future generations, the natural inequality of man, the Russian attitude on heredity, "One World" theories, inner- and outer-directed man, selective breeding and other vital questions.

This stimulating history of evolutionary thought lucidly explains the biological laws of man, his composition and future possibilities. It sets in modern perspective and in vivid, dramatic terms the greatest scientific debate of our time and its implications for our own and future generations.

"I do not recall any other semi-popular book which goes so deeply into the subject, which deals so fully with the complicated details, or expounds them more clearly."—Joseph Wood Krutch, *N. Y. Herald Tribune*.

OTHER BOOKS OF SPECIAL INTEREST

Nature and Man's Fate

by GARRETT HARDIN

A MENTOR BOOK
Published by
THE NEW AMERICAN LIBRARY,
New York and Toronto
The New English Library Limited, London

To G. W. Beadle

*Published as a MENTOR BOOK
By arrangement with Holt, Rinehart and Winston, Inc.*

SECOND PRINTING

Line illustrations are by Evan Gillespie.

Grateful acknowledgement is made to the following publishers
for permission to reprint material from their publications:

Doubleday & Co., Inc., New York, N. Y. and Rupert Hart-Davis, Ltd.,
London, England, for quotations from *The Next Million Years*,
copyright, 1952, by Charles Galton Darwin.

Harcourt, Brace & World, Inc., New York, N. Y. and Edward
Arnold, Ltd., London, England, for a quotation from *Two Cheers
for Democracy*, copyright, 1951, by E. M. Forster.

The Viking Press, Inc., New York, N. Y., for two selections from
The Love Letters of Phyllis McGinley, copyright, 1954, by Phyllis McGinley.

A condensation of Chapter 13 has appeared in *The Saturday Evening Post*.

MENTOR BOOKS are published *in the United States* by
The New American Library, Inc.,
1301 Avenue of the Americas, New York, New York 10019,
in Canada by The New American Library of Canada Limited,
295 King Street East, Toronto 2, Ontario,
in the United Kingdom by The New English Library Limited,
Barnard's Inn, Holborn, London, E.C. 1, England.

FIRST PRINTING, JUNE, 1961

PRINTED IN THE UNITED STATES OF AMERICA

Prologue

THE lecture was over. I had tried to explain heredity to a general audience in one hour's time, a task that requires about forty hours in a college course. I asked for questions —and got them.

"You say that X rays and atomic radiations cause mutations, and that almost all mutations are bad?"

"Yes."

"But isn't it true that all evolutionary progress has been made possible by new mutations?"

I could see it coming—but I answered simply, "Yes."

"Don't those two statements contradict each other?"

So: he had seen the binding point. Now what was I to do? I knew there was no real contradiction—but could I convince others with less than a twenty-hour lecture? That was plainly out of the question, so I tried to resolve the apparent paradox in a few words. But I don't think the questioner was satisfied. I hope he wasn't.

His question had uncovered a point that has only recently become clear: that the truth or falsity of the theory of evolution is now seen to be a matter of the most practical political importance. It doesn't much matter whether you think man was created out of the dust six thousand years ago or came from the apes a million years earlier; whether the story of Noah's ark is true, or dinosaurs once lived. Believe what you will of evolution in the past: but you had jolly well better believe it will take place in the future if you hope to make political decisions that will give your descendants a reasonable chance to exist. The principles of evolution are inescapably relevant to the analysis of man's predicament.

The theory of evolution had its official birth in 1858-59. Its essential truth is now universally accepted by scientists competent to judge. Yet even today, a century after its birth, the great majority of mankind either has not heard of the theory or thinks it false. Why is this so? Is it because the theory is intellectually difficult? Not at all. T. H. Huxley, when he first learned of his friend Darwin's theory, said, "How extremely stupid not to have thought of that!" The principles of the theory are really quite simple. Yet it was only after more than a half century of unconscious avoidance by society that they were first openly stated by Charles Darwin. Even then he did not state all of the principles explicitly. One of the principles—the Principle of Competitive Exclusion—though basic to his entire theory, was not given explicit formulation until our own time. Have we even now uncovered all of the elements of the theory? Experience makes us doubt that we have. Evolution has such intimate significance for our daily life that it creates immensely great psychological resistances to seeing even the most "obvious" truths.

When there is resistance to seeing truth, the man who is in some sense outside of the group that maintains the resistance has an advantage. It is the matter of the Emperor's New Clothes. So it is that we find a most diverse collection of thinkers have contributed to the development of the theory of evolution. There was an engineer whose specialty was transatlantic cables; a brilliantly successful speculator in stocks who wanted to know what kept the economic wheels turning; a very British explorer who thought nothing was more important than children—of which he had none; a cloistered monk whose interest in gambling and probability led him to discover that life begins with a lottery; and above all others, of course, there was Charles Darwin, the idle rich man's son, who forged the theory out of his own lonely experience—and thereby insured that the next twenty years of his life would be even more lonely as he struggled to gain courage to say what the world dreaded to hear.

But, *Ah,* you may say, *all that was a hundred years ago. We have nothing to be afraid of now. We can speak freely.* Really? Have we forgotten so soon that it was only a decade ago that many men lost their lives in Russia because of their evolutionary beliefs? *But that was in Russia!* someone says. Yes: but there were many in our part of the world who defended the attitude of the Soviets. Science, real living Science, is always under attack, and the attack does not always come from the same quarter. In Darwin's day the opposition to the theory of evolution came principally from the right; in our own time, it is stronger on the left. Science is a heresy so extreme that no merely political school of thought can embrace it in all its aspects.

The primary aim of this book is to bring the reader abreast of the latest thought in evolutionary theory, to show him its implications for the future. But our present concepts have grown by an organic process out of old ideas which have left their traces even as the gill arches of ancestral fishes are still to be found in parts of our hearing apparatus. To understand the present we must know the past. With John Maynard Keynes I believe that "a study of the history of opinion is a necessary preliminary to the emancipation of the mind." In sketching the history of evolutionary opinions I have made no attempt at all-inclusiveness but have, at the risk of error, selected those elements of the story that (I think) still live in the conflicts of our own time. I have also consciously avoided making the story seem too simple. History is not a chain but a tapestry. Even at the risk of confusion, I have tried to preserve something of the richness of the intertwined threads that make up the pattern of evolutionary thought. The tapestry is not yet finished, yet I think we can already see the pattern clearly enough to realize that curious and investigative man, while seemingly concerned with the historical origin of ferns and bees, has really been trying to ascertain the meaning of Nature in the determination of his own fate.

Contents

Who Will Bell the Cat?

IN the evening of the first day of July, 1858, at a meeting of the Linnaean Society in London, a scientific paper was presented bearing the imposing title, *On the Tendency of Species to Form Varieties; and on the Perpetuation of Varieties and Species by Natural Means of Selection.* The authors were Charles Darwin, Esq., Fellow of the Royal Society, Fellow of the Linnaean Society and Fellow of the Geological Society; and Alfred Wallace—just Esq. Neither author was present in person. Wallace was on the other side of the world, and Darwin, though only forty miles away, was enjoying his usual delicate health as he awaited the reaction of the Fellows. The paper was read by his close friends, Sir Joseph Hooker, botanist, and Sir Charles Lyell, geologist.

There was no explosion. In fact, probably most of the attending Fellows were utterly unconscious of the historic importance of the moment. At the end of the year the President of the Society blandly expressed his disappointment that 1858 had "not been marked by any of those striking discoveries which at once revolutionize, so to speak, the department of science on which they bear." Hooker, by contrast, reported that the interest at the July meeting was "intense"—but friend Hooker was a prejudiced witness. Certain it is that there was no obvious public notice of the birth of the modern theory of evolution until more than a year later, when the evidence for it was fully presented in Darwin's *Origin of Species.* With this publication, on the twenty-fourth of November, 1859, the floodgates of abuse and praise were loosed. No scientific book since Newton's *Principia* has had so widespread an effect on public thought, and it is doubtful if even Newton's great work has as direct a bearing on man's fate. Darwin used over four hundred pages to explain and document his theory, but the basic idea of evolution can be given in a few words: *All living organisms are truly related to one another by common inheritance.*

There are three important historical questions connected with the birth of the theory of evolution:

First. The basic framework of the theory was already

present in Darwin's mind in 1838. Why did he wait twenty years before publishing the first notice of it?

Second. Many men before Darwin conceived the idea of evolution. Some published it. Then, too, there was Wallace. Why, then, do we give Darwin so much credit?

Third. Since the idea was old—at the very least, a half-century old—why was the reaction to the *Origin* so violent?

To answer these questions we must go back more than half a century, and attempt to re-create the climate of opinion that developed in England as an aftermath of the French Revolution.

Miscarriage Before the "Origin"

To say that the idea of evolution was "in the air" before the *Origin* is to make a gross understatement. The idea had, in fact, already been nailed down on paper, and that repeatedly. Only a few years before the epochal meeting at the Linnaean Society, that much-esteemed Victorian philosopher, Herbert Spencer, had firmly come out for a theory of evolution, first in 1852, and again in 1855. Before Spencer, evolution was championed in a book entitled *The Vestiges of Creation,* which was published anonymously. This book was unquestionably widely read, for it was in its tenth edition at the time the *Origin of Species* saw the light of publication. And before the *Vestiges,* there was the Frenchman, Lamarck, who proposed a theory of evolution in the very year Darwin was born, 1809. (A year made remarkable, incidentally, by the birth of Abraham Lincoln also—on the same day as Darwin. Tennyson, Gladstone and Mendelssohn likewise shared this natal year.) And before Lamarck there was another Frenchman, Maupertuis. And before Maupertuis—well, one can (as always!) find traces of the idea as far back as the Greeks (Anaximander and Empedocles, to be explicit) if one is willing to dig hard enough and interpret with sufficient liberality. But the quasi-scientific speculations of these old Greeks were not foremost in the minds of Victorian Englishmen, whereas the pronouncements of Spencer and the author of the *Vestiges* were. "Everyone" had heard of the idea of evolution. But few there were to honor it.

A generation after the *Origin,* that great champion of Darwinism, Thomas Henry Huxley, in recalling the attitude of scientists toward evolution during the years immediately preceding the fateful publication, insisted that learned men were mostly just bored with the idea. Confronted with the arguments of evolutionists and antievolutionists, scientists were inclined to say, " 'a plague to both your houses!' and disposed to turn aside from an interminable and apparently fruitless discussion, to labor in the fertile fields of ascertainable fact." Mere anticipation of a bored audience would hardly account, however, for Darwin's long hesitancy in publishing; there must have been some more powerful reaction that he feared. There was. Oddly enough, we catch our first glimpse of the cause of his fears in the life of his grandfather, Erasmus.

Erasmus Darwin (1731-1802) published three works in which the idea of evolution figures prominently: *The Botanic Garden* (1789-1791), *Zoonomia* (1794-1796), and *The Temple of Nature* (1803). To modern eyes they are curious works, following as they do the tradition of Lucretius in presenting scientific theories in verse (few would now call it poetry). It is interesting to follow the change in sentiment toward Erasmus' works, as shown in an excellent study by Professor Garfinkle of Amherst College, on which the present account leans heavily. At first, critical opinion was almost wholly laudatory. One journal said that the defects of Darwin's work "are so few that it is enough to hint at them generally, while the [merits] occur in every page and might give occasion for undistinguishing panegyric." Another critic enthusiastically suggested tht Erasmus Darwin's works would do for biology what Newton's had done for physics. The poet, Samuel Taylor Coleridge, spoke favorably of Darwin, and the great optimist, William Godwin, making a tour (in 1797) of the "lions" of the day, included Dr. Darwin, "so extraordinary a man"—in his itinerary. Dr. Darwin's works were avidly bought and read by the intellectuals of England and America and were translated into German, French, Spanish and Italian.

But the honeymoon of Dr. Darwin and the English critics did not last long. As early as 1793 one journal (then in the minority) strongly criticized evolutionary theory, pointing out that only from the Bible could man gain a knowledge of the origin of things. Two years later the same journal asked haughtily what sort of reception "does a work deserve in which the author discards all the lights and all the authority of revelation, only to substitute the sports of his own imagination?" From this time on the anti-Darwinian chorus swelled in volume. One review spoke of Erasmus' work as teeming with "monstrous absurdities" and expressed abhorrence for the author's "total denial of any interference of a Deity in the creation and preservation of everything that exists." The critic of another magazine protested that the publication of such works was an "insult on good taste and good sense." Yet another protested that the "tendency of Doctor Darwin's poetry to degrade the human species and to exalt animals of an inferior nature . . . [is] in no way adapted to improve either the judgment or the morals of his readers." Probably the most effective critical blast of all was a parody in verse called *The Loves of the Triangles*, after *The Loves of the Plants*, the title of part of Darwin's *Botanic Garden*. One of the three authors of this lampoon was George Canning, Undersecretary of State for Foreign Affairs. The connection of such literary criticism with responsible political position in a conservative government is not without significance.

Why the about-face? Erasmus Darwin's works had not changed in character. But the world had. Dr. Darwin's books were the product of the eighteenth century, the "Age of Enlightenment," a century in which learned gentlemen mentioned God very respectfully—but often without perceptible conviction. When the mind's wanderings led into byways uncharted in the Mosaic map of creation, it was only gentlemanly to mention what one had come across without calling attention to the lack of agreement with the sacred map. The Enlightened Gentleman said nice things about both tradition and innovation without admitting their contradictions. That was (and is) tact.

But every age nurses the next age's character in its bosom. The pleasantly tolerant spirit of the Enlightenment was accompanied by the growth of a more rigorous insistence on the fundamentals of Protestantism by the Evangelicals and the Methodists, headed by John Wesley. Protestants, by their own choice deprived of an institutional source of certainty in Church and Papacy, made the Bible their source of infallible truth. It was the growing Evangelical movement that clipped Erasmus Darwin's wings.

During the 1790's, political conservatives increased their power by a ruse not unknown to us today: they asserted the blood kinship of liberal thought with godlessness. Whether the connection is necessary, or even true, we need not here inquire. We need only note that it was easy to argue convincingly at the close of the eighteenth century. A large proportion of the intellectual godfathers of the French Revolution had unquestionably been skeptical men (remember Voltaire!), and the French Revolution, like all revolutions, early began to devour its own children. Cannabilism is a grisly sight. One can hardly blame bystanders for seeking to eliminate the crime by stamping out the seditious thoughts held to be responsible. As Élie Halévy was later to remark, "The French Revolution had opened the eyes of the gentry and the wealthy traders to the risks to which their light attitude toward religion was exposing the social order of which they were the principal beneficiaries." Evidently religious beliefs were *useful*, these men thought. Perhaps not useful for themselves, but for other people. Particularly for "the lower orders," who needed controlling.

The change in critical attitude toward Erasmus Darwin's works was, then, only a part of a larger reactionary movement in England following the bloody end of the French Revolution. We are not surprised to note that the editors of one of the journals most critical of Darwin announced their intention of censoring all opinions "devoted to the cause of sedition and irreligion, to the pay and principles of France." Elsewhere they asserted that Dr. Darwin's ideas threatened the very foundations of civil order. Another journal asserted that he proposed "to substitute the religion of nature for the religion of the Bible."

Reading over old reviews of Erasmus Darwin's works in the light of subsequent events, one cannot help but feel that the weapon that ultimately gave this Darwin's works the *coup de grâce* was not so much the sharp knife of outspoken criticism as it was the duller, but perhaps more effective, bludgeon of the conspiracy of silence. Now the hypothesis of a conspiracy of silence is, by its very nature, next to impossible to prove. However, we know that at least one journal did explicitly urge the public not to read Darwin's works. And another one pointed out that they were dangerous for "young readers"—and where reading is concerned, who is to say when dangerously suggestible youth finally gives way to safe maturity?

In any case, after Erasmus died in 1802, there was decreasingly less reason to refer to him or his works at all. *Out of sight, out of mind*—this is especially applicable to the unwanted or the suspect. With the drawing together of the forces of reaction—political, economic and theological—in the first two decades of the nineteenth century, Erasmus Darwin and the freedom of speculation that he stood for were largely forgotten. Over the intellectual life of England, night fell; or if not night, at least a long twilight. The truth had been *settled*. In 1810, just one year after the birth of Charles Darwin, the Reverend Edward Copleston, vicar of St. Mary's, Oxford, stated firmly: "The scheme of Revelation, we think, is closed, and we expect no new light on earth to break in upon us. Oxford must guard that sacred citadel." It will be a matter of no little interest to see how. Oxford, led by its Bishop Wilberforce, guarded the citadel exactly fifty years later.

". . . and I'll Take the Low Road": Geology

After the appearance of Charles Darwin's great work, it was natural that a few men of long memory should recall his grandfather's verses and suggest them as the origin of Darwin's theory. It seems unlikely, however, that Grandfather's work was a *direct* stimulus. We suspect that Charles's strait-laced and domineering father did not encourage conversation about Grandfather, whose irregularity had extended beyond theological views and into his personal life. For, after the death of his first wife, Erasmus had kept a mistress by whom he had two daughters. This might all have been very well for the eighteenth century, but in the Victorian atmosphere of the Darwin house in Shrewsbury one can well imagine that discussion of the life and works of such a grandfather might have been discouraged. It is probable that the attitude in this household, as in most educated households of the time, was like that expressed by Coleridge in 1815 in a letter to his fellow poet, William Wordsworth, when he said flatly that the idea that man could have descended from an orangutan was "contrary to all history, to all religion, nay, to all pos-sibility."

In such an atmosphere, further progress of the idea of evolution along the high road of biology was difficult. Prog-ress came in another way—through the study of the earth beneath man's—and orangutan's—feet; through the study of the rocks and their evolution in past ages. That man came from an ape was *unthinkable,* but that the mountains had once been under the sea—well, that was a pretty tall story, too, but at least one could entertain the idea as a *hypothesis.* After all, those objects embedded in the rocks near the top of the mountain do certainly look like sea shells. Perhaps . . . well, we're willing to *speculate* a bit. . . .

Men had speculated about the rocks of the earth for at least two thousand years, particularly about fossils. How did it happen that one could see objects that looked like fishes or sea shells embedded in rocks at the tops of mountains many miles from the nearest salt water? What we regard as the "obvious" answer was given at least as long ago as the sixth century B.C. by Xenophanes of Colophon. And Leonardo da Vinci (of course) understood. But there was poor continuity to this knowledge, interrupted as it was by many kinds of mystical or irrational speculations. As usual, there were al-ternative verbal "explanations": Avicenna in the eleventh century spoke of a "stone-making force"; and Albert the Great, of a "formative quality" (just as Molière much later explained—but sardonically—the sleep-producing effect of opium in terms of a "dormative quality"). In despair, many dismissed fossils as "jokes of nature." The scientifically minded, using what passed as science at that time, said that emanations from the stars concentrated on certain rocks, producing fossils. But if you say this, retorted Leonardo, "in what way will you show that this influence produces in the very same place shells of various sizes and varying in age, and of different kinds?"

Not until the latter part of the eighteenth century was a genuinely modern systematization of the evidence of the rocks put forward, when James Hutton published his *Theory of the Earth*, first as a brief paper in 1785 and subsequently as a book (1795). Hutton's thesis, simply stated, was that the "eternal hills" are anything but eternal, that they are being continually eroded into fragments which are swept out to sea, where they are deposited in beds that are, in time, consolidated into new rocky layers; these, by gross movements of the earth's crust, are thrust up into new mountains which undergo the process of dissolution all over again. Such a story is not readily reconcilable with the book of Genesis, for it makes the creation of our world a continuing process, and it implies—by any rationally acceptable standards whatever—that the world has existed far longer than the few thousand years calculated on the authority of the Bible. The basis for this calculation is itself a curious chapter in man's intellectual history. In older printings of the King James Bible there is a thin center strip of small type, consisting largely of cross references. The center strip of the first page of Genesis begins with the words "B.C. 4004" placed alongside the story of creation. This is the documentary evidence that led many of Hutton's contemporaries to believe that the sacred writings say explicitly that the world was created in 4004 B.C. Considering that the book of Genesis was written several centuries B.C., this is remarkable evidence, indeed—rather like finding a coin in the ruins of Pompeii with the inscription "35 B.C." on it. The fact is, of course, that the statement "B.C. 4004" is no *proper* part of Genesis. This particular figure, first printed in a Bible in 1701, is the guess of one James Ussher, Archbishop of Armagh in Ireland. This imaginative Irishman arrived at the date, we must suppose, by meticulous collation of the "begats," though how he deduced so exact a figure from such inexact data is rather a mystery. An even more inspired contemporary of Ussher's, Dr. Lightfoot of Cambridge, figured out that the world was created precisely on the twenty-third of October of that immemorial year *at precisely 9* A.M. The irreverent cannot but wonder—was this standard time or daylight saving time?

The geologists' new view of the world as an object hundreds of thousands of years old (at least) met, of course, with spirited opposition. "Well-established beliefs," said Bernard de Fontenelle, the first great popularizer of science, "can be successfully attacked only by degrees,"—but Hutton was not one to settle for anything less than a complete revolution. No one ever accused him of tact; but then, should we expect this quality in a revolutionist? His deficiency probably helped delay the acceptance of his ideas. Even more important was the unfavorable climate of opinion of the times. Hutton ran headlong into the same stone wall that had stopped Erasmus Darwin. Anything foreign was suspect. Witch hunts were encouraged by the stringent Sedition Acts and Combination Laws, coupled with the suspension of Habeas Corpus. When external censors flourish, the internal censor waxes in strength. What controversy is so purely intellectual as to be without political or theological implications? Certainly rocks are not "safe." Only after Napoleon was out of the way and the tension in England was beginning to relax in a period of new prosperity did a few courageous men cut away the shackles of external censorship, thereby weakening the internal censor. With this revival of the spirit of free inquiry there came a new champion for geology, another Scot, Charles Lyell, born in the very year (1797) of Hutton's death. The revolution which Hutton began Lyell finished. His *Principles of Geology,* in three volumes, was first published in the years 1830–33. Lyell's work met with instant success and soon swept away all important opposition to the geological view of the world.

"The Man Who Walks with Henslow"

At the time of the publication of the first volume of Lyell's work, Charles Darwin was a young man of twenty-one, enrolled in Cambridge. One would hesitate to call him a *student* in that university. "My time was sadly wasted there," he wrote many years later in his *Autobiography*, "and worse than wasted. From my passion for shooting and for hunting, and, when this failed, for riding across country, I got into a sporting set, including some dissipated low-minded young men. We used often to dine together in the evening, though these dinners often included men of a higher stamp, and we sometimes drank too much, with jolly singing and playing at cards afterwards." And then he tries to speak as a good Victorian should: "I know that I ought to feel ashamed of days and evenings thus spent, but"—and here the honest Darwin, the great and accurate observer, speaks out—"but as some of my friends were very pleasant, and we were all in the highest spirits, I cannot help looking back to these times with much pleasure." By all accounts, his life cannot have been much different from that of the great majority of the idle young English gentlemen in the universities. His great passion was for hunting, which he indulged in most at the beautiful country estate of his favorite cousins, the Wedgwoods of pottery fame. "My zeal was so great that I used to place my shooting-boots open by my bed-side when I went to bed, so as not to lose half a minute in putting them on in the morning; and on one occasion I reached a distant part of the Maer estate, on the 20th of August for black-game shooting, before I could see: I then toiled on with the gamekeeper the whole day through thick heath and young Scotch firs."

It must have been a pleasant life, this being a young gentle-man in nineteenth-century England. Yet, even in this life, there were psychic tensions. Charles knew that he was in line for a large-enough fortune so that he need never worry about his livelihood, but he was nonetheless under real pressure to make something of himself. His father, Dr. Robert Darwin, a very successful doctor, in a fit of annoyance once exclaimed, "You care for nothing but shooting, dogs, and rat-catching, and you will be a disgrace to yourself and all your family."

What was one to do with such a son? His father first sent him to Edinburgh University to train for medicine, but Charles, finding most of the lecturers intolerably dull, skipped class extravagantly. More important, he tells us that he "saw two very bad operations, one on a child, but I rushed away before they were completed. Nor did I ever attend again, for hardly any inducement would have been strong enough to make me do so; this being long before the blessed days of chloroform. The two cases fairly haunted me for many a long year." Plainly, medicine was not for him. With respect to this, he made no direct approach to his father, but the truth trickled home, and presently Charles was removed from Edinburgh.

What now? What else *could* a *gentleman* do? Well, there was always the ministry. So off Charles went to Cambridge, obediently determined to become a clergyman. But not at the expense of youthful fun, of course—as we have seen. The riding and the shooting continued, yes, and there was even drinking and card-playing. And to these sports young Charles now added another: beetle-collecting. . . . Thus begins a bril-liant scientific career? Not exactly. He cared nothing about the beetles, really. His passion was, as he admitted, merely for collecting for collecting's sake. "I will give a proof of my zeal," he says. "One day, on tearing off some old bark, I saw two rare beetles, and seized one in each hand; then I saw a third and new kind, which I could not bear to lose, so that I popped the one which I held in my right hand into my mouth. Alas! it ejected some intensely acrid fluid, which burnt my tongue so that I was forced to spit the beetle out, which was lost, as was the third one."

Yet, in the end, there was more than sport in Darwin's collecting activities. Although he himself did nothing serious with his beetles, one of his rarer specimens, properly tagged, found its way into the hands of an expert who published an account of it, with "the magic words, 'captured by C. Darwin, Esq.'" Said the inspired captor: "No poet ever felt more delighted at seeing his first poem published. . . ."

Another crucial influence in his life was John Stevens Henslow, a gentle professor of botany, and Charles's senior by thirteen years. Darwin writes: "Before coming up to Cambridge, I had heard of him from my brother as a man who knew every branch of science, and I was accordingly prepared to reverence him. He kept open house once every week when all undergraduates, and some older members of the University, who were attached to science, used to meet in the evening. I soon got . . . an invitation, and went there regularly. Before long I became well acquainted with Henslow, and during the latter half of my time at Cambridge took long walks with him on most days; so that I was called by some of the dons 'the man who walks with Henslow. . . .'"

Thus it was that Charles's vocation was determined for him by the two most potent motivations known: vanity and love. The importance of vanity is axiomatic, but in our "tough-minded" world we too often deny the power of love. We must never forget what Goethe said: *We learn only from those whom we love.* Science, with its emphasis on the impersonal beauty of its method and discoveries, may fool both participants and spectators into thinking that personal love is of no importance in proselytizing new practitioners of the art. Nothing could be more mistaken. It is questionable whether there is a single instance of anyone's being drawn into science except through the love of someone already in the field. For Darwin, it was love of the young botany professor that was decisive.

The Odyssey of the "Beagle"

Henslow played a deciding role in Darwin's life in one other way: through the botanist's influence, Charles was offered a berth in H.M.S. *Beagle*, a man-of-war that was about to set out on a map-making voyage. This journey determined his career, setting him to speculating along the lines that ultimately led to the *Origin of Species*. When Charles learned that there was an opening on board for a naturalist (without pay), he was eager to accept, but his father dismissed the idea as preposterous, finally adding, "If you can find any man of common sense who advises you to go I will give my consent." That was enough for the obedient son, who immediately wrote to refuse the offer. The following day he rode to the Wedgwood estate for the fall shooting. In his usual open way, without, we may be sure, any subtle strategy, he told his relatives the opportunity he had just passed by. His uncle Josiah, after taking time to mull over the matter, said he thought that Charles should go, and stated that he would be glad to ride the thirty miles to Shrewsbury to give his brother-in-law his opinion. The offer was gleefully accepted, the journey made, and Dr. Darwin, who had a high opinion of Wedgwood's judgment, "at once consented in the kindest manner."

So it was that Charles Darwin set forth on what was certainly one of the most important voyages ever taken, not only for him, but for the entire world. Yet how can one do justice to such an epochal journey? It would hardly make a satisfactory movie. No pirates were met and repulsed. There was no mutiny—Captain Fitz-Roy was too efficient an autocrat for that. There were no beautiful ladies—except for the lovely ladies of Lima who, in their tight-fitting gowns, reminded Darwin of "nice round mermaids," averring that "they are better worth looking at than all the churches and buildings in Lima." But there is no indication that he did anything more than look at them. (How times have changed—no Victorian book would even acknowledge such a doubt.) Nor was there a fiancée left sighing at home.

The real adventure of the *Beagle* took place inside the developing young naturalist. It was a time of tempering for him. He who had hitherto known nothing but the life of a gentleman now had to endure desperately cramped quarters while suffering from seasickness and frequent, unavoidable conflicts with a moody captain, who was a bit of a martinet. It was during this voyage that Darwin discovered the fearful truth that he was to wrestle with for most of his adult life—that plants and animals probably had an origin quite different from that believed in by the polite world of England—*his* world. Even before the voyage, he was given a foretaste of seditious thought when Henslow, the beloved mentor whom he "reverenced," urged him to get a copy of the first volume of Lyell's *Principles of Geology* (just published), to read and study it, *but on no account to accept the views therein advocated.* That Henslow should so hedge his advice was entirely natural. He was not only a competent scientist; he was also in holy orders. The combination, which was common at the time, frequently subjected a man's soul to schismatic strain. It was this strain that the Reverend Mr. Henslow passed on to his young friend, who was thus initiated into the adult estate of the intellectual in nineteenth-century England. Charles soon realized that he was faced with a difficult choice. Should he accept the "uniformitarian" principle of geology and explain the past always in terms of present geologic processes, regardless of the consequences to his beliefs? Or should he, at some point dictated by theology, make a barricade against rationalism saying, *thus far, and no further?*

Burdened with this psychic load, Darwin boarded the *Beagle,* taking as one of the few books space permitted, Lyell's *Principles* to read and ponder over. He had plenty of time for it. It took two months to reach South America, and nearly five years to get around the world. There was plenty of time, though idle days were now a thing of the past. Collecting on the high seas, preserving and dissecting specimens, writing descriptions and scientific letters home to be published in scholarly quarterlies, keeping a systematic journal of events, taking long trips inland from the ports where they laid over for considerable periods—never before had Darwin worked so hard, or so much enjoyed his life and the prospect of the future. What a change from his college days!

Perhaps the best proof of Darwin's mettle was that he stuck to a heavy research program in the face of a handicap that would have prostrated lesser men and sent them packing home —seasickness. His first letter mentions it; and in one of his last letters, almost five years later, he complains that he was suffering more than ever. Some scholars think that this ordeal by sea is at the bottom of his persistent poor health on land. Perhaps. We will return to this problem later.

Read Lyell . . . but on no account accept his views. In the face of the manifold evidences of titanic but slow geological processes visible throughout South America, Darwin soon found he could not accept the second part of Henslow's advice. He became a thoroughly modern geologist: and he gave up the thought of becoming a clergyman in the conservative Church of England.

At first he accepted change in geology but not in the biological realm. As late as 1834 he wrote uncritically of the "creation" of animals, in the Biblical sense. Later he admitted that when one finds an animal which played a very insignificant part "in the great scheme of nature, one is apt to wonder why a distinct species should have been created." His doubts were heightened when, in the fall of 1835, he visited the Galápagos Islands off the west coast of South America. Here he was impressed with the fact that the finches of one island were always slightly different from those of a neighboring island. "The Zoology of Archipelagoes will be well worth examining," he said, "for such facts would undermine [the belief in] the stability of species." This was only a note for his private use; a public statement had to wait for many years. He had first to work through, in his own mind, the reasons for the small but constant differences among the inhabitants of an archipelago.

Why should the birds on adjacent islands be so much alike, and yet different? Why should they be so much like birds on the nearby continent, and yet different? These phenomena are not peculiar to the birds of the Galápagos, but are generally observed of both plants and animals on all well-isolated oceanic islands. If one assumes that every species has been especially created, very puzzling questions are raised. On this hypothesis of "Special Creation," as it is called, one would ask: Why these particular species? Evidently (the answer would be) because the Intelligence that created them adapted them to this particular environment. . . . And what about the close resemblance to continental species, five hundred miles away? Evidently the environments closely resemble each other and require very similar creations. But it is at this point that the Special Creation rationalization runs into difficulties—for if we study the environments closely, we see that there is, as Darwin pointed out in the *Origin,* less resemblance between the Galápagos Islands and the mainland of South America than there is between the Cape Verde Archipelagoes, and the Galápagos—but the Cape Verde fauna are closely similar to that of neighboring Africa. Why are not the animals on the two sets of islands similar? Of course, they are five thousand miles apart, but surely that distance is a small matter to an omnipotent creative force! (This force we must assume, of course, operates according to principles of human rationality.) It seems odd, on such assumptions, to have fauna and flora of oceanic islands resemble those of the nearest and most accessible mainlands rather than those of other islands of similar environment, however far away.

On the hypothesis of evolutionary change, the explanation fits far better into a pattern. When any island is formed at some distance from a neighboring body of land, it must remain bare of terrestrial life until immigrants reach it. The chance of successful immigration is always slight, of course; but there's lots of time. Sooner or later organisms will reach any island, however remote. But some kinds of organisms have a better chance than others: organisms small enough to be borne by the wind (many insects, for example); or with wings of their own (birds); or other wind-capturers (spiders and their threads, seeds with winglike extensions); or hitch-hikers (eggs and larvae, which may be borne in the mud on birds' feet)—these have a better chance than large, heavy, non-fliers. So we are not surprised to find that mammals are rare on islands—except bats, which can fly, and sometimes mice and rats which, it is reasonable to suppose, may have got to an island as stowaways in a boat during some early, unrecorded visit by man.

If we assume that evolution has accompanied geographic dispersal, the distribution of island species makes sense. The pattern is rational; but it is not without its mysteries. Why, for example, should the finches on the various Galápagos Islands differ? Why are they not all the same? The islands, though in sight of each other, are separated by deep seas generally wider than the British Channel; small birds like finches move from one island to another only very occasionally. It looks as though mere isolation causes racial characteristics to change. But why? The answer is best deferred. For the moment, it is enough to point out that we will not say, "Isolation causes evolution" (as we might say, "Gravity causes a rock to fall"), but rather that *Isolation is accompanied by evolution,* regarding this as a broad generalization of our observations, rather than as an explanation.

This was the generalization that struck Darwin at the Galápagos Islands. From this point on, his life's work was cut out for him: to gather evidence for a theory of evolution. Henceforth his letters express an increasing impatience to get home. The voyage had served its hidden purpose. He had found that the golden apples he sought were in the Hesperides of home. "I see very clearly," he writes to his sister Caroline, "it will be necessary to live in London for a year. . . . Will you ask Erasmus [their older brother] to put down my name for the Whyndam or any other club. . . . Tell Erasmus to turn over in his mind for some lodgings with good big rooms in some vulgar part of London." Gone are thoughts of riding and shooting and dogs; those temptations are five years and a world behind him—and there is a dream ahead. Now we find, in the last letter written home, that most moving statement, a statement that is part prophecy, part promise and part prayer: "I trust . . . that I shall act—as I now think—that a man who dares to waste one hour of time, has not discovered the value of life."

Belling the Cat

IT'S a rare conversion that doesn't have its backsliding. Darwin returned to England in October of 1836 determined not to waste an hour of his time, but he reckoned without his family; or rather without his two families, for his Wedgwood cousins were almost like brothers and sisters. The returned voyager was coerced into many a party at Maer and Shrewsbury—not that much coercion was needed—and it was six months before he could tear himself away to set up bachelor quarters in Great Marlborough Street in London. He was anxious to get at the riddle of species change. In July, 1837, he began writing in the first of many notebooks on the subject.

> I worked on true Baconian principles, and without any theory collected facts on a wholesale scale, more especially with respect to domesticated productions, by printed enquiries, by conversation with skillful breeders and gardeners, and by extensive reading. When I see the list of books of all kinds which I read and abstracted, including whole series of Journals and Transactions, I am surprised at my industry. I soon perceived that selection was the keystone of man's success in making useful races of animals and plants. But how selection could be applied to organisms living in a state of nature remained for some time a mystery to me.

In this statement we see an instance of Darwin's firm grasp of what James B. Conant (chemist, university president and international statesman) has called "the strategy of science," an art which is almost impossible to describe, but for which the masters have an intuitive feeling. It is not obvious that the way in which various varieties of domesticated plants and animals have been developed by man has anything to tell us about the hypothetical evolution of species in nature. In fact, a keen critic might argue (as some have) that to pass from one instance to the other is to argue by analogy—a notoriously treacherous procedure. But analogy, unsatisfactory though it may be as proof, is a useful guide to discovery. The *formal* similarity of different problems hints at the sort of unknown factors we should look for. With a simple diagram we can show the parallelism that struck Darwin. In Fig. 1, the first line represents man's way of modifying a domesticated species to suit his needs or frivolous desires. Suppose, for example, that he has a pack of dogs that range in length from 16 inches to 36 inches, with a mean (average) of 24; and suppose that, for some reason or other, he decides that 30 inches is the "right" length for a dog: how does he get dogs to be the way he wants them? The answer is known to all: by *selection*. He allows only those dogs to breed that are nearly 30 inches long; the others he kills, sterilizes, or gives away—it does not matter (for this purpose) how he removes them from his breeding population. The next generation of his animals will be found to be statistically different from the first. They are not all the desired 30 inches—no such luck—but the variation among them is less, and the mean has been *biased* away from the original 24 and toward the desired 30. He has only to continue the same process for a sufficient number of generations to achieve the "pure" breed that he desires.

May not a similar process operate in nature? This was Darwin's hunch. It leads to a parallel analytical description shown

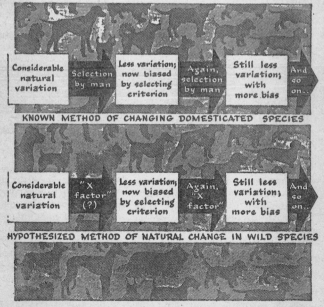

| Considerable natural variation | Selection by man | Less variation; now biased by selecting criterion | Again, selection by man | Still less variation; with more bias | And so on.. |

KNOWN METHOD OF CHANGING DOMESTICATED SPECIES

| Considerable natural variation | "X factor" (?) | Less variation; now biased by selecting criterion | Again, "X factor" | Still less variation; with more bias | And so on.. |

HYPOTHESIZED METHOD OF NATURAL CHANGE IN WILD SPECIES

Fig. 1. Darwin's problem in 1837-38: What is "X"?

in the second line of Fig. 1. But what is "X"? By hypothesis it is not man. Of course, we might say "X = God." That would make the system work, but it would be an unsatisfactory "explanation" both scientifically and theologically: unsatisfactory scientifically because science, *by definition,* is not equipped to deal with gods; and unsatisfactory theologically because it's a messy hypothesis. If you are going to have a god modify or create species, why not do it directly, as described in Genesis, rather than by means of such a clumsy, human-conceived mechanism as this? . . . No, gods will not do, and man is out. What then is X?

The problem haunted Darwin for a long time. The solution came to him not directly from his voluminous readings in the biological sciences, but from some browsing that he did in the field of economics, or "political economy" as it was then called.

In October 1838, that is, fifteen months after I had begun my systematic enquiry, I happened to read for amusement 'Malthus on Population', and being well prepared to appreciate the struggle for existence which everywhere goes on from long-continued observation of the habits of animals and plants, it at once struck me that under these circumstances favourable variations would tend to be preserved, and unfavourable ones to be destroyed. The result of this would be the formation of new species. Here then I had at last got a theory by which to work. . . .

So there is the "X"! Though the "X" *plays the role* of a person ("man"), it is not a person or a personal god or anything of that sort. Rather, it is the *result of a process,* or complex of processes. Always and forever, a successful species of plant or animal can, as Malthus emphasized, produce far more offspring than the world can support. The result is a "struggle for existence"—Malthus's own phrase, which Darwin borrowed. The result of this struggle is necessarily the survival of *only a fraction* of each generation produced. Is this fraction a random sample of the initial population or is it biased? *Biased,* said Darwin. If the mean of a population of dogs—*wild* dogs now—is 24, and the environment is such that a 30-inch dog has a competitive advantage over all others, then, statistically speaking, 30-inch dogs will produce more offspring than either shorter or longer dogs. A set of processes, operating with only statistical precision, produces the effect labeled "X." Darwin called it *natural selection.*

Such was the evolutionary mechanism that Darwin conceived in October, 1838. Did he immediately sit down and give an account of his discovery and dispatch it by the next post to a science journal in order to insure "priority"? Not he. *Not for four years* did he write out an account of his momentous discovery, *even for himself*. Here again, Darwin shows the master's grasp of the strategy of science. He was in possession of the basic element of evolutionary theory—but it was only *one* element. There were many more elements to be found, many subsidiary hypotheses to be discovered and tested against facts which were also to be uncovered. Reading, questioning others, reasoning, and even experimenting on a limited scale, were needed in such large measure that it would take years to see clearly the great prodigy of a theory he had got hold of. And if he tried to describe his catch too soon he might, like the fabled blind men of India, ridiculously describe his elephant as if it were a tree, a snake, or a wall, because he had hold only of its leg, its tail or its chest. Darwin thoroughly appreciated the danger. "I was so anxious to avoid prejudice," he said, "that I determined not for some time to write even the briefest sketch of it." *Some time* turned out to be four years. That is a long time for a man just entering his thirties, a man anxious to make a name for himself, a man whose mind is big with discovery.

It was during this period that Darwin's life assumed the pattern that was to characterize it for the rest of his days—and to stimulate the fascinated speculation of psychiatrists, both amateur and professional, ever since. He had come to London to work, but in the end he had to flee the city because it was too exciting. Dinners with fellow scientists and scientific meetings—the great majority of which are hard to sit through without dozing, even if you are a scientist—were such stimulants to his mind that he found it hard to get on with his work, sometimes for days at a time. For one who had vowed never "to waste one hour of time" this plainly would not do. He must give up London.

In the meantime, Darwin had married. The courtship and marriage were as unostentatious as everything else about his life. He simply married a Wedgwood, as his father had done before him, and as his sister Caroline had just done. The closeness of the two sets of first cousins had always made such a match highly probable. Both families rather expected, and hoped, that Charles would marry one of the Wedgwood girls, but were taken somewhat by surprise when his choice turned out to be Emma. The courtship must have been indeed a quiet one if the family were thus surprised, for the activities of these proper Victorian young people were very open and "groupish." The engagement was announced November 12, 1838, and the wedding took place on the twenty-ninth of January following. Emma, like Charles, was one whom all their friends affectionately identified as "transparently open" in all human relationships. Their married life, like that of those other Victorians, the Gladstones, the Peels and the Brownings, was as nearly an unspoiled idyl as one could hope to find.

There were, of course, strains put upon it. Perhaps the greatest was the necessity of leaving London. Emma loved the theatre and music—she had even studied a little with Chopin —and it was no small sacrifice to give up all that London had to offer one of her tastes. But Charles's fickle health demanded it and so, in 1842, after nearly four years of London life, the search was begun for a place that was not too far from the metropolis, but was yet quiet, and not too expensive (Darwin was always considerate of the family money). At length a house was found near Down, a village of about three hundred people, only twenty miles from London, but accessible only by coach. "The choice of Down," as his son Francis later wrote, "was rather the result of despair than of actual preference; my father and mother were weary of house-hunting. . . ."

In a contemporary letter, the ever-honest naturalist described his home as "a good, very ugly house," and the scenery as only "moderately pretty." But—and this is the point: "its chief merit is its extreme rurality." His life from this time on is best summarized by quoting from the *Autobiography*.

Few persons can have lived a more retired life than we have done. Besides short visits to the houses of relations, and occasionally to the seaside or elsewhere, we have gone nowhere. During the first part of our residence we went a little into society, and received a few friends here; but my health almost always suffered from the excitement, violent shivering and vomiting attacks being thus brought on. I have therefore been compelled for many years to give up all dinner-parties; and this has been somewhat of a deprivation to me, as such parties always put me into high spirits. From the same cause I have been able to invite here very few scientific acquaintances.

My chief enjoyment and sole employment throughout life has been scientific work; and the excitement from such work makes me for the time forget, or drives quite away, my daily discomfort. I have therefore nothing to record during the rest of my life, except the publication of my several books.

Thus we hear the two leitmotifs of his adult life: work, and ill-health. The reason for the work we think we understand; but why the poor health? It is a matter of no small interest when a man who does great work is sick; we cannot help but wonder whether there is some connection between his work and his health.

The Puzzle of Darwin's Illness

In Darwin's time, the openly admitted hypotheses were physical ones, in the narrow sense, of course. Many hypotheses were entertained by himself and his doctors: heart trouble (he was bothered by palpitations during the three months he waited in Devonport for the *Beagle* to begin her voyage); "stomach trouble"; the aftereffects of his years of seasickness; aftereffects of some of the serious and mysterious fevers of his South American days; or just "hypochondria"—a label which, though it may describe, does not explain. Ordinary medicine did him no good, and so he had recourse to hot baths, to cold baths, to being wrapped in dripping sheets, to douches, to periodic walks, to fasting, to horseback-riding, and to banishment from work and home for several weeks to visit the popular "hydropathic" establishments of the day. Many of these measures worked—for a while. But only for a while. In the end his misery came back, and only overwhelmingly interesting work would give him temporary relief. His doctors never understood his trouble, or if they did, they kept their knowledge to themselves. After his death, with the advent of Freud, it was natural that his trouble should be identified as a "neurosis," first by Kaempf (1921) and more recently, and very sympathetically, by the English psychiatrist, Dr. Douglas Hubble (1943). The argument for this diagnosis is quite convincing because there are, in the voluminous letters and memoranda of the Darwin circle, so many naïve and unconscious revelations of psychological stresses and strains. As Hubble points out:

. . . here is a clinical picture drawn with a clarity and detail which are accounted for by two fortunate circumstances unlikely ever again to be conjugated. The first that Darwin and his family were trained in the exact recording of their observations, and the second that no one in Darwin's circle recognized the origin of his illness or thought of withholding it from posterity. . . .

It is inconceivable that today anyone, rich or poor, great or small, could travel through forty years of happy invalidism without having it explained by doctor, nurse, kind friend or aggrieved relation that his illness was neurotic in origin. Darwin suffered from a variety of symptoms which can be recognized as neurotic because they were associated with unpleasant emotions, because they were relieved by the pleasurable excitement connected with his work, because even he recognized that his illness brought him gains and he frequently used it to avoid difficult situations, because no physical illness was discovered in him and he lived to a good age.

What was the origin of his stress? No one can read the

Autobiography and letters without seeing the central role Dr. Robert Darwin must have played in his son's life. As an adult, Charles could recall almost nothing of his mother, though he was eight years old at the time of her death. But his father was omnipresent in his thoughts, in his letters, in his life. On one occasion he spoke of him as "the largest man whom I ever saw"—and he *was* large: six feet two, and weighing 24 stone, that is, 336 pounds. "The wisest man I ever knew," said Charles of his father, and through Cambridge, and during the voyage of the *Beagle,* and well into his married period, Charles asked the elder Darwin's advice and deferred to his judgment. (A Wedgwood cousin expressed something less than delight with the doctor's two-hour monologues, which passed for conversation in the Shrewsbury home.) And Charles insisted he was "the kindest man I ever knew," though he admitted he was especially mortified on that occasion when his father told him that he cared "for nothing but shooting, dogs, and rat-catching," and would be a disgrace to himself and his family. That this rebuke should stick in the son's memory all his life indicates how strong a "father-figure" Dr. Darwin was for him. Hubble is surely right when he says that the desire to please this beloved, imposing and never-rejected father-figure was a dominating factor in Charles Darwin's life, on the one hand, driving him to do some of the greatest work ever done in the biological sciences, and on the other, ruining his days and nights with a gnawing anxiety that he was unworthy of his father, that largest, kindest and wisest of men.

And yet . . . there is something left out of the psychoanalyst's story. What is left out is society, and the scientist's position in it. This has changed a great deal in the last century or so, and we can hardly understand all the forces pressing in on Darwin unless we appreciate how different was the scientist's position in his time. In a word, the difference lies in *professionalization.* Nowadays a scientist is a professional; in Darwin's time, he was an amateur. The difference between the two positions is profound when it is a question of engaging in a revolution, which is what Darwin proposed to do. The strongest social bonds of the professionals are within the esoteric brotherhood, and it does not take an impossible amount of courage for one to announce a truth that is unwelcome to ninety-nine percent of the populace outside the academic walls, provided one has the support of his fellow scientists within. Professionalization brings protection from the psychological consequences of heresy—if by "heresy" one means heresy for the outside world. (Whether professionals are any more tolerant of truths that are heretical *to them* is a moot question.)

Professional scientists were almost unknown in the nineteenth century. Many competent scientists were men of independent means, like Lyell and Darwin, and those who were not generally worked at something else. A fair share of the naturalists were parsons. The small corps of professional scientists within the universities was so diluted by the superior numbers of their sometimes-condescending colleagues in languages and literature as to make difficult the attainment of a strong *esprit de corps,* which might protect a heretical scientist against the disapproval of the outside world. The effective world of the scientist was little different from that of anyone else of his social and economic class. It is never easy to speak contrary to the preconceptions of the class one really lives with. Darwin lived in the warm embrace of a large and loving family, cherishing friends whose vested interests lay in the continuance of society as it was. In such a situation it was no light matter to suggest that perhaps the Book of Revelations was not closed, that perhaps man's place in nature had not always been but little lower than that of the angels. As late as January, 1844, Darwin, writing to his friend, Joseph Hooker, could admit only with the greatest diffidence whither his thoughts had led him: "I am almost convinced (quite contrary to the opinion I started with) that species are not (it is like confessing a murder) immutable."

We must grant that the confession is partly humorous—but only partly. Considering his society and his time, we may be sure that he did not make the rueful comparison of murder and belief in evolution just to get a laugh. The dominance of qualifying, parenthetical clauses in the confession, the insincere insertion of "almost" to qualify his conviction—insincere, we may say, because Darwin had already been in possession of his theory for six years, and had written out a first draft of it almost two years earlier—these rhetorical signs show Darwin's distress. Being an evolutionist *was* scarcely more acceptable than being a murderer, as was clearly and publicly shown before the year 1844 came to a close.

Chambers, The Anonymous Murderer

The "murder" was committed by an Edinburgh publisher and writer, one Robert Chambers. It was done anonymously. Who today has even heard of Robert Chambers? Yet in his day he was as well known as H. G. Wells in ours, and for much the same reason. He had a wonderful knack for popularization. He had written many books about Scotland, which sold very well; he was the publisher of a number of popular magazines as well as various highly successful annual volumes of select stories and deifying poems. An amateur interest in geology had not only led him to write some books on the subject (successful, of course) but also had convinced him that plants and animals must have evolved from common ancestors. But how could he publish such heresy without endangering the fat little publishing business that he and his brother enjoyed together? Plainly, if he *must* publish, it should be done anonymously, and through another house. Was this cowardly of him? Perhaps; but if we allow only those who have shown greater courage to join the chorus of critics, the outcry will not be deafening. Besides, anonymous publications were much commoner then than now; noblemen, from a nice sense of modesty, often refrained from claiming credit for works which they felt were highly creditable.

The *Vestiges of the Natural History of Creation* was first published in 1844. At once it was avidly bought by the public and publicly damned by the critics. Highly unfavorable reviews appeared in the *Athenaeum, Blackwood's,* the *North British Review,* the *Edinburgh Review,* and the *British Quarterly Review,* all influential journals. Among the important critics were Whewell (who was supposed to understand the philosophy of science better than anyone else), Agassiz (a noted naturalist), Sir John Herschel (a famous astronomer, whom Darwin had met in South Africa on his trip around the world), Silliman (an American chemist and geologist) and the Reverend Adam Sedgwick, now almost sixty years old. Sedgwick we must take especial note of because he was one of Darwin's teachers. Charles had toured Wales with him during his Cambridge days. Though Sedgwick was not his warmest friend, he was one whose good opinion Darwin valued. Toward the end of his *Beagle* days Charles had received a letter from his father reporting that Professor Sedgwick had prophesied that Dr. Darwin's son "should take a place among the leading scientific men," which flattering prediction had made Charles bound like a mountain goat over the crags of Ascension Island, making the volcanic rocks resound under his geological hammer. We may, then, be sure that Sedgwick's opinion of Chambers's book would be especially significant to the young man who was now, indeed, taking a place among the leading men of science, and who was secretly nourishing a work which might increase his reputation entirely—or utterly destroy it.

"How," asked the Reverend Mr. Sedgwick, surveying Chambers's evolution treatise in amazement, "are we to account for the popularity of the work?"

Men who are fed on nothing better than the trash of literature, and who have never waded beyond the surface of the things they pretend to know, must needs delight in the trashy skimmings of philosophy; and we venture to affirm that no man who has any name in science, properly so called, whether derived from profound study, or original labour in the field, has spoken well of the book, or regarded it with any feelings but those of deep aversion. We say this advisedly, after exchanging thoughts with some of the best informed men in Britain.

Then there follows a lovely passage to which one so much wishes one could know the reaction of Florence Nightingale —she who had, just before, begun her visits to the hospitals.

It is our maxim, that things must keep their proper places if they are to work together for any good. If our glorious maidens and matrons may not soil their fingers with the dirty knife of the anatomist, neither may they poison the springs of joyous thought and modest feeling, by listening to the seductions of this author; who comes before them with a bright, polished, and many-coloured surface, and the serpent coils of a false philosophy, and asks them again to stretch out their hands and pluck forbidden fruit—to talk familiarly with him of things which cannot be so much as named without raising a blush upon a modest cheek;—who tells them—that their Bible is a fable when it teaches them that they were made in the image of God—that they are the children of apes and the breeders of monsters—that he has *annulled all distinction between physical and moral,* and that all the phenomena of the universe, dead and living, are to be put before the mind in a new jargon, and as the progression and development of a rank, unbending, and degrading materialism.

After fathering that most promising entrant in the Non-Stop Sentence Derby one might expect the good parson to be rather out of breath—but he isn't. The critical dismemberment of the *Vestiges* continues for a total of eighty-five well-filled pages (*those* were the days of *real* reviews!), reaching this not unexpected summary:

We conclude, then, that our author's work is not merely shallow and superficial, but utterly false throughout to all the principles of sound philosophy. Of all the books we ever read, it puts before us the largest congeries of positive misstatements and positively false conclusions.

Then, at the last minute—perhaps remembering his manners?—Sedgwick adds, "But it is pleasantly written. . . ." On this point there seemed to be critical agreement. Another reviewer put the point more aciduously: "We readily attribute to it all the graces of the accomplished harlot."

But nothing that Sedgwick or anyone else could say about the book stopped people from reading it. It went through three editions in the year of publication; by the time the *Origin of Species* had been published, the tenth edition was out. It was published also in America and was translated into German and Dutch. Of the English editions alone, 23,750 copies were sold. Not until the twelfth edition, in 1884, did the author's name appear on the title page, though long before this his guilt had been an open secret. The *Athenaeum* for December 2, 1854 identified Chambers as "generally credited with the work." Even earlier than this, in spite of the elaborate precautions he had taken in handling manuscript and proof, Chambers had been suspected of authorship, and the suspicion had harmed him as he had predicted it would. In 1848, he submitted his name as a candidate for the Lord Provostship of Edinburgh, a position he much coveted, and for which his eminence as an author and successful business-man qualified him. But others wanted the honor as well, and one of the cannier of these rivals let it be known that if Robert Chambers persisted in his campaign, he would be asked in public whether he was, or was not, the author of the *Vestiges?* The hint was sufficient. Chambers withdrew his name.

And what about the *Vestiges*—is it an earlier *Origin*? Should Chambers be given at least part of the generous credit now bestowed on Darwin? No biologist who bothers to read the *Vestiges* now thinks so. It is filled, as contemporary critics pointed out, with errors of fact and interpretation. Those eighty-five pages of Sedgwick's review include more than pious posturing and rhetoric. The way in which crystals grow led Chambers to assert that the plant forms are determined by the laws of electricity. From uncontrolled agricultural experiments he inferred that oat plants can metamorphose into rye plants over the winter. (For scoffing at such reports a hundred years later, scientists were to die in Russia.) These errors were but two among many. But what about theory? What was his theory of evolution? The fact is, Chambers had no theory, properly so called (if we may borrow a favorite Victorian phrase of criticism)—no theory, only a magical word, *development*. He analogizes evolution to the development of an embryo: that's all.

There was, however, one good thing to be said for the book, and that was said by Darwin, who was always considerate of the feelings of others. In the preface to the sixth edition of the *Origin*, after gently insisting that the *Vestiges* did not really explain anything, he praises it for the role it played in drawing the enemy's fire first: "In my opinion it has done excellent service in this country in calling attention to the subject, in removing prejudice, and in thus preparing the ground for the reception of analogous views."

On the negative side, we can now point out the harm the *Vestiges* did in delaying the publication of a *real* theory. By 1844, Darwin had finished a second sketch of his theory—a long one this time—but he took no steps toward publishing it. Letters written in that year paint a picture of a man who is really frightened—frightened of what will happen to him if he publishes a second *Vestiges,* frightened that he will die before he publishes. Convinced that his days were numbered, he wrote out a long will, giving his wife minute directions for finding a suitable literary executor. He lived thirty-eight years more.

Down: A Design For Living

How does any great work get done? Here is a mystery to which there are as many answers as there are examples, for each work of genius is irrefragably individual. With an eye toward the future, we are interested in all the answers, whether we are thinking in terms of the good of all humanity, or in terms of some unit of lesser size, a nation, for instance. How did Darwin's work get done? What was his life like?

His daily life was a curious mixture of leisure and minute-pinching. On the one hand, he spent a great deal of time walking, playing and talking with his children (he had ten, of whom seven lived to adulthood). Family life was *every* day, not merely weekends, as it is for commuter families now. Work life was every day, too; the interpenetration of the two produced a pattern that must seem terribly fragmented to those who would like to plan men's lives. A typical day for Darwin went as follows:

	Morning
7:45	Breakfast *alone*.
8:00– 9:30	Thinking and writing in his study.
9:30–10:30	In the drawing room, lying on the sofa while letters were read aloud to him. If the post was light, part of a novel would be read to him.
10:30–12:00	Back to the study for the second, and last, period of writing.
	Afternoon (the timing is less precise from here on).
12:00– 1:00	He would often announce *"I've* done a good day's work," and—rain or shine—would set out on a walk with Polly, the white terrier.
1:00– 1:30	Lunch with the family.
1:30– 2:00	Lying on the sofa, reading the paper.

2:00– 3:00	Sitting in an armchair by the fire, busy with correspondence.
3:00– 4:00	Up to his bedroom, where he lay on another sofa, smoking a cigarette, while listening to a second installment of the novel—which, to be first-class, should (he said) contain "some person whom one can thoroughly love, and if a pretty woman all the better." It must, in any case, have a happy ending.
4:00– 4:30	Another walk.
4:30– 5:30	A little more work.
5:30– 7:30	More rest, another cigarette, and some more of the novel.
7:30	Dinner.

After dinner, he would beg to be excused, saying that he was an old woman who must leave with the ladies. Sometimes there was company that he felt he could not abandon, and he would talk for a while, which he loved to do. For this dissipation he paid dearly. Even a half hour's conversation would so excite him that the next day was spoiled for work. Much more favorable to his ambition was a game of backgammon with the children, then an hour's reading of a scientific work before going to bed, hoping for sleep. But all too often his mind was too busy with a problem.

If we add up the hours of work, we find that it comes to only *four*. And this only on good days. We agree with Dr. Hubble's wonderment, that four hours' work should suffice for the performance of the most important scientific work of the nineteenth century.

In the strictest sense, Darwin was a fortunate man. He was financially independent: he started life with a sufficient fortune and ended up with a considerable one—£282,000 at the time of his death. How much would this be in our money now—two million dollars? Four million? We must remember not only the change in the value of money, but also the non-existence of income taxes. In any case, there was plenty of money and plenty of servants. We find scarcely a mention in the letters of the many servants there must have been, though we do know that one jewel of a manservant was with the family for fifty-eight years. Only with a great deal of "help" could a scientist have performed such prodigies of intellectual labor in a house throbbing with a half-dozen or so children, not to mention the miscellaneous long-staying relatives so typical of the times.

And above all there was Emma Wedgwood Darwin. Like her husband, she was praised as being "transparent," a Victorian term which seems to be the equivalent of our "sincere." She deserved the name. Asked how she liked Tennyson's

Queen Mary, she replied that she found it "not nearly so tiresome as Shakespeare." There is something a little puzzling about this because she was fond of at least some of Shakespeare's plays. However, it shows her manner of speaking what came to her mind at the moment, without pausing to see what sort of picture she was painting of herself. Such frankness is often coupled with an acid character, but not in Emma. She could safely be frank with her friends because she apparently had no antagonisms to work out on others. "Though she was the most unselfish person I have ever known," said her daughter Henrietta, "there was no trace in her character of the self-suppression which is often found in those who have had to struggle for unselfishness. . . . With her there seemed to be no evil to conquer."

Her husband was equally laudatory in his *Autobiography.* All in all, Emma seemed to be all that a man like Charles Darwin would want in a wife, save in one respect: she was fearful of where his thoughts might lead him. Even before their marriage Emma expressed her loving fears in a long letter to him on the general subject of religion. Knowing that his beliefs were not orthodox, Charles consulted his father, who advised him to conceal his doubts and thus avoid causing needless misery. What should he do? Go against his father's advice? Or be less than frank with his wife-to-be? He followed the latter course of action. This was the year 1838, the year in which he read Malthus, the year in which he saw clearly the theory he must work on, the year in which his chronic ill-health began. The coincidence of these events may not be purely accidental.

The Confidant Is Found: Hooker

Genuinely original thinking is rare because it requires the rarest and most improbable concatenation of personal circumstances. "Every man of genius," Havelock Ellis said, "is a stranger and a pilgrim on the earth, unlike other men, seeing everything as it were at a different angle." To be a man of genius one must have the opportunity to see things from a different angle, to be alone, to be alienated from the crowd. But the burden of alienation is not to be borne forever: the man of genius must also have someone to whom he can reveal himself. To love is to reveal one's self, Kierkegaard has said. Charles was unable to love Emma completely. He had need of someone else, though he doubtless did not know it. He was in possession of a great new truth . . . but was it the truth? How could he know if he had not shared it with another? (Can *I* alone know any truth? This is the doubt that, planted in the minds of even the strongest of men in our time, has made them falsely confess state crimes in a way that is incredible to those who are happy enough to live in a less enveloping society and are thus unaware of the profoundly social nature of all truth.)

Darwin found the confidant he sorely needed in the person of Joseph Dalton Hooker, a young botanist. Just as there would probably never have been a *Principia* had Newton not had his Halley, or a *De Revolutionibus* had Copernicus not had Rhaeticus, so is it very doubtful if the *Origin* would ever have come into being had Darwin not found Hooker. The botanist was practically tailored for the part. At about the time that Darwin was reading Malthus "for amusement," this twenty-year-old son of a distinguished botanist was trying very hard to persuade the explorer, Ross, to take him as naturalist on the coming voyage of the *Erebus* and the *Terror* to the Antarctic; but with little success, for, said Ross, putting the matter as kindly as he could, he wanted "such a person as Mr. Darwin." Hooker, with the logic of youth, pointed out that Mr. Darwin himself had not been such a man when he began his voyage. *True*, said Ross; but he would not say, *Come*. Fortunately, Papa had influence, and Joseph got a post on the *Erebus*. For him, as for Darwin, the long sea voyage launched a distinguished career. And just as Henslow had handed Lyell's book to Darwin to read on the voyage, so Lyell now handed Hooker Mr. Darwin's *Journal of Researches* to serve as a model for his endeavors. Young Joseph confessed that this book "impressed me profoundly, I might say despairingly, with the variety of acquirements, mental and physical, required in a naturalist who should follow in Darwin's footsteps, whilst they stimulated me to enthusiasm in the desire to travel and observe."

It was not surprising that Hooker should return to England prepared to reverence Darwin, who was eight years older than he, as Darwin had reverenced Henslow. Hooker must have been made particularly susceptible to the friendly overtures of a revered mentor because of his personal circumstances. He was a delicately built young man and extremely nearsighted. The long letters he wrote his father while on board the *Erebus* reveal a desperate avoidance of the threat of warm human contacts, coupled with an immature clinging to his family. In one of his letters he scolds his father for proudly handing his letters around to others to read. "My letters," says Joseph,

. . . were written for *my near relations alone,* and contain such messages to others as are requisite for them to know; my repugnance to any such notoriety is so strong that if these wishes cannot be complied with I must give up writing anything but simple statements. You may remember that I was always very averse to any society but that of persons whose pursuits were similar to mine, . . . this may be owing to a peculiar temperament of mine or more probably to a fault; still I cannot help it, and care to be known by few but Botanists and men of Science. With them my own industry must introduce me, and what other real friends I have I can write to. . . . A few friends are all my narrow mind has room for. . . .

Joseph had two sisters and a brother, whom he, in his friendlessness, held doubly dear. It takes no great ability to imagine how his already-withdrawn personality must have been devastated by the appearance of two black-edged letters delivered to him at the bottom of the world, one announcing the death of his brother, the other of a sister, both of consumption. A bit later his father wrote that he proposed to give up the family home in Glasgow and move to London to take over the direction of the Kew Gardens. What did Joseph think? Joseph says he hopes his father will take the new position, admitting, however, that he will always have a warm spot in his heart for the "dirty Town" of Glasgow, but adding bitterly, "It is true I have no friends there, but equally I have none elsewhere. . . ."

The Ross expedition returned to England in September, 1843. Not long thereafter, in December, Charles Darwin, always on the lookout for fresh facts to test his theory, wrote a letter to this lonely young man (whom he knew slightly, through Lyell), warmly congratulating him on his safe return and expressing a desire to hear the results of the expedition. Here was the kind of friend Joseph really wanted, a man of Science, and one of the best. His reply (which has not come down to us) must have clearly revealed his longing for friendship, for only a month later, January, 1844, Darwin reveals to him what he had kept from all others for more than five years, the "murder" he was nursing in his bosom. At the cost of repetition it will be useful to repeat that quotation, in a fuller setting:

I have read heaps of agricultural and horticultural books, and have never ceased collecting facts. At last gleams of light have come, and I am almost convinced (quite contrary to the opinion I started with) that species are not (it is like confessing a murder) immutable. Heaven forfend me from Lamarck nonsense of a "tendency to progression," "adaptations from the slow willing of animals," etc! But the conclusions I am led to are not widely different from his; though the means of change are wholly so. I think I have found out (here's presumption!) the simple way by which species become exquisitely adapted to various ends. You will now groan, and think to yourself, "on what a man have I been wasting my time and writing to."

Hooker was no doubt flattered by Darwin's confiding in him in so delicate a matter. His reply must have been more than friendly, for by February twenty-third we find his revered model abandoning the polite greeting, *My dear sir,* of the preceding letters and brashly addressing him, *Dear Hooker* —and then immediately apologizing: "I hope you will excuse the freedom of my address." Thus began what can quite properly be called one of the world's great love affairs, a scientific love affair that, over forty years' time, poured itself out in fifteen hundred pages of handwritten technicalities invaluable to the scholar who wants to follow the development of Darwin's thought. To this warm friendship and to the letters necessitated by the seclusion required for the protection of Darwin's wretched stomach, we owe a record of the day-by-day development of the theory of evolution that is, for completeness, unequaled in the history of science. It is small wonder that historians and philosophers of science return to this source material time after time for fresh insight into the still-mysterious workings of the human mind in its striving to paint a rational picture of the world.

The Confounded Barnacles

By the end of 1844, then, Darwin's position was this: he had clarified his thoughts by writing a second sketch of his theory—some 230 handwritten pages—and had acquired new psychological strength through the always-sympathetic support of young Hooker. Was this not the time, then, to begin the big work in earnest? Yes, wrote Darwin to Hooker early in 1845: "I hope this next summer to finish my South American Geology, then to get out a little Zoology, and hurrah for my species work. . . ."

The "little Zoology" took *eight years.*

It began innocently enough. Like the geology, it was something left over from his *Beagle* trip—a matter of some curious barnacles that he had picked up in Chile, whose structure was quite new to science. It was natural to want to "clean up" this matter before taking on something new. But to make sense of the new barnacles he had to become thoroughly acquainted with the more common sorts. And after this, there were fossil forms to be looked into. Before he was through, he published two large monographs of the living forms, of

399 and 684 pages respectively, and two small quartos on fossil species. And what did this contribute to the *Origin of Species?* Just five references, totaling 2 pages out of 415, less than one half of one percent; and not one of these references was essential, each being merely an additional exemplification of principles already established. And for this he gave eight years of his life. Was it worth it?

This question must have been often asked at the time of the assessment of Darwin's life toward the close of the century, for his good friends were very defensive of barnacle investigation—*too* defensive, one feels. T. H. Huxley said that Darwin had never done a wiser thing than this:

> Like the rest of us, he had no proper training in biological science, and it has always struck me as a remarkable instance of his scientific insight, that he saw the necessity of giving himself such training, and of his courage, that he did not shirk the labour of obtaining it.

And Hooker says that the taxonomic work had the merit of opening Darwin's eyes

> . . . to the difficulties and merits of the works of the dullest of cataloguers. One result was that he would never allow a depreciatory remark to pass unchallenged on the poorest class of scientific workers, provided that their work was honest, and good of its kind. I have always regarded it as one of the finest traits of his character,—this generous appreciation of the hodmen of science, and their labours . . . and it was monographing the Barnacles that brought it about.

But the improvement of his character can hardly have been his *motive* in undertaking the work. Is it not far more likely that he subconsciously welcomed this diversion because it postponed the day in which he would reveal his subversive thoughts about man's origin? Chambers's work was still being savagely reviewed as Darwin began working on barnacles. Would his own work on species be no better received? He had already published one "bad" paper—on the geology of Glen Roy—in 1839. In his *Autobiography* he acknowledged: "This paper was a great failure, and I am ashamed of it." When it was attacked in 1847, Darwin said that the publicity "made me horribly sick." Was he not subconsciously afraid that his heretical "species work" would be just as bad and even more mercilessly attacked?

With eyes opened by Freud, we see his persistence in carrying on a detailed study of barnacles principally as a neurotic escape from the real challenge. Like most neurotic adaptations, it failed. Darwin's son, Francis, tells us that during the barnacle years his father suffered perhaps more from ill-health than at any other time of his life. Although he often spoke of the beauties of his tiny Cirripedes (barnacles), he also not infrequently referred to them in some such terms as "my confounded Cirripedes," and to his occupation as "hateful work." Though financially independent, Darwin was nevertheless a man in bondage. Ambition and fear bound him to a job he hated, and his response was that of any slave or frustrated job holder—"absenteeism." Out of his eight barnacle years, an aggregate of two were devoted to helpless illness.

Darwin stuck with his barnacles to the bitter end, finishing in 1854 the labor begun in 1846. Then he sent off "ten thousand Barnacles" to museums and collectors all over the world, thus clearing the decks for the species work. The tempo of queries to Hooker on evolutionary questions was now stepped up, and Darwin's health improved (somewhat). Early in 1856, Sir Charles Lyell, who by this time had also been taken into confidence, advised Darwin to write out his theory for publication, and Darwin began to do so.

The Painful Birth of the "Origin"

But now a new problem presented itself: from long postponement, the theory had become almost overripe. His first attempt to boil down the accumulated facts of nearly twenty years' collecting produced the beginnings of an "abstract" that would have been three or four times as long as the *Origin* finally was. What to do? Afraid, perhaps, of producing a second *Vestiges,* Darwin was more unwilling than most authors to cut out a single instance, to omit a single corroborative detail in the presentation of his theory. Lyell counseled haste. The work continued to expand. It is interesting to speculate whether the theory ever would have been published had outside forces not intervened. But—as when we ask: *What if Cleopatra's nose had been an inch longer?*—we will never know the answer for outside forces *did* intervene, in the form of a communication sent by a young naturalist stationed in the Malay Archipelago. The young man's name was Alfred Russel Wallace, and the communication was a personal letter, accompanied by a brief paper in which Darwin's theory of evolution by natural selection was described to a *T.* "I never saw a more striking coincidence," said Darwin: "if Wallace had my MS. sketch written out in 1842, he could not have made a better short abstract! Even his terms now stand as heads of my chapters."

In agony, Darwin wrote to his old friend and counselor, Sir

Charles: "Your words have come true with a vengeance—that I should be forestalled. . . . So all my originality, whatever it may amount to, will be smashed. . . ." For he must, of course, publish Wallace's sketch. Wallace had not specifically asked him to, but the implication was obvious. How could he now publish his own views ahead of Wallace's without its presently being said (when the full facts were known): *He has stolen from a fellow worker who is too far away to defend his own interests?*

A week later Darwin wrote again to Lyell, this time pouring out his feelings more fully: *I am sorry to trouble you . . . this is a trumpery affair . . . if I could honourably publish . . . I cannot tell whether to publish now would not be base and paltry . . . Wallace says nothing about publication . . . trumpery feelings . . .* And then, he had procrastinated twenty years while he put out thirteen papers on geology and eight on biology, not to mention a book of travels, one of geology, one on coral reefs and four on the hateful barnacles—yes, he who was working on a three-volume "abstract" of his theory, and having hard work holding it down to that minimum size, admitted that, did honor permit, *he should be extremely glad now to publish a sketch of his general views in about a dozen pages or so*. But how could he? He appealed to Sir Charles for help; he was worn out with musing; he had entire confidence in Sir Charles's judgment and honor. . . .

The letter should have acted as a cathartic for his "trumpery feelings," but the obstruction was evidently a severe one, for the next day we find him again writing to Lyell, saying much the same thing, trying desperately, against heroic temptation, to be wholly honorable; and then adding a hopeful postscript: "I have always thought you would make a first-rate Lord Chancellor; and I now appeal to you as a Lord Chancellor." As if the woes of his professional life were not enough, scarlet fever entered the house at Down at this time, carrying off the youngest child, Charles Waring. In a panic, all the other children (except Henrietta, who was too feeble to be moved) were bundled out of the house. Two of the nurses took ill, but recovered. However, grueling though the personal ordeal was, it was not an unmixed sadness, for little Charles, the tenth and last child, born in Emma's forty-eighth year, had from the first been without his full share of intelligence, and his honest parents, "after the first sorrow . . . could only feel thankful at his death."

Darwin's two closest friends in science, Lyell and Hooker, put their heads together and came up with a solution that would save both his honor and his claim to priority: they would present both Wallace's paper and a brief one by their friend—who must write it immediately—to the Linnaean Society. They would at the same time stand as character witnesses, being able to vouch for his long priority. And that is how it came about that the theory of evolution by natural selection was announced jointly by Charles Darwin and A. R. Wallace in July, 1858.

And what of Wallace? How did he happen to arrive at the same theory? And why do we not give him equal credit? To take up the first question first, it is clear that this good naturalist, fourteen years Darwin's junior, was living in much the same climate of opinion, a world in which the idea of evolution, though not yet scientifically respectable, was in every scientist's mind. Moreover, Wallace had for some time been in correspondence with the dean of naturalists, who had lately been less secretive about his thoughts. Darwin had evidently said something about his "species work" to Wallace, for on the twenty-second of December, 1857, we find Darwin writing, in reply to a question:

You ask whether I shall discuss 'man.' I think I shall avoid the whole subject, as so surrounded with prejudices; though I fully admit that it is the highest and most interesting problem for the naturalist. My work, on which I have now been at work more or less for twenty years, will not fix or settle anything; but I hope it will aid by giving a large collection of facts with one definite end.

With such a hint, it is not entirely wonderful that an active, speculative mind should arrive at Darwin's theory. The final clue, interestingly enough, was for Wallace the same as it had been for Darwin: Malthus's *Essay on Population*. Wallace read it in a lull between bouts with malaria, was immediately struck by the importance of the "struggle for existence," dashed off a sketch of the theory of evolution by natural selection and sent it posthaste to Darwin, with the results that we have seen.

And what about the credit? Here we enter a very human realm in which there are no laws (in the legal sense) for assigning credit, but where there do appear to be "laws" of human behavior in the descriptive sense. In the first place, it is greatly to Wallace's credit that he behaved with the greatest magnanimity from beginning to end, dismissing his essay as a slight affair and insisting that the honor all belonged to Darwin, who had labored so heroically in producing his *Origin of Species*. When Wallace got around to writing a book on the subject he even called it *Darwinism*. Secondly, there is involved a principle of human reputations that may seem not quite fair, but is none the less inescapable: *to him that hath shall be given*. Darwin's reputation, already well established by his theory of coral-island formation, his work on the geology and natural history of South America, and the very solid monographs on barnacles, naturally took to itself the credit for the new theory. It is easier to remember a well-known name than the name of a newcomer; thus reputation acts as a self-regenerative circuit.

Finally, Wallace's place in the scientific hall of fame has no doubt been influenced by his behavior after 1858. He published a considerable amount of good natural history and interesting travel books, but in addition, at one time or another, he came out strongly for socialization of land, for spiritualism, and violently against vaccination. A man's following is not so much the sum of all the people who favor his various ideas as it is the residue left after subtracting the gentlemen and those vested financial interests who were shocked by Wallace's socialism, the scientists who scoffed at spiritualism, the medical men who defended vaccination, and the conservative religious folks who were shocked by evolution —and who is left to sing Wallace's praises? It is small wonder we have almost forgotten his part in belling the cat.

But was the cat really belled in 1858? Not quite. The joint paper attracted little overt attention. Darwin, in his *Autobiography,* says that he can recall only one published notice of it, by an Irish professor, who resorted to that immortal ploy of the undiscerning critic: *what is new is false and what is true is old*. Perhaps, as Hooker thought, everyone else was holding his fire until Darwin came forth with the promised full barrage.

Darwin began almost immediately on the big work, applying himself as he never had before. He consented to write it on a third the scale of his original plan, and thus was able to finish the manuscript by late May, 1859. Then he collapsed. The summer was spent alternating proofs and douches. Revisions were extensive, costing some seventy-two pounds, but the last of the index was finally got off on the first of October, and the Darwins fled to a water-cure establishment near Leeds, where they stayed for three months.

On the twenty-fourth of November, 1859, Mr. John Murray brought out a slim green volume with this title page:

ON
THE ORIGIN OF SPECIES
BY MEANS OF NATURAL SELECTION
OR THE

PRESERVATION OF FAVOURED RACES IN THE STRUGGLE
FOR LIFE
BY CHARLES DARWIN, M.A.

The cat had been belled.

3

Darwinism, Deity and Process

THE *Origin of Species* was given a lively reception. How lively, and what was the eventual outcome, we shall see later. First we need to find out just what is in the book itself. One might read it, of course—it is a great "classic." But that is just the trouble. It is axiomatic that the first statement of a theory is not the neatest. Later students, more disinterested than the author and with the wisdom of hindsight, can always boil it down. Certainly the *Origin,* loaded as it is with multiple illustrations of even the smallest point, is capable of great compaction. The book will always be a mine of great interest to the professional biologist, but its essence can be much more briefly stated.

Also, it must be admitted that the *Origin* is often marred by a characteristic left-handedness of presentation. "There seems to be a sort of fatality in my mind," Darwin once complained, "leading me to put at first my statement or proposition in a wrong or awkward form." His friend T. H. Huxley, himself a fluent and precise writer, ruefully and affectionately complained that "Exposition is not Darwin's *forte*—and his English is sometimes wonderful. But there is a marvellous dumb sagacity about him—like that of a sort of miraculous dog—and he gets to the truth by ways as dark as those of the Heathen Chinee."

The darkness was not entirely of Darwin's making. He inherited the word "evolution," with all its ambiguity and uncertainty, and used it without question. It refers not to a single idea but to a complex of analytically separable ideas that are partly independent of, partly dependent on, each other. The four most important of these we may call the processes of *adaptation, secular change, speciation,* and *extinction.* The biological meaning of each of these terms will be explored in turn, the first one being the subject of the remainder of this chapter.

The Idea of Cybernetics

The most characteristically Darwinian feature of the theory of evolution is the process of adaption, which was conceived as a part of a mechanism for explaining change. Yet, paradoxically, the adaptive process is one which, by itself, makes for stability rather than change. Only under exceptional circumstances, and only a small percentage of the time, is it part of a change-producing mechanism.

We can most readily understand the process if we look at it in a larger framework than was available in Darwin's time. We will consider adaptation as a member of a class of systems called *homeostatic systems*, or *cybernetic systems*. The Harvard physiologist, Walter B. Cannon, coined the first name and described many such systems in his delightful book, *The Wisdom of the Body* (1932). As an example of such systems, consider the diagram of the mechanism involved in keeping a man's body temperature constant (Fig. 2). Initially (at left) we will suppose that body temperature is the normal 98.6° Fahrenheit. Any change impressed on the body by outside influences we will represent by a discontinuous arrow (——>). Suppose the body temperature is raised: what happens? As everyone knows, the body sweats more. Increased sweat leads to increased loss of heat by evaporation, which presently brings the temperature down to normal again. The various stages described are indicated in the upper row of

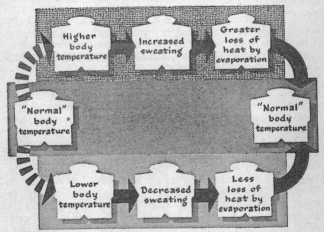

SYMBOLISM:
Broken arrow (IIII▶) indicates hypothetical, or random, impressed change.
Solid arrow (■■▶) indicates necessary, response change.

Fig. 2. The cybernetic system that controls body temperature.

boxes, connected by solid arrows (——>) to signify that these changes are necessary, that is, ones that are built into the physiological system of response. A similar response system is brought into play if the temperature falls below normal (lower row of boxes). Both rows of boxes taken together represent what Cannon christened a homeostatic system, *i.e.,* a system that, to translate literally, keeps the temperature "like steady." . . . It hardly needs to be said that our diagram is a great simplification of the facts: there are other devices for changing the body temperature (*e.g.,* bristling hair, shivering, flushing) and more elements (*e.g.,* sense organs, nerve fibers, central nervous system). But the sense of the diagram is correct.

Cannon's description of homeostasis was immediately recognized as useful by biologists and was soon applied (by Cannon and others) to a wide variety of biological variables: the level of sugar in the blood, of water in the body, and of oxygen in the blood, to mention only three. Somewhat later, various engineers became aware that many man-made self-correcting systems are formally analogous to natural systems. In systematizing knowledge of such systems, the mathematician, Norbert Wiener, although he knew of Cannon's work, felt obliged to create a new name for his study, namely *cybernetics,*

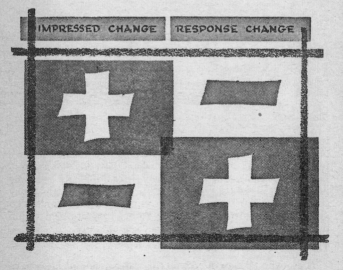

Fig. 3. The reason for the phrase "negative feedback."

derived from Greek roots meaning steersman. In 1948, Wiener

published a book under the Greek title, and the word is now as well established as Cannon's. Self-adjusting systems will hereafter be indifferently referred to as homeostatic or cybernetic systems.

Engineering practice has introduced the useful term "negative feedback" into the discussion of adjustive systems. The meaning of this term should be apparent from the table shown in Fig. 3. When the impressed change is +, the response change is −; and vice versa. The response (feedback) is the negative of the stimulus that evokes it. Negative feedback is characteristic of all self-adjusting systems, the essence of which can be diagrammed as shown in Fig. 4.

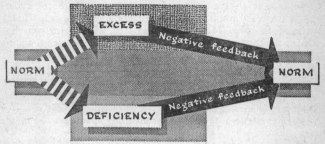

Fig. 4. The essence of a cybernetic or homeostatic system.

Positive feedback, by contrast, leads to a runaway process. For example, if the body temperature rises to something like 107° F. (the exact point varies among individuals), the negative-feedback system breaks down to be replaced by positive feedback. Increased temperature causes the chemical reactions of metabolism to go faster, which increases the temperature, which increases the chemical reactions further, which . . . and so on. A "vicious circle" is established; positive feedback is in control; there is no end in sight but the destruction of the living system of the individual. A similar positive feedback system also takes over when the body temperature falls 10 or so degrees below normal, resulting in a runaway process in the opposite direction. In general, self-maintaining systems (like life) are self-adjusting only within limits. To keep them going, we must see to it that they are held within the limits in which negative feedback is operative.

The Flow of Ideas

Those who take an interest in the transmission of ideas have often pointed out how a concept may first be developed in the "exact sciences" (physics, chemistry) and then move out into the less exact (biology, psychology), perhaps eventually reaching those dimly scientific regions called the social sciences. There is a hierarchy of prestige among the sciences that makes it easy for us to see examples of transmission in this direction. What has been less often noticed is that ideas may just as well go the other way: in the idea of cybernetics we have a clear-cut example. *The principle of the survival of the fittest,* said John Maynard Keynes, *is just a vast generalization of Ricardian economics.* We need now to see what this cryptic statement means, in order not only to understand the origin of an important idea but also to see the source of some enduring conflicts in human thought.

An idea is always older than its name. The idea of cybernetics was used implicitly by the French physiologist, Claude Bernard, in 1878. The Scottish physicist, Clerk Maxwell, also used it in 1868 in developing the theory of the steam-engine governor. But long before both of them Adam Smith had just as clearly used the idea in his *Wealth of Nations* (1776). The "invisible hand" that regulates prices to a nicety is clearly

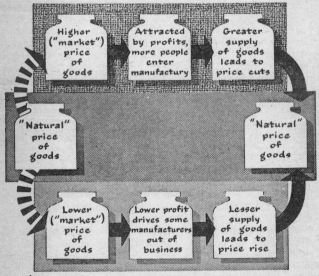

(⚎▶) indicates hypothetical, impressed change
(➡) indicates necessary, response change

Fig. 5. The cybernetic system that controls commodity prices in a free market.

a homeostatic device. Fig. 5 shows the implicit structure of this idea. In a free market, says Smith in effect, prices are regulated by negative feedback. The line of thought begun by Smith was carried through in greater detail in the early 1800s by the London stock speculator and brilliant amateur economist, David Ricardo. Because his work is more thorough (and perhaps also because "Smithian" is un-Englishic) the name "Ricardian economics" is often applied to this system of thought.

It is more than a system of thought; it is a feeling—a feeling borrowed in part from the French "physiocrats," who coined the phrase *laissez faire*. Behind this slogan is the idea that not only are the stars in the heavens ruled by laws but so also are the affairs of men. It is our duty to find these natural laws, and then not interfere with their workings. Any conscious action we take (*e.g.*, establishing a tariff) is likely to do more harm than good. The assurance that *laissez faire* is the best course springs from a kind of piety, a religious feeling in which "Law" (note the capital *L*) takes the place of "God."

Ricardo had this piety, and in the working out of his system he did not shrink from the consequences of logic. Goods are commodities; so also is labor, he said, and its price is governed by a cybernetic system like that shown in Fig. 5, *mutatis mutandis*. But *mutatis mutandis*—"with the necessary changes" —what potential misery is hidden in the learned phrase! What if the market price of *this* commodity—the labor of living, breathing men—declines? The result will surely be more painful than the bankruptcy of a manufacturer. Ricardo admits as much.

> When the market price of labour is below its natural price, the condition of the labourers is most wretched: then poverty deprives them of those comforts which custom renders absolute necessaries. *It is only after their privations have reduced their number,* or the demand for labour has increased, that the market price of labour will rise to its natural price, and that the labourer will have the moderate comforts which the natural rate of wages will afford.

The italicizing above was done—need it be said?—*not* by Ricardo.

Every clearly expressed idea provokes its own negation, which often takes the form of an uncomplimentary descriptive epithet fastened on the original idea. Ricardo's cybernetic scheme for labor control became known as the "Iron Law of Wages," stimulating Karl Marx to some of his most impassioned rhetoric. We will not here inquire into the relative merits of the opposing positions in economic thought. Our only interest is to mark them, and then see how the same opposition was later carried over into biology as Charles Darwin introjected into the scientific world the cybernetic scheme that pervaded the economic thinking of the society in which he grew to manhood.

The Darwinian Cybernetic Scheme

To naturalists before Darwin it was not at all obvious that there was any problem in the maintenance of constancy within a species. "Like begets like," goes the old saw. There is enough truth in the saying to cause us to pass blindly by the consequences of its untruth. The fact is that offspring are never entirely like their parents. Occasionally a child exhibits a characteristic never seen before—and this novelty may be transmitted to subsequent generations. In the face of perpetual individual variation, how is it possible for a *species* to remain unchanged for tens of thousands of generations? How is it that the lions depicted by the early Egyptians look like the ones we see today, approximately one thousand lion-generations later? It was Darwin's genius that led him to realize that *constancy is maintained only by perpetual change*. It takes a cybernetic scheme of perpetual adjustment

Fig. 6. The conservative Darwinian cybernetic scheme that preserves species constancy in the face of ever-recurring heredity changes.

to keep a species at its best, or (as is usually said) its "fittest."

The way in which this cybernetic scheme works is shown in Fig. 6. For an example, we consider only the weight of a species. However variable the environment, there is a certain weight that is (on the average) best for the species. The mean weight of the population will, in fact, be this weight. Should the mean weight depart from this figure, there will be an increased mortality among the members which will, in fact, be selective, tending to carry off in greater numbers those members that depart furthest from the "fittest" weight. By this process, the "fittest" survive. In the Darwinian scheme, the concept of the "fittest" has the same normalizing role as that played by the "natural" price of commodities or labor in economics, or the "normal" temperature in animal physiology. The quantitative value of each of these concepts can be determined only empirically and *ex post facto;* they have, nonetheless, a real meaning.

Augustine to Paley to Darwin

"I am fearfully and wonderfully made," said the Psalmist: so also is the entire living world, every organism being marvelously *fitted* to the demands of its environment. Nothing is perfect: but marvels abound. How are we to account for them? Darwin had an answer: adjustment brought about by "natural selection." But his answer was not the first, and it had to struggle with two older explanations.

The first of these we may call the Augustinian, in honor of St. Augustine, Bishop of Hippo; he was not the first who proposed it, but he was perhaps the most influential, so we will identify it by his name. In Augustine's view the world was created for man's benefit: bees give honey for man's use; for the same reason, a cow gives milk. It sounds pleasantly plausible, but such a homocentric view raises the "problem of evil": Why does the rattlesnake have fangs? (Or, as William Blake asked, *Did God make the Tyger?*) One can explain the evil created by the Augustinian mode of thought only through the use of a most dubious device—by saying that evil really exists for our own good, in some mysterious sense known only to God. Such an explanation may be true or it may be false, but it is logically objectionable because it is *too* good. Literally anything, true or false, may be explained by it. "The infinitely mysterious ways of the Lord" is a *panchreston,* an "explain-all." No puzzle disturbs the thoughts of those who embrace a panchreston: neither do they discover new truths.

The trap is escaped only by asserting that the world does not revolve around man. The destruction of the homocentric universe was the work of many hands, Copernicus's and Newton's among them, but for our purposes we are most interested in the thoughts of the Reverend William Paley, a noted Cambridge figure of the latter part of the eighteenth century. Like Augustine, Paley was not a strikingly original thinker, but his writings epitomized a point of view in an unforgettable way. Paley's most noted work, published in 1802, bore the title *Natural Theology, or Evidences of the Existence and Attributes of the Deity collected from the Appearances of Nature*. The principal argument is indicated in the title: that the adaptedness of natural structures and organs is an evidence that there is a God. Everywhere we look, said Paley, we see "Design in Nature": in the structure of flowers designed to achieve cross-pollination by bees, in the parts of the bee so wonderfully designed to achieve this act, in the arrangement of man's muscles and bones to insure movement, in the structure of his lungs to secure the benefits of air, and above all in the structure of his eye—here, surely, is the result of conscious design. "There cannot be a design without a designer"; hence God exists. The examination of this marvelous organ, the eye, Paley said, is a sure cure for atheism.

"Everyone" in nineteenth-century England knew of Paley's works. Darwin once remarked, "I do not think I hardly ever admired a book more than Paley's *Natural Theology*. I could almost formerly have said it by heart." One of the ideas Darwin got out of it was what we may call *Paley's Principle:* The functions and structures of an organism are to be explained in terms of its own good—not in terms of the desires or needs of any other species, man not excepted. The rattlesnake has rattles not to save man from being bitten, but to warn him away in order that he—the rattlesnake—may survive. That man survives also is no part of the "Design" that "Nature" had in mind in making the rattlesnake. With this type of non-homocentric explanation Paley escapes the false problem of evil raised by Augustine. The fangs of the rattlesnake are not evil but good—good for the rattlesnake itself, the necessary center of this discourse. An Augustinian, confronted with a remarkable natural phenomenon, must seek its utility for man; if he cannot find it, he is in a bad way. (This is the meaning of the classical remark of the country bumpkin on seeing his first giraffe: "There ain't no such animal"—that is, the animal could do man no good, therefore it does not exist.) A Paleyan, in contrast, asking: *What is the function of this structure or ability in the life of the organism possessing it?* necessarily becomes a close and attentive student of nature. Paley made naturalists: Darwin was one of them.

But Paley's Principle created a new problem: How can one

account for imperfection—imperfection from the point of view of the organism itself? To suppose a divine Designer is to postulate perfect Design. Paley supposed the eye was perfect—but the physicist, Helmholtz, scrutinizing the human eye a half century later, pronounced it so imperfect an instrument that, he said, had he purchased it from an optician, "he would have thought himself fully justified in returning it." The human body shows countless other features that are certainly not well designed for our kind of life: the vermiform appendix (which is not big enough to do vegetarians any good, its only function being—contrary to Paley's Principle!—to support the medical profession); our ear-wiggling muscles (not good enough to focus the sound as a horse's do—good only for laughs); and the valves in the *horizontal* blood vessels that run between the ribs (where they are not needed) instead of more valves in the vertical vessels of the legs where they would help prevent varicose veins. Paley's system of thought cannot explain such imperfections. Darwin's can, by roughly two means: *First*—An organism need not be perfectly adapted to survive—"51% adaptation is good enough." There is no operational way of determining the percentage, but the principle is surely a sound one: an organ need not be perfect to have survival value. *Second*—Evolution is a process that takes time. At any particular moment a particular species may have a number of features that have not yet evolved to their full extent.

In Augustine's system, error is evil. In Paley's, it is a reflection on the wisdom of God. In Darwin's, it is merely an evidence that the world is made by on-going processes. When a Darwinian comes across poor design, he does not say, "poor God," but rather, "Rome was not built in a day." Evil and imperfection, which cannot be satisfactorily accounted for by Augustine or Paley, become, in Darwin's view, natural parts of a larger and more rational world. It is a more humane world, and therefore a more beautiful one.

"Natural Selection": A New God?

In retrospect we can see that the Darwinian contribution to biology was a part of a larger movement in the history of scientific thought—indeed, of all *rational* thought—the substitution of the dynamic for the static, with a consequent change in emphasis from substance to process. The solid, immovable earth of the ancients was set in constant motion by Copernicus. The primitive notion of absolute rest was, by Newton, replaced by the idea of constant velocity. The stars, which the ancients thought were embedded in some sort of substantial sphere, have now been cut loose from all moorings and made part of an ever-expanding universe. Nor are the earth's "eternal hills" any longer eternal; in the scale of geological time, they are no more than tiny bumps of brown sugar melting away under the onslaught of rain and wind, only to be replaced by other brown bumps, equally "eternal," thrust up by the unceasing agitations of the earth's crust. The constancy which man's spirit apparently craves is to be found neither in hills, nor earth, nor stars nor—perhaps—even in the universe. If there is any sort of constancy at all, it is not one of substance or position, but one of process. Whether even *this* is forever constant we cannot say from certain knowledge. But many *feel* that it is—and that feeling will probably be, at least for a time, a good guide to new discoveries.

Metaphor is both the mother-lode from which new truths are mined, and (to mix metaphors) the honey with which they are made palatable. But it is always dangerous. The source, the attractiveness and the danger of metaphor in the development and acceptance of evolutionary thought are easily observed. Darwin took over the term "natural selection" from the agricultural breeders because of its formal resemblance to deliberate, human selection. But Darwin had no sooner done so than he was accused of having created a new god. Where men before him had said, "God is responsible for the probing bill of the humming-bird," Darwin now said, "Natural Selection is responsible . . ." But what is this natural selection, his critics protested, if not God under a new name? It stands in the same position in the same sort of sentences, does it not? If x replaces y everywhere, are not x and y synonymous? Is not natural selection God?

No, said Darwin, it is only a metaphorical expression. "Natural selection" stands not for a person or a force; it is shorthand for a process. It is language that deceives us. Our language breeds gods: it is admirably suited to dealing with substances and persons, but poorly adapted to dealing with processes, which it constantly tends to degrade to things or beings. Perhaps no single ability is so characteristic of the true scientist as the ability to think in terms of process in spite of language. The next few pages are an attempt to show what these processes are that the biologist has in mind when he uses the phrase "natural selection." If the going gets a little rough at times, don't worry. Good science, like good music, is not completely understood at the first hearing; it must be returned to several times.

What we *really* mean by "natural selection" can best be shown by discussing a series of graphs. A population of

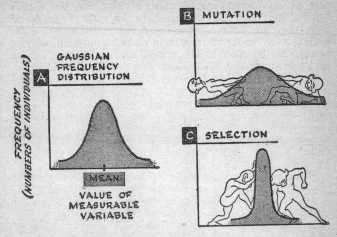

Fig. 7. The effects of mutation and selection on a Gaussian ("normal") distribution curve.

organisms consists of individuals that vary with respect to any single measurable quantity, and the frequency of the various classes is, in the general case, given by a Gaussian, or bell-shaped, curve (Fig. 7), in which the *mean* (average) value is (in general) the *fittest* type. As generation succeeds generation, the population is subjected to two opposing forces. The process of "mutation," by its continual production of new hereditary types, tends to cause the curve to spread out in both directions (Fig. 7), thus diminishing the relative frequency of the most fit types. On the other hand, the process of natural selection results in the elimination of proportionately more of the individuals that are farthest from the mean, and through this differential mortality tends to squeeze the curve inward from both sides (Fig. 7), thus increasing the relative frequency of the "fittest" class.

In time, an equilibrium is struck between these opposing forces. If selection is mild (with respect to the character studied), the stable equilibrium curve will be a broad one (Fig. 8). If selection increases in severity, the curve will become more pinched in shape, the relative frequency of the "fittest" increasing (Fig. 8). But since the production of hereditary novelties through the mutation process can never be stopped, *under no conditions* will the curve consist of a single line, the members of the "fittest" class (Fig. 8), though this is what the phrase "the survival if *the* fittest" may suggest. This is merely one of the criticisms that must be levied against

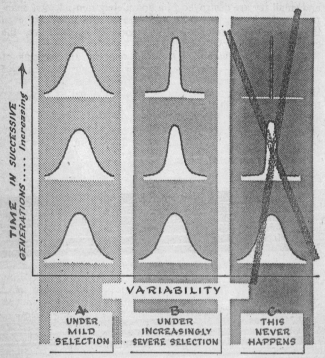

Fig. 8. The effect of natural selection in reducing variability. Never does natural selection result in "the survival of the fittest" only, as shown in C.

this immortal and all-too-popular phrase. Other shortcomings will be pointed out later.

Some other characteristics of the selection process need to be explicitly stated. First, it should be noted, that *the adaptation process operates with only statistical precision.* The race is not always to the swift, nor victory always to the strong. Whether a slower-than-normal rabbit does or does not get caught by the fox is at least partly a matter of luck. It follows, therefore, that the fact of survival of an individual does not necessarily imply his individual lack of fitness.

The process of adaptation is cybernetically effective even when most mortality is a chance affair. A single female salmon lays millions of eggs from which, on the average, only two develop into breeding adults. Undoubtedly most of the eggs and small fry are destroyed in a completely non-selective manner by predators, accident, and disease. If, however, even the smallest percentage of the mortality is selective, the cybernetic process will work.

The whole individual is the unit selected. In speaking of adaptive fitness, it is usually convenient to consider variables one by one: length, weight, speed, intelligence, etc. But the environment does not so analyze the individual; it selects or rejects the entire organism. To speak metaphorically, Nature makes an average of all the characteristics, and then makes her decision. Averaging length, weight, speed and intelligence is surely like dividing apples by oranges—but that is what happens.

Natural selection makes no distinction between genetically and environmentally determined variations. Everyone knows that the size of an adult animal is determined by both its heredity and its environment, particularly by the nutrition received during youth. Nature, in selecting or rejecting the individual, does not inquire into the origin of its adaptation. But the individual who successfully runs the gantlet can pass on to his offspring only what he possesses in the way of hereditary capabilities, divested of his environmental "luck." This makes for a certain inexactness in the selective process; some might even use the word "injustice." Be that as it may, Nature's confounding of heredity and environment in the selective process is one of the explanations of the continuing variability in succeeding generations. Perfection is not a characteristic of the single individual or the unique act of Nature; at best, it is a statistical property of the population as a whole. The generation of error is without end.

4

Is Evolution Progress?

THE study of the history of ideas shows that when a novel theory is first born, it is judged not so much on its own merits as it is on the basis of its supposed association with other ideas already well known to us. In other words, we judge unfamiliar ideas as we judge unfamiliar people—by the company they keep. But there is this difference: the idea doesn't really keep any company; we assign it its associates. The greater part of the rejection or acceptance of a new idea proves on close examination to stem from judgments of "guilt by association," or innocence by the same means. So it was with the idea of evolution during the first part of the nineteenth century. As we have seen, it was rejected by most men because of its association with ideas of atheism, radicalism, revolution, sedition and ungentlemanliness—all completely irrelevant to the truth or falsity of the theory. But the idea survived nevertheless, and for reasons that were perhaps equally irrelevant—its association with another idea that was then rapidly increasing its holds on men's minds, the idea of progress.

It is difficult for twentieth-century men to realize that the idea of progress is an extremely young idea. Of course a few of the ancients had a word to say for progress—a few of the Greeks, for instance. But the idea never really caught on among the masses of men until about two hundred years ago, as J. B. Bury has shown in his history, *The Idea of Progress*. During most of man's existence, a properly conducted public-opinion poll would have shown that, almost without exception, men interpreted human history—both past and to come—in terms either of a Golden Age concept, or in cyclical terms. The Golden Age concept takes various forms, among them the Garden of Eden story. Details vary, but the sense is always the same: *Things were once wonderful, but look at the mess we're in now.* Such an interpretation is natural to old age, and can always be supported by facts, if they are properly biased and selected. An equally plausible interpretation, also supportable by carefully chosen facts, is the cyclical theory of history: *Things are always getting either better or worse, but there's never any real change or genuine direction to history.*

This cynical view of history has probably always been less widely believed than the Golden Age view—perhaps because cynics are rarer than pessimists?—but, rather interestingly, has, in our time, been revived in modified form by Arnold Toynbee, in his *Study of History*.

In contrast to these interpretations, the idea of progress asserts that there is, in some sense, a progressive improvement in man's life. Not at all times, but viewed over a long period of time. Not at all places simultaneously, but ultimately everywhere. The idea must not be stated with the precision of a mathematical theorem, for it is not such; it is primarily a *feeling* that governs a man's view of the world and motivates his actions. The feeling has been immensely important in the development of the Western world during the last two hundred years, and now is becoming explosively effective in the Eastern.

The idea has not a single author, but many. Among the more important ones was a French nobleman, Antoine Nicolas de Condorcet, who, during the French Revolution—in fact while he was in hiding to save his life (which he lost)— wrote a magnificently optimistic *Sketch for a Historical Picture of the Progress of the Human Mind*. In this, he divided the past history of mankind into nine epochs, striving to show how each had led *upward* to the next; and predicted a tenth epoch, into which mankind was just entering—"The last of life, for which the first was made," as Browning might have said. Condorcet's analysis was entirely plausible—far more plausible on the eve of the nineteenth century than it had ever been before, and his views captured the imagination of men. No longer was history to be viewed as a "tale told by an idiot, full of sound and fury, signifying nothing." Running through all the hubbub was a persistent leitmotif that made sense. It was beautiful. Man was moving ever upward, and who was to say what he might not do? *I will show,* said Condorcet,

> . . . that Nature has set no limit to the perfecting of the human faculties, that the perfectibility of man is truly indefinite; that the progress of this perfectibility, henceforth independent of any power that might wish to arrest it, has no other limit than the duration of the globe on which Nature has placed us.

Heady stuff! Small wonder that, in the battle for men's minds, the pessimistic growlings of Ecclesiastes and much of the rest of traditional religious writings lost ground in the nineteenth century. Judged by his actions, Western man now worships the great god Progress more faithfully than ever he did

Jehovah. In this religious conversion Condorcet played no small role.

Human history made sense. Perhaps natural history did, too? Was not the succession of forms revealed in the rocks evidence of a *progression* from lower to higher forms of life? Perhaps to be *descended* from an ape was a repulsive thought; but why not say instead that we have *ascended* from—well, why not say from an innocuous amoeba, without mentioning any closer cousins? "From amoeba to man" became a catch-word after Darwin. *Upward! Progress! Evolution!* Even today, "the common man," insofar as he accepts evolution, probably does so because the theory rides on the coattails of that popular of all gods, Progress.

But is evolution progress? The philosopher, Bertrand Russell, has wryly remarked, "A process which led from amoeba to man appeared to the philosophers to be obviously progress—though whether the amoeba would agree with this

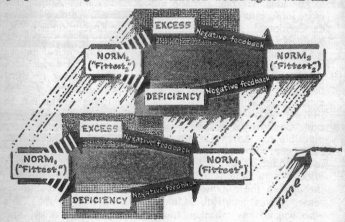

Fig. 9. Showing how the Darwinian cybernetic system, in the presence of environmental change, produces secular change in the definition of "fittest."

opinion is not known." Biologists have been by no means agreed in their opinions. The issues are complex, so the whole question is best approached as we would approach a dangerous animal, from the ambush of other questions that may not at first sight appear related. We must surround the question before closing in.

The Idea of Secular Change

Darwinian adaptation, recall, is not in its essence a progressive change, but merely a dynamic way of preserving the status quo. In terms of the diagrams given in the preceding chapter, we can represent progressive change in two ways; First (Fig. 9), we conceive of an initial cybernetic system (the system involving Norm₁) as being subjected to strain as the result of an environmental redefinition of "fittest," the

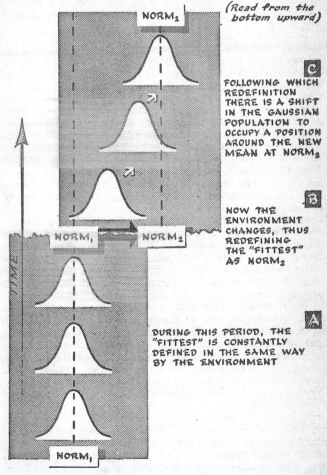

Fig. 10. Evolutionary secular shift in terms of change in a Gaussian distribution.

newly defined norm being called Norm$_2$. (For example, the mean temperature may drop, thus favoring larger organisms than formerly.) Under the new definition, the whole cybernetic system slides, as it were, to a new position—at which dynamic stability will be maintained until the next redefinition of "fittest," *i.e.*, the next change in the environment. Second, in Fig. 10 we see the same process expressed in a different system of graphs, in terms of changes in a Gaussian distribution curve.

Both figures attempt to depict what we call "secular change," that is, a drift in the state of the world that is not merely part of a temporary fluctuation. As we thus graph the idea, we must remind ourselves of the unavoidable dangers of any mapping process: that of implying direction. By convention, we think of one direction of the paper (toward the "top") as being upward; and another (toward the right side) as being onward. It is all too easy to think of diagrams like those just given as representing evolution "upward" or "onward." A moment's reflection shows, however, that the orientation of the diagrams could just as well have been reversed. All they represent, really, is change. If there is *direction* to the change, that fact must be revealed by logical investigation; direction must not be inferred from the conventions of map-making.

Man himself has, unwittingly and unwillingly, brought about some well-authenticated cases of evolution in a small way by altering the meaning of "fittest" for some of his pests. In California, scale insects attacking citrus trees were for many years successfully controlled by cyanide fumigation. In three different species, at different times and places, insects have been found which could no longer be killed in this way. In each instance, there must have been present, at the time fumigation began, several mutant forms that just happened to be resistant to cyanide. The mutants survived fumigation and bred a new generation that was more resistant than the initial one. Successive fumigations continued the selection process. With the passing of the years, the resistant forms spread out from each center of origin, displacing the "normal" types. For the insects, cyanide had become a new aspect of "natural selection."

A similar phenomenon was observed with houseflies upon the advent of the insecticide, DDT. When this substance was first developed, men optimistically believed that houseflies would become things of the past. Soon, however, it was found that flies were no longer susceptible to it. Experimental analysis showed that the resistant flies were genetically different from the original strains. Continued use of DDT resulted in the displacement of the "normal" type by the resistant type.

Another instance of the same phenomenon is that of penicillin-resistant strains of disease-causing microbes, which constantly threaten to replace the "normal" strains, as the antibiotic continues to be used, particularly when it is used sparingly, thus favoring the gradual selection of resistant strains. The effectiveness of other antibiotics is similarly limited by the natural-selection process.

What about the relevance of these phenomena to the concept of progress? Would we say that each of the changes described is an example of "progress"? Our first impulse may be to say, *Not from man's point of view*—since the change makes the human situation more difficult. This, however, is a relatively trivial point. Is the change progressive from the point of view of the pest? It is tempting to say, *Yes*—to say that the pest, in response to the threat of a new selecting agent, develops a new and superior form. But it is important to note that the new form is superior *only in the new environment*. If it is set in competition with the old form in an environment that is lacking the special selecting agent, the resistant strain is speedily displaced by the non-resistant strain through a process of natural selection. In other words, the resistant strain is not a kind of Superpest that possesses some sort of generalized superiority; it is merely a variant that has developed a specialized resistance to a particular agent, for which development it has had to pay a price (in some sense) in the loss of other elements of vigor. Is this progress? It does not seem quite like what we have in mind when we use the word. With each pest we have two possible cybernetic systems, each one with a different norm-element. Is one norm "higher" than the other? Only if it is, will we be willing to say that the shift from one cybernetic level to another is a form of progress.

By far the greater part of the evolutionary process consists of small steps of the sort discussed, in which the shift from one cybernetic system to another cannot usefully be said to involve *direction* at all. Over a long period of time, the shift may (for the most part) be in the same *sense*—but must we speak of this as direction? The horse of today has evolved from a four-toed ancestor about the size of a dog. The evolution involved the proliferation of many forms now extinct, and frequent reversals in "direction," *i.e.*, from larger to smaller. But even if we ignore the extinctions and the reversals, should we say that horses have evolved "progressively" "upward" from the little *Eohippus* of thirty million years ago to the big, modern *Equus*? Surely we are not to succumb to the superstition of our time that holds that bigness is, per se, superior to littleness? And if we do not make this error, how can we say that the evolution from *Eohippus* to *Equus* was a progress? The former undoubtedly enjoyed as good a cybernetic equilibrium with its environment as the latter.

Even those who are not tempted to equate Bigger with Better are likely to succumb to another temptation: to think of parasites as immoral, and the evolution from the free-living state to a condition of dependence as being somehow a "downward" evolution, a "degenerative" or "retrogressive" evolution. "Degenerative" it certainly is, if one means by this no more than that unneeded organs wither away in the process—but is this bad? What virtue would there be in a tapeworm's having eyespots, living as it does in the perpetual darkness of the mammalian gut? Is extravagance a virtue? And as for "retrogressive,"—well, a tapeworm is like nothing on its family tree. It has not gone backward to become an earlier species; it has gone forward (if we must use direction words) to develop new adaptations to its particular situation. Not any old worm can be a successful parasite; it takes special gifts.

So we see that the concept of progress, for all its historical importance in sheltering the idea of evolution, is not easily applicable to facts of biology. There may be a sense in which it is useful to say that progress has occurred; but we have not yet discovered it. Perhaps we will later. For the present, it is best to agree that neither adaptation alone, nor adaptation coupled with secular change, necessarily constitute progress.

Limitations of Darwinian Evolution

The coupled processes of adaptation plus secular change, as just described, we may refer to as the "Darwinian evolution process." It is the heart of Darwin's theory. Before passing to other aspects of the total theory of evolution, it would be well to point out important characteristics of this logical core.

Secular shift plus adaptation will not, by themselves, account for the multiplication of contemporaneous species that has occurred repeatedly during the course of evolution. Through very extensive shifts of the "fittest" norm, a breeding population may, in the course of time, become so different from what it was much earlier that one would want to call it by a different species name—but it would still, at a given point in time, be only a single species. The subdivision of one species into several that exist contemporaneously requires other processes.

A secular shift in the norm of a cybernetic system can be successfully accomplished only if the shift is not too great. There must, at every stage, be at least a few members of the existing population (in one of the "tails" of the Gaussian curve) which are near enough to the new norm to be able to reproduce. If none are, then the population that is suddenly subject to a new norm will be eliminated. As an example in point, malaria-carrying species of mosquitoes, unlike houseflies, apparently produce no genetic variants that are resistant to DDT; consequently, it was possible, just after the Second World War, to eliminate virtually all of the mosquitoes from Sardinia by thorough spraying of the entire island, thereby freeing it completely from malaria. Another instance: the early use of penicillin was attended by many avoidable failures because it was used too sparingly. The doses used killed less than 100 percent of the microbes infecting the patient. The minority of microbes that survived, being genetically resistant, would produce a new population in which additional spontaneous genetic variation would produce still more resistant forms. If the dosage was increased only gradually in dealing with a difficult case, the process of adaptation plus secular shift nullified the therapy. With an understanding of the evolutionary theory underlying the problem, the procedure was modified; nowadays one prescribes heroic dosages of penicillin or none at all.

In the evolution of any structure or function, every intermediate stage must be of additional advantage to the species. There is no way in which a species can evolve by foresight, producing the maladapted beginning of an organ which, when completely evolved, will have adaptive value. In the words of a leading contemporary authority, Theodosius Dobzhansky, *evolution is opportunistic:* natural selection seizes upon the best variation available at the moment, regardless of its ultimate potentialities. How then are we to account for the evolution of such a complicated organ as the eye? "The eye to this day gives me a cold shudder," wrote Darwin to the American botanist, Asa Gray, in 1860; and long after Darwin ceased to be troubled by this challenge to his theory, his detractors were insisting that it was an unanswerable refutation of his views. Look, they said, if even the slightest thing is wrong—if the retina is missing, or the lens opaque, or the dimensions in error—the eye fails to form a recognizable image and is consequently useless. Since it must be either perfect, or perfectly useless, how could it have been evolved by small, successive, Darwinian steps?

The objection is a formidable one, but it no longer looks unanswerable. For one thing, such objectors forget the soundness of old Desiderius Erasmus' realistic principle: *In the land of the blind, One-Eye is King.* Were all other organisms blind, the animal which managed to evolve even a *very* poor eye would thereby have some advantage over others. Oysters have such poor eyes—many tiny sensitive spots that can do no more than detect changes in the intensity of light. An oyster may not be able to enjoy television, but it can detect a passing shadow, react to it as if it were caused by an approaching predator, and—because it is sometimes right—live another day. By selecting examples from various places in the animal kingdom, we can assemble a nicely graded series of eyes, passing, by not too big steps, from the primitive eyes of oysters to the excellent (though not perfect) eyes of men and birds. Such a series, made up from contemporary species, is not supposed to be the actual historical series; but it shows us how evolution could have occurred.

The principle that intermediate stages must be of adaptive value can be used to explain the absence of structures that would be useful to organisms, but of which we can conceive no useful intermediate stages. The English biologist, J. B. S. Haldane, has remarked, "If I were designing an animal as a construct with no historical background, like the ideal state [*e.g.,* Plato's *Republic*], I should very probably give it an eye with a concave mirror rather than a lens," for such an optical system is free of chromatic aberration, to mention only one advantage. But it is difficult to conceive of a series of stages leading to a reflector-type eye in which the early stages would have been of any use, and so we find no such eye in the entire animal kingdom. An engineer, Henri Morgenroth, has pointed out to me that a similar difficulty has probably precluded the development of the wheel and axle in the animal kingdom, and consequently has ruled out the possibility of flight by means of revolving propellers.

No species can evolve any structure or function that is exclusively for the benefit of another species. This is "Paley's Principle," which was discussed in the preceding chapter. It is basic to all thinking about evolution.

Speciation: An Answer to Environmental Complexity

A. N. Whitehead has said, "Seek simplicity; and distrust it." It is difficult to imagine a more fruitful guide for scientific research. To see anything at all, we must abstract a few elements from the infinite totality; but when we do, we undoubtedly warp the truth. Therefore we must secondly—and it must be *secondly,* not at first—we must secondly turn a suspicious eye on the simplicity we have found and see in what way it is false to facts. Then we introduce new elements into the theory, thus complicating it. Then we look for new simplicities. Then . . . and so the process goes on, indefinitely. Such is the dialectic of intellectual inquiry.

In constructing our logical systems of evolution, we have spoken repeatedly of the environment—*the* environment, indeed! As though any organism were subject to only one environment. There are a multitude of environments, as many as the fineness of our analytical methods permits us to recognize. It is not enough that we should make only gross distinctions into the environments of forest, grassland and sea; close observation shows that each of these is subdivisible much further. "The" tropical rain forest, as the zoologist, W. C. Allee (1926), has shown, consists of at least seven different environments, ranging from the treetops, about 125 feet above the ground, through the various levels (or "stories") of the trees, down to the forest floor and the dirt itself. The levels differ from one another in temperature, illumination and humidity; in each may be found a distinctive assortment of animals and plants. Some organisms range through many levels, but others are confined to one or two for the greater part of their lives, living literally within calling distance of organisms with which they have as little to do as with the inhabitants of another continent.

Nor is variation in space all: there is also variation in time. Winter is certainly a different environment than summer, and July than May. With short-lived species like fruit flies of the genus *Drosophila,* in which the generations succeed one another in a matter of a couple of weeks, it has been shown by Dobzhansky that the hereditary make-up of a population in summer is statistically different from that of the same population in the same place in the spring. For longer-lived species of plants and animals, long-term secular changes, such as those involved in the waxing and waning of glacial periods, may produce similar fluctuations.

A living organism is not, therefore, subject to one environment, but to a variety of environments with varying degrees of spatial and temporal separation. To which of its many environments does a species adjust? *To all of them.* It strikes a sort of balance between the various selective pressures, thus assembling a sort of hereditary stew that does well enough for all its environments, though it is far from perfectly adapted to any one. Compromise is the order of the day.

Where the range of a continuously interbreeding population is great, the mixture of hereditary elements at widely separated regions may be demonstrably different. Especially is this true along a north-south transect of a species range. In many species of mammals and birds, individuals from colder regions are larger than individuals of the same species living in warmer regions. This generalization is called "Bergmann's rule." It is commonly explained as an adaptation to temperature: a larger animal has less body surface per unit weight, and consequently can conserve body heat better. The same type of explanation is given for the related "Allen's rule," that animals in colder regions have more-reduced appendages (*e.g.*, heat-radiating ears and tails) than do their relatives in warmer climes. In passing, be it noted that the rules apply only to members of the same species. It is unreasonable to expect the rules to hold for animals built on markedly different plans, *e.g.*, an elephant of the tropics compared with an arctic lemming.

At least part of the difference between northern and southern varieties of a single species is hereditarily determined. In terms of our cybernetic scheme, the norm of "fittest" is different at the two extremes of the ranges, hence the different adaptations. Will the animals in time not come to be different species? Not so long as interchange of hereditary material between the two regions is possible through interbreeding with animals living in the intermediate zones. For one species to split into two something else is required, namely *isolation*.

It is an interesting commentary on the slowness with which the human mind works to note that Darwin did not see that isolation is essential for the multiplication of species until at least five years after he had grasped the logic of evolutionary adaptation, in spite of the fact that it was the consequences of isolation in the Galápagos that had first started him puzzling about evolution. We now speak of the process of subdivision and multiplication of species as *speciation*. In recalling the difficulty he had in seeing the essentiality of isolation, Darwin exclaimed, "How I could have overlooked it . . . is astonishing to me, except on the principle of Columbus and his egg. . . . I can remember the very spot in the road, whilst in my carriage, when to my joy the solution occurred to me."

The solution, as we now see it, is roughly this. So long as interbreeding is possible through the entire range of a species, the cybernetic adjustment to the different environmental norms is kept imperfect by the mixing process of heredity; the total heredity is a compromise solution to the conflicting definitions of fitness. But whenever one small region is cut off from the rest, as by the rising of an impassable range of mountains, or the subsidence of land into a barrier sea, then the population which is isolated need no longer compromise with the needs of other regions. As a result, it will make a much better adjustment to its particular environment. It will soon, therefore, come to differ from the "parental" population. As time goes on, the physical environment may undergo further changes, which will entail still further alterations of the local population. Ultimately the two populations may differ so greatly from each other that we feel obliged to give them different species names; we then say that speciation has occurred.

At what precise point in time do we say, *There are now two species?* This is like asking, "When does night change to day?" The process is a continuous one, which we can represent as in Fig. 11. It is an essential consequence of the theory of evolution that only by an arbitrary decision can we decide exactly when first to say, *Now there are two species where before there was only one.* This conclusion represents a sharp break with the pre-Darwinian attitude toward species. At least since the time of Linnaeus, naturalists, almost without exception, took it for granted that species were "atomistic," *i.e.,* sharply discontinuous. A specimen belonged either to one species or to another; there could be no uncertainty. Species were always truly distinct, they thought. Of course, the more closely they studied nature, the oftener they found exceptional specimens and species—instances in which (as we Darwinians would say) speciation was still incomplete, being at the moment of

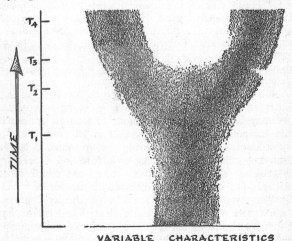

Fig. 11. At what precise point in time does one species become two? At T_2? At T_3? At T_4? The decision is necessarily arbitrary. (From Hardin, *Biology: Its Human Implications,* 2nd ed., W H. Freeman & Co., San Francisco; 1952. By permission.)

observation at the stage represented (say) by time T_3 in our diagram. The atomistic, Linnaean taxonomists (classifiers) disposed of such embarrassing instances by verbal fiat: the offending intermediate forms were said to be "not good species," which justified the naturalist's discarding them. How the bias of such a traditional practice protected taxonomists from thinking is clearly evident from a comment Lyell made in 1867:

> In regard to shells, I have always found that dealers have a positive prejudice against intermediate forms, and one of the most philosophical of them, now no more, once confessed to me that it was very much against his trade interest to give an honest opinion that certain varieties were not real species, or that certain forms, made distinct genera by some conchologists, ought not so to rank. Nine-tenths of his customers, if told that it was not a good genus or a good species, would say, "Then I need not buy it." What they wanted was names, not things.

All excuse for such an attitude—if, indeed, there ever was an excuse—disappeared with the advent of Darwinism. A modern taxonomist must live with uncertainty, or live falsely. "Whoever wants to hold to firm rules," one zoologist has remarked, "should give up taxonomical work. Nature is much too disorderly for such a man. He would better turn to collecting postage stamps." Nevertheless, there are, even today—one hundred years after Darwin—a few such stamp-collector taxonomists still cluttering up the literature with unenlightening discussions of "the species problem," as it is dignified. Fortunately, their race is a vanishing one.

It should be clear by this time that no thoroughly satisfactory definition of a species can be given. As a first approximation, we may say that organisms belong to separate species if they are incapable of breeding together at all (a dog and a cat, for example) or if the offspring they produce is sterile (as is the mule, the hybrid offspring of a mare and a jackass). Two organisms will also usually be considered members of different species if they are physiologically incapable of breeding together, even though they may be genetically compatible. An example will make this point clear. Vanderplank has found that interbreeding between two species of tsetse flies is prevented by the incompatibility of their genital structures. In the act of mating, the male of one species usually punctures the abdomen of the female of the other species—an unkind cut, indeed! Experimentally it is possible to alter the offending organ, following which surgery, hybrids are readily produced. A more amusing form of structural isolation (within a species in this case) is found in a four-eyed fish of the genus *Anableps* in which the intromittent organ of the male is sometimes on the right-hand side, sometimes on the left; and a corresponding genital variation occurs among the females. Males that are left-handed (so to speak) can mate only with right-handed females, and reciprocally for right-handed males and left-handed females. Justice demands that such creatures be confined to County Limerick, Ireland; but, in sad and sober fact, they live in South America.

Two populations of organisms which cannot interbreed will certainly be assigned different species names. But the necessary criteria of specific status do not include so severe a condition; it is enough if two populations merely fail to interbreed. There are many pairs of species of birds, insects and mammals which will produce fertile hybrids when the male of one species is confined with the female of another, but which will not interbreed at all in a state of nature. The reasons for their failure to do so are often of the sort we call "psychological." Sturtevant (1915) and, later, Spieth (1951) have studied the courtship of various small garbage flies, discovering that it is a matter of vast importance to a courted female (given free choice) how the male dances around and how he flutters his wings. Similar innate species-specific courtship patterns and instinctive responses are known in hundreds of species of animals, and often serve to maintain reproductive isolation between populations which otherwise might interbreed. The psychological reactions are innate, that is, inherited, but Cushing (1941) has pointed out that there is considerable evidence that the mating of many species of birds is determined by experience—*i.e.*, a bird *learns*, largely as a result of early conditioning ("imprinting") by members of his own species, which is the correct kind of bird to associate with. Lorenz has been a leader in the study of such imprinting. Of course, the ability to learn or to be imprinted must itself be innate. It is quite reasonable to suppose, as Cushing does, that the speciation process in many of the "higher" animals may occasionally be aided by a social conditioning process which teaches the individual to distinguish between in-group and out-group, as human beings certainly do.

Effective as psychological factors may be in maintaining isolation of populations, it is difficult to see how they can ever initiate the isolation (except possibly in man). Far easier is it to imagine that the initial isolation is a geographic one, which cuts off an appreciable-sized group of the population from the rest of the species, thus permitting it (for whatever causes) to accumulate those variations, psychological and others, that may enable it to retain its identity as a separate population, should the geographical isolating barriers later disappear. The phrase "geographical barriers" may call to mind such mighty obstacles as mile-high mountains and thousand-league oceans, but much more modest impediments may serve the cause of speciation. As Lamotte (1951) observed, a mere cart track in the mud may bar the way to a snail (at least for a time). By contrast, the American golden plover annually flies from the Arctic to the tip of Patagonia near the Antarctic. Barriers are relative matters.

Speciation: Possible Outcomes

Whenever a species is subdivided by an environmental barrier, the isolated populations can be expected to become genetically different from each other in the course of time, for the simple reason that no two different regions are ever *exactly* alike, and each will therefore select for a slightly different norm. After the descendant populations have become genetically differentiated, the barrier may disappear. Then what happens? There are three possibilities: reunion, coexistence, extinction.

Reunion. If the once-separated populations have not developed physiological or psychological barriers to interbreeding, two genetically different populations may simply fuse, so to speak. The extent to which separation, differentiation into "races," and refusion has occurred in the past cannot be readily determined, but there is an increasing amount of evidence that it is a common-enough occurrence to deserve the epithet "normal." For technical reasons, the best evidence is available among the plants, though the phenomenon occurs among animals as well. Very thorough studies of the speciation process have been made by Clausen, Keck and Hiesey at the Carnegie Institution of Washington laboratory at Stanford. As one result of these studies, it was finally possible to assert, with considerable confidence, the substantial accuracy of the "family tree" shown in Fig. 12. The word "tree" is used only for traditional reasons. The true relationships of species are the result not only of an arboreal branching process, but also of an untree-like fusing or anastomosing process. When viewed from a distance great enough to blur the fine details, a "phylogenetic tree"—a metaphorical genealogical tree—may really look like an ordinary tree; but viewed more closely, many of its portions clearly are more net-like than tree-like. Failure to realize this has spawned many ridiculous arguments as to whether man, for example, has a "monophyletic" (from one species or a "polyphletic" (from many species, by hybridization) origin. The question is purely a matter of focus. From a sufficient conceptual distance, man may be regarded as monophyletic. Up close, when greater detail can be seen, his origin is just as clearly polyphletic. From the great emotional heat this controversy engenders, one might

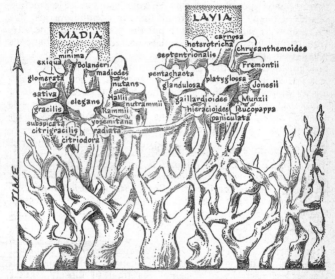

Fig. 12. Evolution, as it has probably occurred in a group of plants: showing how "nature is too disorderly" for those who seek to find clean-cut "phylogenetic trees" and unidirectional evolution everywhere. (From Clausen, *Stages in the Evolution of Plant Species,* Cornell University Press, Ithaca, N. Y.; 1951. By permission.)

suppose that a consequence of great scientific or sociological moment hinges upon the conclusion. None of the disputants ever condescends to tell us what it is.

Coexistence. How isolation may be followed by coexistence of descendant species is seen in the phenomenon that the zoologist, Ernst Mayr (1942), calls "double invasion." Many well-isolated oceanic islands are inhabited by pairs of closely related bird species. For such birds to reach, and colonize, a distant isle is evidently so improbable an event that the time between two such events is enough to allow for speciation to take place between the first island population and its parental continental population. In keeping with this line of reasoning, we find that islands remote from a mainland (in terms of the traveling ability of birds) show no examples of "double invasion." At the other extreme, an island of easy access is invaded so frequently that specific differences between it and the mainland cannot develop at all.

Extinction. Finally, the disappearance of a barrier between two speciated populations may be followed by the extinction of one of them. Why? Why don't the two populations just live in peace with each other? Or to put the matter more generally, what principles are involved in determining what happens when two species or races which formerly dwelt apart are brought together in the same geographical area? Each instance is a particular case, but there is a general principle underlying all of them, a principle that has been utilized for at least a hundred years; but which, for deep and curious reasons, has existed largely at the unconscious level of evolutionary theorization. This principle we call—

The Competitive Exclusion Principle

In a finite world it is impossible for species that are competitive in very respect to coexist indefinitely. Or, with less accuracy, but greater brevity: *Competitors cannot coexist.*

Examples of the operation of this principle are legion. Everyone knows how, when Australia, a long-isolated part of the world, was opened up to colonization by animals from our part of the world, there was a rapid displacement of species after species of marsupials (pouched mammals) by placental mammals. Predation aside, each displacement of a marsupial species has been by a placental mammal of closely similar habits of life; or, as biologists commonly put it, by an animal that occupies the same "ecological niche." The threat of the extinction of almost all the native marsupials has led to strong control measures, aimed at preventing further immigrations, or at controlling the competition already in operation to prevent it from working through to its logical conclusion. Similar examples of competitive displacement are to be found in the natural history of many islands.

However (a critic may object)—what about examples on the other side of the argument? What about those instances in which an immigrant competes with the native animal without either one displacing the other? What explanation do you offer when competitors do coexist? To this, the evolutionist has an answer that must, at first glance, appear to be a very strange one: *The Competitive Exclusion Principle is established by indubitable theory, and all factual instances of the contrary must be dismissed as spurious.*

This surely sounds very unscientific! It sounds like the dogmatism of the past, like the worst sort of Platonist asserting the supremacy of ideas over mere facts. Yet, appearances are deceiving: it *is* a quite scientific statement. The Exclusion Principle *is* established by theory, and facts must be interpreted in the light of it. To appreciate the reasons for this surprising state of affairs we must first understand the theory.

The theory is mathematical, and for that reason it is part of a closed book to most people. But like most mathematics, the sense of it, and not a little of the conviction of it, can fortunately be conveyed in ordinary words, appealing to the reader's "intuition." To illustrate the working out of the principle we will use a simple analogy. (We will admit, however, that the analogy is a strained one.)

Let us imagine a very odd savings bank which has only two depositors. For some obscure reason the bank pays one of the depositors 2 percent compound interest, while paying the other 2.01 percent. Let us suppose further (and here the analogy is really strained) that whenever the sum of the combined funds of the two depositors reaches two million dollars, the bank arbitrarily appropriates one million dollars of it, taking from each depositor in proportion to his holdings at that time. Then both accounts are allowed to grow until their sum again equals two million dollars, at which time the appropriation process is repeated. If this procedure is continued indefinitely, what will happen to the wealth of these two depositors? A little intuition shows us (and mathematics verifies) that the man who receives the greater rate of interest will, in time, have *all* the money, and the other man none (we assume a penny cannot be subdivided). No matter how small the difference between the two interest rates (so long as there is a difference) such will be the outcome.

Translated into evolutionary terms, this is what competition in nature amounts to. The fluctuating limit of one million to two million represents the finite available wealth (food, shelter, etc.) of any natural environment, and the difference in interest rates represents the difference between the competing species in their efficiency in producing offspring. No matter how small this difference may be, one species will eventually replace the other. In the scale of geological time, even a small competitive difference will result in a rapid extermination of the less successful species. Competitive differences that are so small as to be unmeasurable by direct means will, by virtue of the compound-interest effect, ultimately result in the extinction of one competing species by another.

The Nature of Theory

Theory in science plays various roles. It summarizes voluminous data succinctly. It presents a picture that is easy to remember. It injects rationality into the world. And, not the least important, it leads us to discover new facts. It is hardly possible for a theory to fulfill the last-named function unless we have a confidence in our theory that is not easily shaken by apparently contradictory facts. Faced with incompatible facts our first impulse must be to say, "The facts are wrong; not the theory." Saying this, we put ourselves in a dangerous position, of course; but only those theories that are capable of achieving so strong a hold on our minds will reach the highest degree of usefulness.

Let us recall an example of this principle in the physical sciences. Newton explained the motions of the heavenly bodies by a beautiful and all-embracing theory that for many generations seemed to fit the facts perfectly. Then, in the first part of the nineteenth century, increasingly more accurate measurements of the motions of planets showed that the orbit of Uranus was not completely predictable from known facts and Newtonian theory. When this became known, did astronomers abandon the theory? Not at all! Instead, Leverrier (in France) and Adams (in England) assumed that the theory must be correct and the facts, incorrect (that is, incomplete). They assumed there must be another and as yet still unknown planet beyond Uranus, whose gravitational attraction accounted for the perturbations of the nearer planet. Using Newtonian theory, they calculated where this planet must be, and when observers looked for it, there it was. Thus was Neptune discovered by asserting the primacy of theory in the face of apparently contradictory facts. (Of course the theory itself is based on a vast body of facts; and ultimately we did abandon Newtonian theory in part. But elucidating the subtle reasons for this abandonment would take us beyond our present needs.)

The Exclusion Principle in biology plays a role similar to that of the Newtonian laws of motion in physics. It is a prime guide to the discovery of facts. We use the principle coupled with an axiom that is equally fundamental but which is almost never explicitly stated. We may call this the *Inequality Axiom*, and it states: *If two populations are distinguishable, they are competitively unequal.* The mood behind this axiom is an old one—that no two things in the world are ever exactly equal. This is an axiom which we readily admit of the material objects of the world, but our admission of it is usually a grudging one, for we are tempted to add, "What of it?"

Perhaps no two postage stamps are quite the same, but does it matter? They serve the same function. Why quibble? The objection is a sound one when mere *things* are being considered, for many differences are without significance. But with *processes,* it is otherwise. Because of the compound-interest effect, no difference between competing populations is trivial. The slightest difference—and our acceptance of the Inequality Axiom asserts that a difference always exists—will result in the eventual extinction of one population by another. Put in another way, the Exclusion Principle tells us that two distinguishable populations can coexist in the same geographical region only if they live in different ecological worlds (thus avoiding complete competition and strict coexistence). Whenever we find, say, two birds that live in the same geographical region and *appear* to lead the same sort of life, close examination always reveals some important differences. One species may live near the forest floor while another lives higher up in the branches; or one may eat seeds and the other berries; or one may eat small seeds, the other large; or the less efficient one in their common way of life may have an alternative source of food not utilized by its competitor. Strict coexistence is impossible. Every persisting species, in a profound sense, lives in a world of its own. No ecological niche is large enough for two occupants.

It is a most astonishing thing how a doctrine that is so central to evolutionary theory should have so long gone without explicit recognition. Only in the past decade or so have an appreciable number of biologists seen the basic importance of the principle and consciously made use of it in their thinking; even now it is not really generally known. Our present appreciation of it, such as it is, stems largely from publications of a Russian biologist, G. F. Gause, who did some very interesting work in both theoretical and experimental aspects of evolutionary theory in this country during the early 1930's, under the stimulus of Raymond Pearl of Johns Hopkins University. Later in the decade he returned to Russia where, for a time, he continued his studies on competition. But as the purge of Western biology began to develop in the late 'thirties, Gause evidently found that competition was much too touchy a subject for objective study in a socialistic society, for he completely abandoned this field and embarked on the "safe" study of pharmacology. Gause's early work is remembered in the Western world, however, by frequent reference to the Exclusion Principle as "Gause's principle." This is a rather curious identification, inasmuch as Gause himself (1934) specifically acknowledged earlier statements of the principle by the American, A. J. Lotka (1932), the Italian,

Vito Volterra (1926), and the Englishman, J. B. S. Haldane (1924). And, though Darwin never stated the principle explicitly, there is no doubt that he was unconsciously aware of it. "Competition will generally be most severe between those forms which are most nearly related to each other in habits, constitution and structure," he said, and he used the principle repeatedly in explaining the extinction of competing forms. That he never stated the principle explicitly and accurately is in keeping with his work in general, which suffers from his admitted limitations in thinking mathematically. Yet one cannot read the *Origin* carefully without feeling that the thought is there, three quarters of a century before Gause. The history of the Principle of Competitive Exclusion brings to mind that wise observation of A. N. Whitehead: "Everything of importance has already been said by someone who did not discover it."

Extinction and the Exclusion Principle

In the light of the Principle of Competitive Exclusion, it appears highly probable that the fate that awaits most species is early extinction, a disappearance in which no progeny-species are left behind. The argument for this conclusion is fairly straightforward. To begin with, we define a "physical isolation" as an event in time, a chapter in biological history: say the separation of one portion of a species from the rest by a physical barrier (such as a mountain chain). The term "physical isolation" is applicable until such time as the physical entity no longer acts as a barrier to the interbreeding of the two populations. How long a time will this be? Obviously, there is no general answer, but the most reasonable assumption is that isolations which are long-lasting are less frequent than ones which are short-lasting. We assume, that is, an inverse relationship between the duration of physical isolations and their frequencies.

Recall now the sequence of development in the process of speciation. Initially, the freshly isolated populations are nearly the same genetically; as time goes on they diverge more and more. When they are distinguishably different, but still capable of interbreeding (if put together), we may speak of them as races. Ultimately, if the physical isolation endures long enough, they become so different from each other that interbreeding is impossible; we then say that the two populations are reproductively isolated from each other, and we speak of them as distinct species. The whole process here described, whether carried through to completion or not, we will refer to as the speciation process.

What are the various possible outcomes of the speciation

process, and what their relative frequencies? In the light of our assumption, it is clear that, most often, the speciation process will go no further than the formation of races before the physical isolation comes to an end and the germ plasm of the two races is melded into one by interbreeding. If, however, the speciation process continues until separate species are formed before the physical barrier breaks down, then what happens? The outcome is plainly dependent on the extent to which ecological differentiation has occurred: Do the two species occupy the same ecological niche, or not— that is, are they completely competitive? It seems probable that the degree of ecological differentiation will also increase with time spent in physical isolation. On this assumption, we would predict that, more often than not, "sister species" will be incapable of coexistence: when the physical isolation is at an end, one sister species will extinguish the other. Rarest of all will be those instances in which physical isolation endures long enough to permit both speciation and ecological differentiation to proceed far enough to permit the reunited populations to live together in harmony in the same geographical region.

What Is the Sense of Evolution?

Historically, the idea of evolution gained acceptance fairly rapidly because it was thought to make good sense. The "sense," in fact, preceded evolutionary theory: it was the sense of a chain, something connected link by link, something that led from "lower" forms to "higher." The idea that living forms could be arranged in such a chain is immensely older than the theory of evolution. The phrase "the missing link," now commonly used in connection with evolution, is a vestigial remainder of a much older conception of the world which the historian of ideas, Arthur O. Lovejoy, has characterized as the idea of the "Great Chain of Being." The idea (which had its birth with Plato) is roughly this: All living organisms represent stages in the idea of "Being," each intermediate form being a more advanced stage than some, and a less advanced stage than the rest. If we had before us all the organisms that have ever existed, we could arrange them, single file, in a continuous chain of increasing complexity. The relationship is purely a logical one. That the idea was widely known before 1859 is clearly proved by the fact that the American circus and side-show entrepreneur, P. T. Barnum, could make money from it. As early as 1842, he advertised that he was showing such scientific specimens as:

The Ornithorhincus, or the connecting link between the seal and the duck; two distinct species of flying fish, which undoubtedly connect the bird and the fish; the Siren, or Mud Iguana, a connecting link between the reptiles and fish . . . with other animals forming connecting links in the great chain of Animated Nature.

Undoubtedly the popular appeal of the idea of the Great Chain of Being helped prepare people for the idea of evolution; it was necessary only to assert that the logical sequence represented a genealogical one.

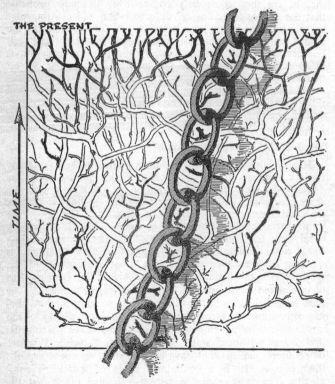

Fig. 13. Hypothetical evolutionary tree. The darker twigs represent the species known to us, either living or fossil. The lighter twigs represent forms of which we have no knowledge. The chain overlaid on the diagram shows the way in which the facts can be distorted to fit the hypothesis of "The Great Chain of Being."

Yet the metaphor of a chain is completely wrong. In the first place, since one species often gives rise to several daughter species as a result of the subdivisive process of speciation, the resulting pattern is much more nearly that of a tree, a phylogenetic tree with many tiny branches that are terminal (extinct) and do not at all lead to further species. (*See* Fig. 13.) In the second place, the theoretical analysis of the relation of the Exclusion Principle to the processes of extinction and race amalgamation (an analysis that is supported by the factual studies of modern taxonomists) leads us to believe that the fine structure of the phylogenetic tree is almost everywhere a net of the sort previously shown in Fig. 12. As a great Swiss biologist, Albrecht von Haller, said, almost a century before the *Origin: Natura in reticulum sua genera connexit, non in catenam*—"Nature has linked her kinds into a net, not into a chain." He then went on to point out the psychological reason for our failing to describe nature properly: "Men are incapable of following anything but a chain, since they cannot express in words more than one thing at a time." And because of this natural bias of language, the error-generating phrase, "the missing link," still muddies the intellectual waters two centuries after Haller's keen insight.

Man is an orderly animal. Confronted with the manifest complexity of a raveled reticulum, he seeks a pattern. Seeking, he finds, of course, pattern—but not one pattern: rather, many. But each of them seems to be trivial, or confined to only one small part of the network, or to involve an unconscionable amount of imagination. Attempts to see a progressive rise from "lower" to "higher" forms of life have met with little favor among professional biologists, who are too keenly aware of the ubiquity of evolution with a reverse sense—from free-living existence to a life of parasitism, for example. In despair of ever finding an important pattern to evolution, some biologists assert that the only generalization that can be safely made is that which has been christened "Dollo's Law": *Evolution is irreversible.* The paleontological record supports this generalization, and no one seriously believes that the law will ever be violated. But is the idea so profound that it deserves a name? Evolution is a part of history. No part of history ever repeats itself. The irreversibility of evolution is no more, and no less, mysterious than the irreversibility of history in general.

The smallest element of change in evolution is one brought about by Paley's Principle (which itself can be regarded as a vast generalization of Hobbesian political theory): *Each species at each moment seeks only its own good.* (We under-

stand the verb "seeks" in a figurative sense only, of course.)
How such a principle of opportunism could lead to an over-
all pattern of evolutionary development is not in the least
obvious. Perhaps the only suggestion we need to consider
seriously is the idea known as "Huxley's barrel of apples."
The world, said Darwin's friend, may be conceived of as a
barrel, space that may be filled by organisms. First, evolution fills the barrel with apples—one kind of organism, living one sort of life. These fill the barrel in one sense, but
in another they do not: there is still space between the apples.
Next, evolution fills in the spaces with marbles—another
sort of organism that lives with the first, but does not compete. Still space is left; so next, evolution produces buckshot;
then sand; then . . . and so on. Thus, said Huxley, there
is at least this sense to evolution, that is constantly making
the world *fuller*.

Half a century later, a most original theoretical biologist,
A. J. Lotka (a student of Raymond Pearl's), recast the idea
in terms of energy (1922). The world, Lotka said, is a sort
of bottleneck in the stream of energy. Our energy comes
from the sun. Where there is no earth to intercept it, the sun's
radiant energy dissipates into all space. That which the earth
intercepts is also eventually dissipated, but only after a delay.
Rock and soil of the earth's surface facing the sun absorb
energy, which is radiated out into space about twelve hours
later when this portion of the earth is facing away from the
sun. Even a lifeless earth somewhat delays the flow of
energy into space, though the effect is not great.

When life came to the earth, the energy bottleneck was
constricted further. With the development of various pigments
(chlorophylls, xanthophylls, etc.), greater ranges of the solar
spectrum became exploited. And by evolving relatively stable
storage compounds (starch, cellulose, etc.) plants have succeeded in putting energy into dead storage, sometimes for
very long periods of time. In burning a lump of coal we
release energy that may have first reached the earth about
three hundred million years ago. Quite a bottleneck.

This much was realized before Lotka. His specific contribution was this *conjecture:* that the evolution of life as a whole
is in the direction of rechanneling more and more of the solar
energy through the living film of the earth before it is dissipated into space. In this sense, said Lotka, there is a sort of
direction to evolution. But the sense of this direction refers
to the entire "biomass" of the earth, the entire collection of
living material, not to any one species or group. Lotka's
conjecture is a recasting of Huxley's barrel-of-apples idea in
terms of energy.

Where does man fit into this picture? In spite of his notorious destruction of other forms of life, it seems highly probable that his net effect has been one of increasing still further the fraction of the sun's energy that flows through the biomass. By diverting surplus waters to desert regions he paints absorbing chlorophylls over sandy plains that would otherwise reradiate solar energy into space almost as soon as it was received. By building dams he captures a modified form of solar energy, some of which he uses to fix nitrogen for use in growing still more energy-capturing plants. Furthermore, there seems now to be a pretty fair probability that man will learn how to capture the sun's energy directly, in significant amounts, through the use of physical and chemical analogues of the chlorophyll apparatus of plants. When this has been successfully accomplished, the proportion of the sun's energy that funnels through the bottleneck of life before dissipating into space should be increased manyfold. At present, plants are almost entirely responsible for this diversion, and their efficiency is only about 1 percent under the best natural conditions. Of the total solar energy that reaches the earth, summer and winter, only a small fraction of 1 percent is channeled into the living world by plants. Man should be able to do better than that. If so, evolutionary progress, in Lotka's sense, will be stepped up considerably.

But is Lotka's conjecture fundamentally true? Is it true that evolution has at all times moved in such a direction as to increase the fraction of energy channeling through the biomass? It is hard to believe that this is so. One can imagine special instances in which the direction of evolution might be reversed for a while. Those great ferns and lush primitive trees of the Coal Ages must have been pretty good at capturing solar energy. When they became extinct (probably because of change of climate), it seems very probable that the smaller, sparser plants of the succeeding ages captured less of the sun's energy, and, if so, evolution had passed through an anti-Lotka phase. The extinction of species is as natural a part of evolution as is their creation. The effect of such extinction on the total living world will depend on just which species happen to become extinct, leaving behind an uninhabited ecological niche. Just now, we stand at a crossroads in evolutionary history that is without parallel in the whole of geological time: one species, the greatest and cleverest of them all, is so far advanced in the arts of capturing and controlling energy—both from the sun and from other sources—and at the same time is so backward in the techniques of controlling himself that he stands in imminent danger of extinguishing all of his kind from the face of the earth. Extinction is a natural process, but it is usually a slow one, often taking tens of thousands of years. This time it may be different: we may leave this world "not with a whimper, but with a bang." We may even take the rest of the living world with us.

Progress?

Attacks from All Sides

IN the history of Western thought we inevitably compare Darwin's *Origin* with Newton's *Principia,* for each brought about an irreversible change in our view of man and his place in the world. But there is this important difference between them: whereas Newton's ideas were accepted almost at once, Darwin's touched off a cascade of attacks and objections that even yet is not at an end. Partly, this is because the biological argument is more difficult, more subtle; even more it is because the human implications of the theory, real or fancied, are more feared.

The first and most dramatic battle that Darwinism had to fight was with the Church. Darwin, reared in the reactionary climate that followed the disillusionment with revolutionary France, knew in his bones the storm that was awaiting him. The spirit of savagery revealed in the attack on the *Vestiges* was not lost to him. Remember how he hinted at this in his letter to Wallace in 1857: "You ask whether I shall discuss 'man.' I think I shall avoid the whole subject, as so surrounded with prejudices." And he did. For almost five hundred pages the *Origin of Species* plods along without a single explicit mention of man, until it reaches the third to last paragraph of the last chapter. Just before taking final leave of the reader, Darwin diffidently writes:

In the distant future I see open fields for far more important researches. Psychology will be based on a new foundation, that of the acquirement of each mental power and capacity by gradation. Light will be thrown on the origin of man and his history.

"Light will be thrown . . ." What a cautious acknowledgment of the suppressed fear that gripped the Victorian mind, the fear that noble man was related to ridiculous monkey. Was Darwin being less than frank in so cautiously indicating his position in the burgeoning controversy? Some said so. Darwin's only answer was, in preparing later editions, to amend the sentence to read *"Much* light will be thrown . . ." —but the italics are not his. Innocuous as the sentence may seem to us, his contemporaries were not fooled. When the

Origin was set over into German, the translator thought it the better part of wisdom to omit the sentence altogether.

The long gestation period of the *Origin* was favorable to its reception in several ways. Besides allowing the maturation of a generation inured to the heterodox ideas of the *Vestiges,* the long pregnancy produced a brain child of formidable size and advanced state of development, one not easily put down. Darwin repeatedly referred to the *Origin* as an "abstract," which it is in its turgidity only, not in its size, which is that of a respectably long book. It was a monumental pile of facts that he amassed, and the early reviews of his book were short and noncommittal. Only after several weeks had passed were the critics sufficiently prepared to be able to wheel out the big guns of the ponderous Victorian book review. By early 1860 a number of important reviews had appeared, most of them damning the implications and spirit of Darwin's work as much as would have been expected. Nevertheless, there was a general recognition that the world was now faced with the work of a master (no mere dabbler like the author of the *Vestiges*), and it was widely felt that the *Origin* should be answered in its own terms, that it should be demolished by scientific facts themselves.

As the time approached for the June meetings of the British Association for the Advancement of Science, a number of skirmishes in the popular press gave promise that the sessions would be livelier than they usually were. The promise was amply fulfilled in the events of that now-historic meeting at Oxford. It was one of those all-too-rare occasions in the history of science that may quite properly be referred to as "dramatic." To a scientist, there is a great deal of drama in the historical development of ideas, but the conflict is spread over so long a time that its dramatic impact is negligible at any particular moment. Seldom is there any crisis as compact as the trial of Galileo, when the great physicist, confronted with the monolithic disapproval of the Church in which he devoutly believed, was forced to deny the evidence of his reason and his senses. This great occasion would have been made more dramatic had the old man muttered in his beard (as he was once reported to have done), "Nevertheless, the world moves"—but he did not. It was left for a distant posterity to say his last words. The great advances of science are usually heralded not with a shout but with a whisper. The shout that greeted Darwinism in 1860 was really exceptional.

What happened at Oxford was very much like a trial. In the defendant's box was Darwinism, the theory with all its implications, or—more accurately—with all the *inferences* others chose to make from it. For prosecuting attorney there was Samuel Wilberforce, fifty-five years old and Bishop of Oxford, an orator who spoke in "such dulcet tones and so persuasive a manner" as to enjoy the sobriquet of "Soapy Sam" among his detractors. The attorney for the defense was Thomas Henry Huxley, only thirty-five years of age, a genuine scholar of science and a master of repartee. Spare in build, quick of thought, and with snapping black eyes, he was to become a figure feared by all so foolish as to oppose him in public debate. The guiding principle of his life was simple: he preferred (and was prepared to defend) truth in the face of all cant, however sanctified by tradition. He would today be called an "egghead."

And the presiding judge was equally well chosen by fate. It was John Stevens Henslow, botanist and geologist, Darwin's beloved teacher at Cambridge, now sixty-four years old and torn between his devout adherence to the Church of England, in which he had taken holy orders, and his love for his young protégé, Charles Darwin, who was shaking his world to its foundations. Henslow presided at the trial with an impartiality praised by all. He must have suffered as only a good judge can. Less than a year later, he died.

It was really a trial, and yet it was never planned as such. In fact, it was not planned at all: only a series of accidents brought it about. The evolutionists had prepared no presentation for the meetings, but the anti-evolutionists were itching for battle. The reading of a provocative paper by one of their number caused the President to call on Huxley to make a few remarks in reply, but Huxley declined, saying that it was not a suitable occasion, that with such a general audience "sentiment would unduly interfere with intellect." He was unable, however, to shut off discussion, for Richard Owen, a famous anatomist, asserted that the theory of evolution was ridiculous, that the brain of the gorilla differed more from that of man than it did from the lowest of the four-legged animals. This was a direct challenge to Huxley, who had spent the last two years working in this very field of primate anatomy. But again, he avoided public combat, contenting himself with denying Owen's statements categorically while saying that he would publish his refutation elsewhere and soon (which he did).

That was Thursday, June 28, 1860. On Friday all was quiet, though there were signs of an impending battle. Huxley, weary of meetings, decided to go home, but Robert Chambers, the generally recognized author of the *Vestiges*, earnestly begged him not to desert the cause. Huxley agreed to stay over one more day.

By the time Saturday arrived, everybody knew that something big was afoot, that it was almost sure that the eloquent Bishop of Oxford would himself raise his voice against the offending "gospel of dirt," as Carlyle was later to label evolution. The room originally planned for the meeting of the zoologists had to be abandoned for a larger one, which was filled to overflowing with scientists, clergy, undergraduates, and ladies in billowy summer dresses. Henslow presided. Those sitting behind him on the platform included the bishop, on his right, and Huxley, with equal fitness, on his left. How the trouble was to start probably no one knew, but the stimulus soon came. A Yankee scientist, one J. W. Draper, in the course of boring the audience thoroughly with a long paper, made a reference to the *Origin of Species*. At the conclusion of Dr. Draper's presentation, Henslow, in calling for discussion, announced that he would squelch any speeches that departed from genuine argument, a threat he made good on four different occasions. The undergraduates themselves, following old English tradition, did some squelching of their own, shouting down a Mr. Dingle, who was so unfortunate as to mispronounce the word *monkey,* with cries of "Maunkey! Maunkey!" until the luckless speaker retired in confusion. Now there came cries from many places for the bishop to speak. To these demands, after a show of modesty, Samuel Wilberforce complied, with his usual brevity. His few remarks took thirty minutes.

Exactly what the bishop said, and what exactly was Huxley's reply, we shall never know, for not one of the seven hundred persons present had the wit to recognize the historic importance of the occasion and act as scribe. The reports we have were made from memory after the event—several hours or many years later. As one would expect, they differ from each other in many details, but in *sense* they are in good agreement. That we may follow the sense of the meeting, rather than become bogged down in a scholarly collation of texts, it will be best to go forward with a sort of composite of several versions.

The bishop lived up to his reputation as a polished speaker. He spoke "in a light, scoffing tone, fluid and fluent," confident of the audience, which was *his.* Clergymen manfully supported him with deep-voiced cries of approbation, while the ladies, many of whom were sitting in the windows, waved and fluttered their white handkerchiefs in admiration of their hero's cleverness. Soapy Sam tried earnestly to found his argument on scientific evidence, in which he had recently been "crammed" by Owen, but, according to Hooker, he boggled his facts from unfamiliarity. But it was not the scientific issues that carried the day. The downfall of the bishop was determined when, intoxicated by his own eloquence, he so far forgot himself as to turn toward Huxley and, with an arch smile, beg to know whether it was through his *grandfather* . . . or . . . through his *grandmother* . . . that he traced his descent from the monkey?

On the instant, Huxley struck his knee, turned to Sir Benjamin Brodie, who was sitting next to him, and whispered, "The Lord hath delivered him into my hands." Poor Sir Benjamin, much slower-witted than Huxley, was only astonished and did not see the point until Huxley spoke to the audience. Apparently many, and probably most, of those present also failed at first to perceive the fatal error the bishop had made; for they who were so soon to turn against him applauded vigorously at the conclusion of his speech.

Huxley arose slowly and moved with great deliberation to the center of the platform; he was very quiet and very grave; a tall, slender, dark figure, stern and serious. He had all eyes and all attention as he returned to the bishop's question. As far as the scientific facts are involved, he said, it is surely realized by all who have given more than passing attention to the problem that the changes in species that evolution brings about take thousands of generations for completion. So much for the scientific facts.

> But if this question is treated, not as a matter for the calm investigation of science, but as a matter of sentiment, and if I am asked whether I would choose to be descended from the poor animal of low intelligence and stooping gait, who grins and chatters as we pass;—or from a man, endowed with great ability and splendid position, who should use these gifts . . .

and at this point, the audience, in a fever of excitement as they anticipated the point he was making, could not restrain their applause

> . . . who should use these gifts to discredit and crush humble seekers after truth—I hesitate what answers I should make.

The ovation was tumultuous, not only from the impertinent undergraduates who were rather "for" Huxley to begin with (since he represented the defiance of authority that is always endearing to the adolescent heart), but also from the older members including the ladies and even some of the clergy. Whatever their individual feelings about evolution, they all recognized that the bishop had made a dreadful blunder: before Englishmen, who loved fair play as perhaps no other people in the world had ever loved it, he had descended to the mire of the *argumentum ad hominem*, to a low attempt to discomfit an opponent by a comic and irreverent reference to his ancestors, implying that his grandfather or—what was infinitely worse—his grand*mother*, was a beast. As the implication of the bishop's fall from grace was brought home to the audience by Huxley, it was small wonder that one lady, as Professor Irvine has so aptly put it, "employing an idiom now lost, expressed her sense of intellectual crisis by fainting."

The Evolution of Theological Opinion

Thus began a war that was vigorously waged without letup for at least ten years, and of which minor skirmishes are still fought at the present day. It was Religion *or* Science—"*God or Gorilla*," as one journalistic partisan entitled his book. (Guess which side *he* was on!) Huxley lectured the length and breadth of England and wrote tirelessly, irritating the religious orthodox and marshaling the scientific faithful to the defense of reason. Now that men had seen a conflict between science and religion, they made the new truth doubly sure by saying it out loud. The Irish historian, William Lecky, published his *History of Rationalism* in 1865, and John William Draper—he who had spoken at Oxford before the bishop—and who, incidentally, was the first man to photograph the moon, and to make a photomicrograph—published in 1874, a *History of the Conflict between Religion and Science*. His position was uncompromising. It was *either-or*. Partisans on the other side were only too eager to return the challenge. A Reverend Dr. Lee asserted that if Darwinism be true, "there is no place for God: . . . by no method of interpretation can the language of Holy Scripture be made wide enough to re-echo the orangutan theory of man's natural history. . . . Darwinism reverses the revelation of God . . . [it] implies utter blasphemy against the divine and human character of our Incarnate Lord." In a similar vein, a Reverend Dr. Hodge pronounced Darwinism theory "utterly inconsistent with Scriptures," and a Reverend Dr. Duffield drew the line with complete clearness: "Evolutionism and the scriptural account of the origin of man are irreconcilable."

Now this is very dangerous talk. It gives one a fine moral glow to deliver an ultimatum—*but what if the ultimatum is accepted?* Dr. James McCosh, when he was made President of Princeton University toward the close of the century, noted that many of the undergraduates were accepting the ultimatum with a will, and were choosing the Gorilla. There was only one prudent course of action for the Church, said Dr. McCosh: stop giving ultimatums. It was not *either-or*; it must be *and*. For his well-intentioned efforts Dr. McCosh received the usual thanks accorded the peacemaker—vituperation from both sides; but in the end, his point of view carried the day.

Of considerable influence was a history published in 1896 by Andrew D. White, then U.S. ambassador to Russia, and formerly the first President of Cornell University. White, a trained historian, wrote the sort of history Draper should have written. In two large volumes he surveyed the origin, development and decay of ecclesiastical opposition to many ideas: ideas in geography (the shape and extent of the earth); astronomy (the heliocentric theory, and the naturalistic interpretation of meteors); medicine (anatomy, vaccination, anaesthetics, naturalistic interpretation of mental disease); history ("the new criticism" of the Bible); geology; and, of course, evolution. In each of these accounts, White pointed to a common element: it was warfare, yes—as Draper had said—but not between Science and Religion, but between Science and *Theology*. Religion, properly understood, said White, has no quarrel with Science; in fact, it welcomes it. The belligerent troublemaker is not the religious spirit, but Dogmatic Theology, the body of received doctrine which is, by definition, insusceptible of improvement or correction. With such, Science will always be in opposition, as a matter of principle, for its conclusions are always subject to change in the light of more facts. Hoping to strengthen the position of true religion in a world already considerably alienated from the Church by the antagonistic attitude of dogmatic theologians, White entitled his book *A History of the Warfare of Science with Theology in Christendom*.

It is essential to realize that some of the most telling blows against traditional theology came not from science but from history, and even from within the fold of theologians themselves. In breaking away from the authority of an institution —the Roman Catholic Church—Protestants had felt it necessary to establish a new authority to maintain stability, and this authority was the Bible. In elevating it to such a position of power, they made it inevitable that sooner or later thoughtful men would read it carefully, with the scholar's eye to meaning and consistency. It was this approach that developed in the nineteenth century and caused so much heartache among the devout. *The Bible is the word of God and is wholly true*—this was the Protestant position: but when we find that one part of the Book contradicts another, where is Truth? The contradictions and inconsistencies are many, and they involve both the letter and the spirit. The only rational approach to such a document is to interpret it naturalistically, as a collection of documents written by many different men, with different ideas of the true, the good and the beautiful.

If there is unity in the Book in any sense, it can only be in a symbolic sense. Plainly, the authority of the Bible can be maintained among studious theologians only by abandoning a literal interpretation of it in favor of a figurative or allegorical one. This approach to the Bible was already being made before evolution became a serious threat. When Darwinism came to the fore, liberal churchmen were quick to point out that there was no *necessary* antagonism between evolution and religion; to reconcile the two, one needed only to regard the word "creation" as a metaphor for "evolution," and the "days" of creation of the book of Genesis as standing for geological epochs. And, decided the Reverend Charles Kingsley (author of *Westward Ho!* and *Water Babies*), "it is just as noble a conception of Deity, to believe that he created primal forms capable of self-development. . . . as to believe that He required a fresh act of intervention to supply the *lacunas* which He Himself had made." On second thought, he added, "I question whether the former be not the loftier thought." On the other side of the Atlantic, that very popular preacher, Henry Ward Beecher, echoed the sentiment: "If it be evidence of design in creation that God adapted one single flower to its place and functions, is it not greater evidence if there is a system of such adaptations going on from eternity to eternity? Is not the Creator of the system a more sublime designer than the creator of any single act?" Facing the revelations of biology, Protestant theologians began to rediscover the beauty of the idea of Nicholas of Oresme of the fourteenth century—that God was not so much a creator of the things of the world as he was of the world as a machine which, once created, he left to run itself. The process of evolution might well be part of a God-created machine.

Such has been the tenor of liberal Protestant thought in the twentieth century. While gaining slowly in power and prestige, it has not lacked for vigorous opposition from the "Fundamentalists" within the churches, who hold that the Bible is literally true. (*And what about internal inconsistencies?* Fundamentalists are silent on this point: or they resort to Orwellian double-thinking.) This sort of religion had its last big field day in the "Scopes Monkey Trial" at Dayton, Tennessee, in 1925. The Fundamentalists there won their case in a court of law (to enforce a state statute against the teaching of evolution in public schools) but lost out in the court of public opinion. Since then, with minor remissions and exacerbations, the Fundamentalist fever has been slowly declining. One should not, however, expect a rapid disappearance of any doctrine that has such great emotional appeal. (Consider, for example, how flourishes still the gentle art of astrology, centuries after its last vestige of scientific support has evaporated. It has been suggested—and it is probably true, though supporting data are unavailable—that more American dollars are still spent each year on astrology than on astronomy. . . . Oh, Progress! Condorcet, thou shouldst be living in this hour!)

So much for the Protestant attitude toward evolution. What about the Catholic? The story is simply and quickly told. Despite occasional remarks by individual clerics, there is no official opposition to evolution in the Roman Catholic Church. This position is probably accounted for by two circumstances. *First,* the Church is not dependent on the authority of the Bible, and hence is faced with no conflict of evidence. *Second,* if we view the Church as a sociological institution, we suspect that in 1859 it was still smarting from the wounds inflicted by the Galileo affair. In 1616 it had condemned Galileo's contention that the earth revolved around the sun. Not until 1822—more than two centuries later—did the cardinals of the Holy Inquisition reverse their position. The institutional memory of the original tactical error must still have been fresh when the *Origin* was published. At any rate, the Church today no longer becomes embroiled in purely scientific matters, and such evolution may be considered to be. Rome does not oppose the theory. Neither can it be accused of being enthusiastic about it.

Aesthetic and Emotional Reactions to Evolution

For countless numbers of people the publication of the *Origin of Species* meant the destruction of a beloved world —the world of Paley, a world in which Design was at once both the work and the evidence of God. Now, from the quiet house at Down, came the picture of a new world, a world in which design grew out of chaos, which seemed to the astronomer, Sir John Herschel, a world governed by "the law of higgledy-piggledy." For some more sensitive souls, the results may have been as devastating as they were for the hero of Winwood Reade's *The Outcast* (1875), who, after reading Malthus and Darwin, dressed thenceforth in black, to show his mourning for mankind, and had the offending books rebound in dark covers for his library table, the first bearing the lettering, "The Book of Doubt," and the second, "The Book of Despair." In Robert Louis Stevenson's story of "The Suicide Club" (1878), one of the members confessed to having been brought to join as a consequence of reading Darwin; and another, the most pitiable of the lot, bore the name "Mr. Malthus."

Every new scientific view of the world brings with it a necessary growth in our conception of beauty. This is the implication of the final peroration of Darwin's book. Paley's view of the world was beautiful, but it was wrong. The correct view of the world is also beautiful. Said Darwin, in the final sentence of the *Origin*:

> There is grandeur in this view of life, with its several powers, having been originally breathed into a few forms or into one; and that, while this planet has gone cycling on according to the fixed laws of gravity, from so simple a beginning endless forms most beautiful and most wonderful have been, and are being, evolved

But growth in the concept of beauty takes time. In the meantime, Darwin was faced with a world in which such maturation had not yet taken place, and the prospect frightened him. "I feel sometimes a little frightened, whether I may not be one of those monomaniacs [who persuade] themselves of the truth of the foolishest doctrines," he wrote to a fellow biologist. His experience raised the painful issue of the psychological meaning of truth: "Though I, of course, believe in the truth of my own doctrine, I suspect that no belief is vivid until shared by others." If for the word "vivid," we substitute the word *true,* we gain an insight into the psychic ordeal of every great pioneer in human thought. The wretchedness of Darwin's stomach is really no great puzzle.

What would his peers think? The day the *Origin* came off the press, the author set about sending presentation copies to men of influence all over Europe and eastern North America, each accompanied by a diffident note: "You will not at all agree with me . . ." "I fear, however, that you will not approve . . ." "I should value your opinion in the very highest rank . . ." and more intimately: "Lord, how savage you will be, if you read it, and how you will long to crucify me alive!" Thus, by prediction voiced, he sought to dull the knife of criticism and perhaps, now and then, to turn the blade aside.

The reaction was strong and varied. His old teacher, Adam Sedgwick, wrote him a long letter, showing that his opinion of evolution had not altered a jot since he had written his devastating review of the *Vestiges,* fifteen years earlier.

> I have read your book with more pain than pleasure. Parts of it I admired greatly, parts I laughed at till my sides were almost sore; other parts I read with absolute sorrow, because I think them utterly false and grievously mischievous. . . . There is a moral or metaphysical part of nature as well as a physical. A man who denies this is deep in the mire of folly. 'Tis the crown

and glory of organic science that it *does* through *final-cause,* link material and moral. . . . You have ignored this link; and, if I do not mistake your meaning, you have done your best in one or two pregnant cases to break it. Were it possible (which thank God, it is not) to break it, humanity, in my mind, would suffer a damage that might brutalize it, and sink the human race into a lower grade of degradation than any into which it has fallen since its written records tell us of history

Not content with thus privately thrusting a dagger into his former pupil, Sedgwick twisted it in public, in an emotional review published in the *Spectator.* Darwin, following a strategy from which he deviated only once or twice in his life, took no public notice of the attack. To a colleague in America he wrote plaintively, "My dear old friend Sedgwick, with his noble heart, is old, and is rabid with indignation. It is hard to please everyone."

Indeed it was. Darwin keenly followed the reviews and sounded out professional opinions through his traveling friends, tallying up those *for* and those *against* him, as in a game or political contest. Always the generalizer, he soon perceived two statistical characteristics of the opponents: advanced age and training as naturalists. By and large, most of the older (and, unfortunately, better established) men were against evolution: most of his support came from the younger and less-well-known workers. Darwin discovered a truth that the physicist, Planck, was to state much later: "A new scientific truth does not triumph by convincing its opponents and making them see the light, but rather because its opponents eventually die, and a new generation grows up that is familiar with it."

Some of the most vigorous professional opposition to the *Origin* came from a group of men who (one might have supposed) should have supported it: the "naturalists," the men with the most extensive knowledge of the variety of living things. But these men were committed to the view of Linnaeus (now dead some eighty years) that species are eternal, and Darwin had little hope for their reform. "I think geologists are more easily converted than simple naturalists, because more accustomed to reasoning," Darwin wrote on one occasion; and on another: "I have long thought that *too much* systematic work [and] description somehow blunts the faculties. The general public appreciates a good dose of reasoning, or generalisation . . . far more than do the regular naturalists."

And how the general public ate up his theory! It was avidly discussed everywhere, not merely because it was shocking in just the right degree, but because much of the evidence on which it was based was widely and intimately known. This was the golden age of the amateur naturalist in England. "Everyone" (a figurative, not a quantitative, term) was a bird watcher, an egg or bird-nest collector, a pigeon fancier, a rabbit breeder, a butterfly chaser, or a plant presser. The facts Darwin drew upon were homely facts to the gentlemen of Victorian England, and so every amateur not only read the *Origin,* but, all too often, felt called upon to criticize it in essay, poem or book. Vicars, curates, country judges; literary men like that bitter old bachelor and champion "on-the-other-hander," Samuel Butler; tortured souls like St. George Mivart, recently converted to Catholicism; and even some of the nobility, notably the Duke of Argyll, pontificated on the new scientific theory with a confidence unknown among the general public in our day, except, perhaps, in the field of psychoanalysis. Today, the frontier of science has, both fortunately and unfortunately, become a crazy quilt of booby traps through which only the technically trained can thread his way. To appreciate how great was the general interest in evolution, one should pick up, quite at random, any issue of the *Spectator,* the *Quarterly Review,* the *Athenaeum,* or any similar journal published during the quarter century following 1859. It is an unusual issue that does not have at least one new criticism or one new "thought" about the development of species. Fortunately, no Ph. D. candidate has yet seen fit to compile a complete bibliography of these contributions.

Early Scientific Criticisms

It should not be inferred from the foregoing remarks that the amateur criticisms were all bad. Quite the contrary: the level of *factual* accuracy (using that word in its narrowest sense) is quite high among these critics, many of whom were careful observers of external nature. When they erred, it was more often than not in their assumptions of what the true method of science was. This was the heydey of belief in the "Baconian method"—to advance science (it was thought), you must gather facts endlessly, without preconception or conscious guide, until finally, by some magical process, the facts group themselves into generalizations which you have only to convert into words. This was the philosophical orthodoxy of the day. Darwin knew it was false. "I am a firm believer that without speculation there is no good and original observation," he wrote, in a letter to Wallace in 1857, and to the careful reader of the *Origin* it was all too evident that his observations had been guided by a theory—the theory of natural selection. *This is not the true Baconian method*, pouted the critics. William Whewell of Cambridge, whose *History of the Inductive Sciences* had established him as the leading authority on scientific method, echoed this opinion: for several years he would not permit a copy of the *Origin* to repose on the aseptic shelves of the library of Trinity College, lest its undergraduates be contaminated with false science.

What did the critics expect? Something wonderful in the way of proof, apparently. Some frankly said they *would not believe the theory of evolution until a change in species took place before their eyes.* What about the multiplication of varieties of dogs? Darwinians asked. Will that do? . . . *No— because these are varieties, and not species; and besides, Man caused that: we mean natural evolution.* . . . Well, Darwinians replied, that takes a long time; for that we have only historical evidence. . . . *Can you show all the links in the chain?* . . . No, of course not; the geological record is imperfect and always will remain so, since it is highly improbable that short-lived intermediate species will be fossilized. Savanna, steppe and desert are unfavorable for fossilizing plants; and birds are extremely unlikely to leave remains in the rocks. (Our written record of human history has many gaps, too, even though school histories are discreetly silent on this matter.)

Let's go on. *What about this struggle for existence stuff— what evidence is there for that?* This was a rather good point. Unfortunately for the orderly progress of ideas, the poet laureate, Alfred Tennyson, had already determined the color of men's thoughts about the struggle for existence when he wrote, nine years before the *Origin*, of "Nature, red in tooth and claw." Taking the poetic phrase too literally as a synonym for Darwin's "struggle," observant critics quite rightly pointed out that their Sunday walks were almost never disturbed by sanguinary sights—*so was there any struggle in Nature after all? Was not peace and harmony the rule?* A difficult point, admitted Darwin, who wrote:

We behold the face of nature bright with gladness, we often see superabundance of food; we do not see, or we forget, that the birds which are idly singing round us mostly live on insects or seeds, and are thus constantly destroying life, or we forget how largely these songsters, or their eggs, or their nestlings, are destroyed by birds and beasts of prey; we do not always bear in mind that though food may be now superabundant, it is not so at all seasons of each recurring year. . . .

I use the term Struggle for Existence in a large and metaphorical sense, including dependence of one being on another, and including (which is more important) not only the life of the individual, but success in leaving offspring Two canine animals in a time of dearth may be truly said to struggle with each other which shall get food and live. But a plant on the edge of a desert is said to struggle for life against the drought. . . .

"Nature, red in tooth and claw"? . . . Perhaps. But such vivid language may mislead us. Whether or not the poet intended to speak in metaphor, his thought is true only metaphorically, and is, therefore, likely to lead the uncritical to erroneous expectations. To the casual eye, the face of nature *is* bright with gladness, as Darwin said: only the eye of the poet or of the statistician (a sort of poet, really) is keen enough to perceive the blood freshly smeared across the guileless smiling visage. Life is so *continuous* and death so quick that the Sunday bird watcher is all too easily "taken in" by nature's innocent-appearing ways. It is the seven-day bird counter who has to correct our Sunday impressions and show us that the poet was not wrong after all. One of the best of these, the British naturalist, David Lack, has written (1954):

When, in February 1942, I stated to the British Ornithologists' Club that ringing returns showed the average age of a wild Robin to be only about a year, my remarks were greeted with outspoken scepticism. It was felt that there must be something wrong with a method that gave so low a figure for so familiar a bird. We ourselves would be shocked if half of our friends died each year, and in fact mankind experiences a death-rate of this magnitude only under unusual circumstances, such as the Black Death in 1348 or in some of the actions by Commando units in the late war. But in wild song-birds this is the normal state of affairs. . . .

Our difficulty in accepting the facts, said Lack, probably stems from our feeling that the average life span should be not far from the maximum life span—but in this unconscious expectation we are quite wrong. A captive robin may live 11 years; a wild one has an average expectancy of less than 1; for a European blackbird the two figures are about 20 and 1.5; for a herring gull, 44 and 2.8. If man's case were comparable, his *average* life span would be perhaps 7 to 10 years. It may well have been so in prehistoric times. If a caveman and his mate had ten children, it would not have been unusual if eight of them died at an average age of one year. If the two survivors lived to the age of forty, probably a ripe old age in a rough society, the average age of the children would be 8.8 years. Even today, the life expectancy of the newborn is not very far from this figure in the most densely populated regions of the world which include a large proportion of mankind. That we are not more keenly aware of this fact is a simple consequence of the bias that is introduced into literary discussions by the fact that people ground under the heel of overpopulation do not write books; nor do they read and criticize the writings of those who are more fortunate. "Nature, red in tooth and claw. . . ." Only the statistician·and the poet know *how* red she is.

What about natural selection? Does it exist? We have already seen that it does, using modern examples from penicillin therapy and the use of DDT; in Darwin's day, the needed examples were not so easy to come by. *And if it exists, is it effective?* Here we are faced with an objection which, in Darwin's time, seemed so telling as to threaten the entire edifice of his theory; an objection which caused him to publish a theory of heredity that was fantastic and quite erroneous. This theory did little direct harm to science (where it was not well received) but, by the irony of circumstances, through its publication, Darwin unwittingly helped Bolshevik politicians to banish and kill scores of able scientists in the Soviet Union three quarters of a century later.

Jenkin's Fateful Objection: The Swamping Effect

Of all the hundreds of critical objections made to Darwin's theory in the nineteenth century, the best by far was raised by a man who was not a professional biologist, a man who, in fact, was not even an amateur biologist in any sense, being neither bird watcher, nest collector nor pigeon fancier. He was, in fact, an engineer who, working with Kelvin, played an important role in developing the first transatlantic submarine cable. His name was Fleeming (pronounced "Flemming") Jenkin and we know quite a bit about him because, by chance, while he was still a professor at Edinburgh, one of his students was Robert Louis Stevenson. At this time, the man who was one day to write *Treasure Island* was training to become a civil engineer, following in the footsteps of a famous father. His delicate health later made him give up this ambition for the less rigorous one of the law, before he answered his true calling. Stevenson's career as an engineering student was, by his own account, not brilliant, but from it he gained a lasting friendship with Jenkin, for the sake of whose memory he was later to write the only full-length biography he ever penned. From this, and from the fictional sketch of "Cockshot" in his "Talk and Talkers," we obtain a living portrait of a man who would otherwise be only a ghostly reference in bibliographies.

Fleeming Jenkin was a familiar type: the keen, honest man who would rather speak the truth than save a friendship.

In the Edinburgh of the day, according to Stevenson, strangers were struck by a "hard and disputatious element"; and Jenkin was regarded, "even in this metropolis of disputation, as a thorny table-mate." It was scarcely possible to make a statement so simple that Jenkin could not see that there was another side to it—which he would defend. And, like Terence, nothing that was human was alien to him; he would discuss and criticize ideas in every field of human interest.

In his later years, whether as a result of his happy marriage, or as a part of a natural ripening process, Jenkin mellowed. The disputatious approach to his fellow man was replaced by one of affection and quiet tolerance. A metamorphosis of thorns to blossoms, unknown in botany, is not uncommon in humanity. Whether this metamorphosis is wholly good for the progress of science is a much-disputed question; for, following it, the individual generally becomes less productive of new, that is heretical, ideas—at any rate, of published ones. So it was with Fleeming Jenkin. But before his thorny period was past, he made two significant critical contributions to the scientific thought of his day, only one of which need concern us here. In the June, 1867, issue of the *North British Review*, Jenkin published a criticism of the theory of evolution by natural selection, calling upon no new facts, but merely pointing out the logical implication of the theory itself in the light of the most reasonable auxiliary assumptions of the day. His argument may be briefly summarized.

Natural selection, to be effective, must have inheritable differences to select among. The greater the difference, the more effective selection will be. On the other hand, as a difference becomes very small, the effectiveness of natural selection must approach zero. It looks as though the "sampling error" of random mortality will far exceed the effect of selection in a species in which mortality is great, for instance in salmon where, of the ten million eggs a female lays, 9,999,998 (on the average) fail to produce breeding adults. Is it not supposing a great deal to believe that a favorable variant will survive under such circumstances?

But Jenkin had a second and, he thought, a more telling argument against natural selection. To illustrate his point, he hypothesized a distant isle, populated entirely by blacks, onto which a single white man chanced. Jenkin supposed the white man to be markedly superior to the natives. "Our shipwrecked hero would probably become king," he said. "He would kill a great many blacks in the struggle for existence; he would have a great many wives and children. . . . In the first generation there will be some dozens of intelligent young mulattoes, much superior in average intelligence to the Negroes. We might expect the throne for some generations to be occupied by a more or less yellow king; but can anyone believe that the whole island will gradually acquire a white, or even a yellow, population?"

Not at all, says Jenkin, for the whiteness will be so diluted by breeding with the general population that it will be as completely lost as a drop of white paint in a barrel of black. Jenkin developed the argument in mathematical terms. It read very convincingly. But it was wrong. Hidden in the arithmetic was the assumption that heredity is fundamentally a blending process: we might call this the "paint-pot theory of heredity." It is an old and widely held theory: we find it embalmed in such phrases as "quarterbreed," "octoroon," and so on. We know now that it is false. But Jenkin and Darwin did not— nor did millions of their contemporaries. They accepted the paint-pot theory as unconsciously as they did the air they breathed. Within this framework of thought, Jenkin demolished the case for natural selection.

Darwin Becomes a Lamarckian

Jenkin had put his finger on a critically weak point in Darwinian theory—its dependence on a mistaken theory of heredity. The unanswerableness of the criticisms led Darwin to make one of the strangest about-faces in the progress of science. Darwin, a long-time anti-Lamarckian, became an unwilling and unavowed convert. How did this happen? And who was Lamarck?

Lamarck was a Frenchman, a chemist turned into a biologist by the Revolution. He was not a very good chemist; he was not quite as bad as a biologist, though he has caused more trouble in science than anyone since Aristotle. He is remembered now chiefly for his attempt to explain evolution. In 1809, the year of Darwin's birth, he proposed that a species adapts to its environment in the same way that an individual adapts to his. Just as a blacksmith's muscles get larger through use, so will an organ increase in size from generation to generation through use. Lamarck's most famous example is the giraffe. This animal, he said, has evolved from short-necked animals because individuals have stretched their necks trying to reach high leaves. Thus each individual has lengthened its own neck, and then has (through heredity) passed the increased neck length on to the next generation, which then carried the process further. The idea is epitomized by the phrase "the inheritance of acquired characteristics." There is a surface plausibility to such a theory. If true, it would certainly explain evolution easily. But how could so detailed a message be carried from the stretched neck to the spermatozoa or the egg, causing it to change in such a way as to alter the neck of the offspring? And if Lamarckism were general, would we not (for example) find that each succeeding generation of human children would speak and walk and read sooner than their parents?

In his own day, few people took Lamarck seriously, least of all Darwin. In his very first letter to Hooker, in 1844, Darwin had said, "Heaven forfend me from Lamarck nonsense of a 'tendency to progression,' 'adaptations from the slow willing of animals,' etc!" Almost twenty years later, four years after the publication of the *Origin*, we find him writing in the same vein to Lyell. He says that he regards Lamarck's book, "after two deliberate readings, as a wretched book, and one from which . . . I gained nothing." Yet he ultimately became a Lamarckian. Why?

This puzzle, which disturbed historians of biology for many decades, was finally resolved by the English statistician, R. A. Fisher, who converted Darwin's qualitative thinking into its mathematical equivalent, in which form it was possible to show the steps in reasoning that led to the naturalist's descent from grace. We will try to translate Fisher's analysis back into ordinary language.

The rub was heredity. Shortly after the publication of the *Origin*, Huxley wrote to the author saying, "it is not clear to me why, if continual physical conditions are of so little moment [in altering heredity] variation should occur at all." In exasperation, Darwin had to agree: "If, as I must think, external conditions produce little direct effect, what the devil determines each particular variation?" From the beginning, Darwin had constructed a theory that assumed only slight variations in heredity, the effect of which would be compounded by the action of natural selection on successive generations. This picture had two important arguments in its favor: (1) At the theoretical level, it is always best to assume the minimum that will make the theory work; and (2) on the observational level, only slight variations are to be seen in nature, for the most part. Real freaks are very rare. Furthermore, they are almost always sterile.

Then Jenkin came along and showed that if variations were indeed non-directional and generally slight, they would be swamped in the hereditary mixing process before they could be naturally selected. Here was a dilemma! Should Darwin assume (contrary to experience) large and fertile variants? Or should he return to the Lamarckian fold and assume that variants of a useful sort (relevant to the environment) were more common than chance would dictate? He chose the latter course and, after acknowledging in the later editions of the *Origin* the justice of Jenkin's criticisms, Darwin published a hereditary theory of Lamarckian design, incorporating it into the two great volumes of materials left over from his "abstract" (the *Origin of Species*), under the title *The Variation of Animals and Plants under Domestication*. The theory is called "pangenesis."

We need not linger over this theory. It is a confused mass of ingenuous arguments, based on facts which were only imperfectly understood in his day. Crudely summarized, the theory asserts that all parts of the body throw off into the circulating fluids some particles called "pangenes," which are gathered together to form the hereditary elements of the sperm or egg. The pangenes are not necessarily constant, but can be modified, in a directional way, by environmental conditions that affect all the parts of the body. Thus was the way opened to a Lamarckian inheritance and an escape from the consequences of blending inheritance. What a paradox—that, to make his non-Lamarckian system of natural selection work, Darwin should, in the end, have to resort to the Lamarckian ideas his theory was designed to supersede!

In passing, we should note the reception Darwin's theory had, for it has a bearing on an old canard fostered by literary people—that Darwinism has always been more favorably received than its merits justify because its author was a member of the inner sanctum of science and hence immune to criticism. This charge was first aired by Samuel Butler (shouted is a better word) and has survived down to the present day. The reception given to pangenesis effectively disposes of the charge of special privilege. Darwin was, by this time, of ripe age (fifty-nine) and full of honors: Honorary Doctor of Breslau, and of Bonn; recipient of the high Prussian Order "Pour le Mérite" and of the coveted Copley medal of the Royal Society; and honorary or corresponding member of no less than thirteen foreign scientific societies (a number that was to swell to sixty-one before his death). Here, surely, was a man whose ideas would pass unopposed if, indeed, science were any sort of closed corporation or conspiracy. The facts suggest that conspiracies exist mostly in the minds of those who feel themselves outside of a happy group. The theory of pangenesis was almost universally criticized by Darwin's fellow scientists. The chorus of opposition included his German translator, V. Carus; the biologists, Fritz Müller and G. Bentham; and the philosopher, Herbert Spencer. Even his three closest friends, Hooker, Lyell and Huxley, stood up solidly against his brain child. Among the few who

thought pangenesis pretty fine was Wallace, who, anti-vac-
cinationist and spiritualist as he was, had a bit of a knack for
picking the wrong horse.

For it *was* the wrong horse. Perhaps no doctrine in biology
in the last two hundred years has had so great an appeal
and has necessitated so many experiments with negative
conclusions as has the Lamarckian doctrine of the inheritance of acquired characteristics. Some of the most important
evidence against it will be presented later, when the needed
background of facts is richer. For the present, let it be
flatly stated that, with few and quite unimportant qualifications, *there's nothing in Lamarckism.* Acquired characteristics
are not inherited. Johnny does not learn to read faster because
many generations of his ancestors have been literate.

The doctrine has, however, had an immense emotional appeal to a world engulfed by a rising tide of socialism. From
Robert Owen's day, in the early nineteenth century, to
Socialist Russia in the twentieth, a heredity system that is
in any important sense determinative has been viewed as subversive of the goals of socialism. Knowledge of the true
mechanism of heredity has posed a serious threat to the
foundations of Socialist theory, as conceived by Marx and
Engel. Faced with this threat, Soviet Russia, in a period
extending from approximately 1935 to 1948, developed a
perfectly consistent and dialectically satisfactory answer: she
purged genetics, the science of heredity, of all who asserted
that heredity was not Lamarckian, depriving hundreds of
competent scientists of their jobs, and killing an unknown,
but not small, number of devoted research men. The attack
was provoked by a man who, it is all too clear from Zirkle's
documentation, was a charlatan, an uneducated opportun-
ist named Trofim Lysenko. Looking for authorities to sanctify
his purge, Lysenko could find only one in the world beyond
the borders of the U.S.S.R. and that one was—Darwin. What
irony! That Darwin, whose life held so much that Communist
agitators regard as despicable, who never "worked" a day in
his life (in the curiously restricted Socialistic sense) and who
yet died a millionaire by virtue of fortunate investments in
stocks and bonds; that Darwin—who politely declined what
was surely, in Communist eyes, the greatest of all honors, the
offer of having Marx's *Das Kapital* dedicated to him (!)—
should yet be cited as a patron saint in a Soviet purge! But
it was not the Darwin of 1859, not the Darwin of the *Origin*
that the Soviets had in mind. It was a different Darwin, the
confused 1868 Darwin of the *Variation* and pangenesis, who
played this curious role.

Perhaps the greatest irony of it all was that the confusion

was completely unnecessary. The *Variation* was published in 1868. Two years before—a year before Jenkin's article—an obscure Moravian monk, studying peas in a diminutive monastery garden in central Europe, had published a beautiful and classically brief paper in which he showed that heredity was not at all the sort of thing Darwin and Jenkin and nearly everyone else thought. Heredity was not a paint-pot operation; it was a game of dice. With the recognition of this difference, all reasons for supporting Jenkin's objections disappeared, and Darwin's pangenesis became only a historic curiosity (life-and-death matter though it may have been to many in Russia). But not a single contemporary understood what the Moravian monk was talking about, and it was almost half a century before the true bearing of his findings on evolutionary theory began to be appreciated.

The monk's name, of course, was Mendel.

6

Heredity: Fate's Lottery

THE two greatest contributions of the nineteenth century
to the theoretical side of biology—the theory of evolution
and the theory of heredity—were published almost simultaneously; but in all other respects, what a contrast between
them! The theory of evolution was a half century overdue
when Darwin revealed his argument in 1858-59, whereas the
theory of heredity, unveiled seven years later, was almost
half a century before its time. Evolution was given a riotous
reception, which unquestionably helped more than hindered its acceptance. The theory of heredity, by contrast, was
greeted with an absolute and deafening silence; so far as the
record reveals, only one bystander took the slightest notice
of it, and he did not understand it all.

The contrast extends to the authors themselves. Where
Darwin was a gentleman and a millionaire, Mendel was a
poor peasant. Darwin was, in later years, definitely an agnostic (though so discreet a one that his remains were interred
in Westminster Abbey); Mendel was an ordained priest.
Of Darwin's life and thought we have perhaps the most complete record in the history of science; of the inner Mendel
we know almost nothing. He kept no diary, wrote no really
intimate letters. It was twenty years after his death before
anyone began to gather materials for his biography, by
which time there was not much to gather. Since his death,
two great wars have swept over his homeland, and it seems
most unlikely that we shall ever learn more than is recorded
in the one biography, written by his countryman, Hugo
Iltis. But even that little is humanly interesting.

The Life of Mendel

The Mendel family lived in Moravia, in Central Europe,
under circumstances of grinding poverty. Or so we would
say, though to the Mendels, things looked pretty good, for
the family was on its way up: for two generations now
they had enjoyed the status of peasants. Father Mendel had
to give only three days out of the week to labor on the
lord's manor; the other three working days he could

squander on his own little farm. Into such a world was born, on July 22, 1822, the boy Johann, the second of three children. A more unlikely candidate to produce the greatest purely intellectual work in biology in his century could hardly have been picked.

How did the life of the intellect happen to capture the imagination of this peasant boy? There are only a few hints. There was a countess who took an interest in the local school for the poor, encouraging the schoolmaster to give instruction in the sciences. Since these subjects were not part of the state-sanctioned curriculum, a local priest called the innovation a "scandal." Then there was, as always, the inspiring teacher, Thomas Makitta by name, devoted to his task for more than forty years. If this devotion bore no fruit other than the awakening of Johann Mendel (and none other is recorded), it was amply justified.

As it became clear that Johann had a passion for learning, difficulties developed within the family. How could a peasant boy be spared to education? He was needed on the farm. But Johann was determined, and he presently had his way. He was sent off to high school in a nearby town. Since the family could not take care of all his expenses, he had to work while he attended school, and even so, had a hard time getting along. Perhaps he might have made it had not his father been seriously injured while working on the lord's manor. The accident required a complete rearranging of family affairs so that a son-in-law could carry on. The resulting financial agreements, though just for Johann, made a reorientation of his life necessary. He had only one chance of keeping contact with the world of learning, and that was by entering the Church. In September of 1843, Mendel entered an Augustinian monastery near Brünn, Austria (later to be called Brno, Czechoslovakia). As he guardedly explained this action in a brief autobiographical fragment written in the third person: "His private circumstances determined his choice of profession." In his new life he took the name by which he is now known, Gregor.

He was certainly poorly suited to the pastoral calling. There is a letter from his superior to the bishop which draws a most interesting character portrait of Pater Gregor. The letter was written on the occasion of recommending him as a "reserve teacher" in a nearby high school. It concludes as follows:

I will content myself with adding that this collegiate priest lives a very retired life, virtuous, and religious, thoroughly appropriate to his condition; also that he is very diligent in the study of the sciences; but that he is much less fitted for work as a parish priest, the reason being that he is seized by an unconquerable timidity when he has to visit a sick-bed or to see any one ill or in pain. Indeed, this infirmity of his has made him dangerously ill, and that was why I found it necessary to relieve him from service as a parish priest.

How fortunate it was that the abbot of his monastery, Prelate Napp, had a keen love of learning, and thus (seeing Gregor's limitations) encouraged him to make teaching his profession. After several years' service as a reserve teacher, Mendel, in 1850, took the examination required for certification as a regular teacher—and failed. Ironically, his performance was poorest in the sections on geology and biology. Following this blow he was allowed to study at the University of Vienna for two years. In 1856, he applied to take the examination again. What happened this time is not at all clear, but certainly he did not pass. Either he failed the examination and the record was lost to posterity, or he got "cold feet" and backed out of it. Whatever the facts, he remained a non-certificated teacher for the rest of his teaching career. . . . Every examination is a reciprocal calibration of both student and examination, and one cannot but wonder, in such a case as this, which it was that was weighed and found wanting?

It was in 1856 also that Mendel began his epochal experiments with peas. Starting with a number of visibly differing strains, he set out to learn how differences in seed color or height of plant were transmitted from one generation to another. What he learned, we shall find out shortly; for the moment we wish to follow the fortunes of his discovery.

In 1865 he reported his findings to the Brünn Society for the Study of Natural Science, reading his paper to an audience of about forty men. It took two successive monthly meetings to complete the reading. One suspects that his audience was as quiet at the end of the second session as had been the audience at the Linnaean Society after the reading of Darwin's and Wallace's papers, but for completely different reasons. What were these good naturalists to make of this weird mathematical approach to the phenomena of nature? Was this science—or was it numerology? Good students today take several weeks to cover the same ground as thoroughly, so Mendel's first auditors may well be excused for failing to appreciate his work.

He needed a wider, abler audience. The publication of his work in the Proceedings of the Society should have given it to him, for this journal was distributed to more than a hundred important libraries in Europe and America. Moreover, the author was given forty separate reprints of his article to distribute as he saw fit. He undoubtedly sent them to the scientific leaders of the day who he thought would be most likely to appreciate his work. Unfortunately, he left no record of his mailing list. We would like to know if he sent a copy to Darwin, in whose work he took a keen interest. We know only that a thorough search of the Down papers made after the rediscovery of Mendel's work in 1900 failed to unearth a copy of the *Versüche über Pflanzenhybriden*.

Of only one distribution of this paper are we sure, and that is of the copy Mendel sent, with an accompanying letter, to Karl Wilhelm von Naegeli, Professor of Botany in the University of Munich. The choice of referee was, on the surface, a wise one. Naegeli, only a few years older than Mendel, was a most eminent botanist, and he was particularly interested in heredity. Surely he would appreciate the new theory? Let us read part of Naegeli's first letter and see. (This reply was sent by return post—two months later.)

It seems to me that the experiments with *Pisum* [peas], far from being finished, are only beginning. The mistake made by all the more recent experimenters is that they have shown so much less perseverance than Kölreuter and Gärtner. I note with pleasure that you are not making this mistake, and that you are treading in the footsteps of your famous predecessors. You should, however, try to excel them, and in my view this will only be possible (and thus alone can any advance be made in the theory of hybridization) if experiments of an exhaustive character are made upon one single object in every conceivable direction. No such complete series of experiments, providing irrefutable proofs for the most momentous conclusions, has ever yet been made. . . . Your design to experiment on plants of other kinds is excellent, and I am convinced that with these different forms you will get notably different results (in respect to the inherited characters). It would seem to me especially valuable if you were to effect hybrid fertilizations in *Hieracium* [hawkweed], for this will soon be the species about whose intermediate forms we shall have the most precise knowledge. What I should especially recommend for experiments are *H. pilosella, H. auricula, H. praealtum, H. pratence, H. murorum, H. tiacum, H. cymosum;* and, on the other hand, *H. murorum, H. vulgatum, H. glaucum, H. alpinum, H. amplexicaule, H. prenanthoides, H. tridentatum.*

A modern biologist, reading Naegeli's condescending letter, is filled with something very like rage. Could the Herr Doktor Professor not see that this little pamphlet of forty-four pages made obsolete several thousand pages of Kölreuter, Gärtner, Herbert, Lecoq, Wichura, Kölliker and Lucas? Could he not read? Apparently not—not in the sense that such a Euclid-bare work as Mendel's demands reading. Naegeli's letter made only the slightest reference to the technical contents of Mendel's paper, a reference as devoid of understanding as a professional book reviewer's.

If Naegeli did not in the least understand Mendel's work, why did he bother to reply at all? From kindness, perhaps; and *noblesee oblige?* The closing part of the passage quoted suggests a less disinterested motive as well. The great professor had for many years been struggling with the riddle of inheritance in the hawkweeds, without success. It took a lot of work. Here was a country priest who plainly loved hard work: why not get him to help out with the hawkweed research, thus advancing the professor's program, and giving the little priest a chance to make a modest name for himself in science, perhaps? It looked like a good bargain and, over a period of eight years, the professor contributed many hours of his invaluable time to writing encouraging letters of misunderstanding to Father Gregor. We must grant that Naegeli meant well. Unfortunately, he could hardly have done Mendel a greater disservice than getting him to study the hawkweeds, for these plants often reproduce in a very irregular way, by what has come to be known as *apomixis*. In this process, a plant may go through the motions of sexual reproduction—pollination and all that—but the embryo that develops in the seed is derived from maternal tissue only. It is obvious that if an investigator doesn't know what the real parentage of a plant is (but thinks he does), he is going to have the devil's own time unscrambling the heredity. This was the puzzle Naegeli quite innocently handed Mendel, and Mendel, of course, failed to solve it. It was many years after his death before the secret of apomictic reproduction was uncovered.

Why was Mendel's work unappreciated in his own lifetime? There are many reasons. For one thing, it was based on simple algebra, an unheard-of approach in that golden age of the descriptive naturalist. For another, the author was unknown, and he said his piece only once. It is exceedingly improbable that a radical new truth will be heard unless it is repeated many times. But events seemed to conspire against the repetition of this particular truth. Two years after the publication of this paper, Mendel was made abbot of his monastery. From that time on he was the busy executive, with only snatches of time available for research. Such research as he did carry on may have made him doubt the generality of the laws he had discovered with the peas, for hawkweeds did not appear to follow them. It is also known that he worked with honeybees, and if he tried to work out their heredity, he must have been similarly discouraged, for the males (drones) have no fathers—a fact not known in Mendel's time. He must have often wondered if his laws of heredity were really true. Darwin said that *no belief is vivid until shared by others*— and Mendel found no others to share his belief, to make it so vivid that he could muster courage to shout it. He died unknown.

In the year of Mendel's death, 1884, Naegeli published *his* magnum opus on heredity, a weighty tome of 822 dispensable pages. In it he did not once refer to the work of the priest at Brünn. Copernicus had his Rhaeticus; Newton his Halley; Darwin his Hooker. Mendel had Naegeli. Surely, if recollections of errors of judgment cause us to turn in our graves, the professor of Munich has joined a mighty band of ghostly whirling dervishes.

What Mendel Found

What did Mendel discover? In brief: *genes*. He did not use that term, however, for the word was not coined until two generations later, but the concept of the gene is clearly implicit in his paper. Like most basic concepts of science, the gene is difficult to define with brevity and in such a way that no exception may be taken to the definition. Perfection in definition is seldom worth striving for; it is better to give an approximate definition that will do for the moment, and then let the meaning grow as experience accumulates. Roughly speaking, *genes are material particles found in the nuclei of cells; particles whose chemical interactions determine how the organism reacts to the environment; particles that are passed on from parents to offspring in regular, predictable ways*.

So general a statement is, of course, rather empty of meaning at first glance; a particular example may help fill it. If your skin is brown, it is because you have the necessary genes for brown skin in the nuclei of the cells of your skin; and these genes you have inherited from your parents. Does this mean that heredity alone determines the color of the skin? Not at all. Although it is true that some men have inherited certain genes that result in a brown skin in almost any environment that a human is likely to live in, yet there are others who are brown "because they have been lying in the sun." But even in the second case, heredity is involved, for only some people have the particular genes that permit the skin to tan when exposed to sunlight. As a matter of method, we should not ask, "Which is the cause—heredity or environment?" but rather, "How do heredity and environment act together to produce the effect observed?" But of this principle more later.

For the moment we need to know more about genes conceived in the simplest way. We will consider an example of genetic action in "four-o'clock" flowers, an example somewhat simpler than the problems attacked by Mendel. Some four-o'clocks have red flowers, others white. The difference is "genetically determined" (that is, it is indifferent to ordinary environmental influences). If a pure-line red four-o'clock is crossed with a pure-line white, the offspring are all pink. So much is not surprising; Fleeming Jenkin, or anyone thinking in terms of the traditional paint-pot theory of heredity would say the two characteristics, red and white, had blended together to form pink. But if this is so, then breeding the pinks among themselves should produce all pink-flowered offspring. *But it doesn't.* It produces three kinds of offspring: red, pink and white. Plainly, the paint-pot theory won't work, for you cannot so easily unmix paints once they are blended together. How are we to explain the results?

Such results were known for centuries, and for centuries they were "explained" verbally. The red and the white flowers coming from the pinks were called "throwbacks" (to the grandparental types); and scientists, including Darwin, spoke learnedly of "reversion" or "atavism." This type of explanation we now call "giving ignorance a name," for it is nothing more. The remarkable thing about the Abbé Mendel was that he was not content with this kind of solution. For some strange and wonderful reason he insisted on finding a more meaningful answer, which he did through counting and speculating.

If you breed two pink four-o'clocks together, you get red, pink and white flowers. If you produce large numbers in this way, and if you look for simple ratios between the numbers, you discover that about ¼ of the plants so produced are reds, about ¾ are pink, and about ¼ are white. How can one explain this result most simply?

The Mendelian explanation is as follows: The genetic character of the pink plants can be represented as Rr, the capital letter (R) standing for the "red allele," that is the "red" form of the gene, received from one parent, the small letter (r) standing for the "white allele" derived from the other. The word *allele* is used for alternative forms of the "same" gene. Both alleles are present in every cell in the body of the pink four-o'clock, including the cells that are going to give rise to the reproductive cells. But in the formation of the reproductive-cell nuclei, a remarkable thing happens: each reproductive-cell nucleus gets *one and only one allele* of a particular gene. Since the new zygote (fertilized egg) is formed by the fusion of only one nucleus from the male side, with only one from the female side, it follows that each gene is represented only twice in the zygote nucleus. How represented? Plainly there are three possibilities: *RR*, and *Rr*, and *rr*, producing (respectively) red, pink, and white plants among the offspring. Qualitatively this checks out. What about the *quantitative* aspect: can we explain ¼: ¾: ¼ ratio?

The Mendelian scientist says *Yes*. The ratio is one long known in probability theory. If you flip a penny and a nickel at the same time, and record the number of times they fall both heads, or one head and one tail, or both tails, you find the same ratio of ¼: ¾: ¼. But what in the reproductive process corresponds to the flipping of coins?

The critical event takes place in the production of reproductive nuclei. The nucleus of a reproductive "mother cell" in a pink plant contains two genes, one *R* and one *r*. In the process of dividing to form pollen nuclei (male) or egg nuclei (female) the number of genes of a given kind is reduced to one per nucleus. Since *R* and *r* are in the ratio of 1:1 (just as the ratio of heads to tails of a coin is 1:1) *R*- and *r*-containing reproductive nuclei are equally probable. Of the pollen nuclei, ½ contain *R* and ½ contain *r;* likewise for the egg nuclei. Since a zygote nucleus is produced by the fusion of one pollen nucleus with one egg nucleus, the frequency of the three types of zygotes will be ¼ *RR*: ¾ *Rr*:¼*rr*. The pinks are twice as frequent as either of the other classes because they can be derived in two ways: *R*-pollen plus *r*-egg, or *r*-pollen plus *R*-egg. (Just as heads and tails with the coins can be obtained by heads-on-penny plus tails-on-nickel, or tails-on-penny plus heads-on-nickel.)

Such is the Mendelian explanation of the four-o'clock data, which present us with just about the simplest problem known in genetics. Mendel, however, was not so fortunate as to encounter such a simple case. The interaction of the genes he studied in peas involves an additional principle called "dominance." If a pure-line pea plant with violet flowers is bred to one with white flowers, all the first generation (called F_1, or "first filial" generation) plants have violet flowers. The violet allele, we say, is "dominant" to the white allele; and white is "recessive" to violet. "Dominance" is a handy word, but a dangerous one: it may suggest that one allele has somehow smothered or stamped out the other, which is not the case. When two F_1 violet plants are bred together, white offspring appear among the progeny ("F_2"), and these white plants, if bred only among themselves, will produce only white-flowered plants, indefinitely. So the "dominant" violet allele has not affected the white allele. The dominance is only one of "expression," not of heredity: when both alleles are present in the same individual (who is said to be *heterozygous* for the gene), we can detect only the V allele; but the recessive v allele is there and will show its effect in later generations whenever it is in the *homozygous* condition (vv). Whenever we cannot tell homozygous dominant individuals (VV, in the present instance) from the heterozygous ones (Vv), the F_2 ratio is altered from one of $\frac{1}{4}$: $\frac{2}{4}$: $\frac{1}{4}$ to one of $\frac{3}{4}$: $\frac{1}{4}$, as a result of the observational lumping together of two different genetic classes. The two *genotypes* (genetic types), VV and Vv, are, we say, lumped into a single *phenotype* (appearance-type) "violet." Such confounding is common but not universal in genetics, so it is small wonder that the riddle of heredity remained so long unsolved. It took real genius to perceive the order underlying the apparent confusion.

Why Did Darwin Fail?

Curiously, the great Darwin did not have the genius required to penetrate the mystery of heredity, a mystery that greatly hindered the proper elaboration of this theory of evolution. He tried. He even carried out some breeding experiments like Mendel's, as is evident from the following passage from his *Variation of Animals and Plants under Domestication*. This account, here somewhat abbreviated, was published two years after Mendel's paper.

> I crossed the peloric [abnormal] snapdragon with pollen of the common form; and the latter, reciprocally, with peloric pollen. I thus raised two great beds of seedlings, and not one was peloric. The crossed plants, which perfectly resembled the common snapdragon, were allowed to sow themselves, and out of a hundred and twenty-seven seedlings, eighty-eight proved to be common snapdragons, two were in an intermediate condition between the peloric and normal state, and thirty-seven were perfectly peloric, having reverted to the structure of their one grandparent.

If we neglect the two intermediate plants as unclassifiable we have in these data a ratio (2.4:1) that is close enough to a 3:1 ratio to be suggestive to the suitably prepared mind. But Darwin missed the hint completely, and went on, in page after page floundering, vacillating between the blending and the particulate theories of inheritance only to end up with "pangenesis," an unholy hybrid of the two theories, contaminated with false and unacknowledged Lamarckism. To us, blessed with hindsight, it is distinctly painful to see him pass the right turnings in the maze of data, blind to their significance.

"In the realm of observation, chance favors the prepared

mind," said Darwin's contemporary, Louis Pasteur. Darwin had the chance that Mendel had. But he did not have the prepared mind, the mathematical mind. In writing of his undergraduate days, he tells us that mathematics was repugnant to him, chiefly because he was not able to see any meaning in the early steps of algebra, and so he gave it up. "This impatience was very foolish," he confessed, "and in after years I have deeply regretted that I did not proceed far enough at least to understand something of the great leading principles of mathematics, for men thus endowed seem to have an extra sense."

Mathematics is still "an extra sense," the development of which is all too frequently neglected in our society. How many insights into nature are even now lying around, closed to the unmathematical mind, but open to him who loves the art of thinking? We will not know until later. Perhaps only when it is too late.

Probing the Unseen with Logic

Two of the greatest intellectual achievements of the nineteenth century were the discovery of the invisible: in physics, the discovery of atoms; in biology, of genes. There are many parallels between these two achievements. If one will accept mere ideas without experimental evidence, both concepts can be found crudely expressed at least as far back as in the writings of the Roman poet Lucretius (first century B.C.). But ideas are cheap (and mostly wrong) and no one treasured these, surrounded as they were by a multitude of other, and quite erroneous, speculations of armchair philosophers. When these ideas were brought up again, with evidence and arguments, in the nineteenth century, they quite naturally met considerable resistance among the scientific fraternity. The idea of atoms, for instance—what right did it have to ask for credence? Particles so tiny that we should never expect to see them—and yet we are to believe they really exist—what is this, the Emperor's New Clothes?

No, says the scientific philosopher: I don't know what you mean by "really exist," and it probably will not be profitable to try to find out. But, operationally, the situation is of this sort. We begin (Fig. 14) with a "model"—say a concept of atoms as indivisible, discrete particles, in constant motion and reacting from encounters with perfect elasticity, and from this model we make predictions that can be experimentally checked. If the experiments turn out as predicted, we say the model has been confirmed. Then, a little later, we think of some other experiments that should turn out a certain way

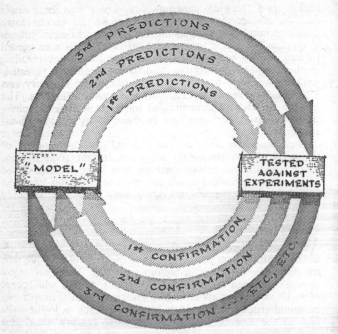

Fig. 14. The idea of a "model." By thus bypassing the difficult
    question, "What is Truth?" scientists get on with the work
    that needs to be done.

if the model is correct: if they do, we say the model has been
confirmed still further. And so on. It is not quite as simple as
this, of course: sometimes experiments don't come out exactly as we had expected them to (*e.g.*, atoms prove to be
destructible), and then we modify the model slightly to fit
the new facts, as well as all the old ones. This leads to new
predictions that must be tested. And thus, by an organic process, our models—our ideas, our theories—grow, until from
many successes and long familiarity, they become as real
to us as the cows and trees and tables with which we have
(we suppose) direct contact. The idea of atoms, viewed with
skepticism by a few good physicists as late as the end of the
nineteenth century, had become so real to us before the middle of the twentieth, that we gambled two billion dollars on
one of its predictions. The successful verification of the
model, in the atomic bomb, was so spectacular that no

thoughtful person seriously asks any more, "Are there *really* atoms?" We cannot see them, but confidence in our logic makes us feel that the existence of these invisible entities is at least as certain as the one-time existence of a man named Julius Caesar. The probability can hardly be less.

The history of the acceptance of the gene concept repeated, in rough outline, that of the atomic-molecular theory. As usual, however, biology trailed physical science in time. The role of the unappreciated Mendel was played earlier by physical science by the unappreciated Avogadro (1811). General acceptance of the gene theory by scientists came about a half century after the scientific acceptance of the atomic-molecular picture of matter. And if a crude generalization of a very complex situation is acceptable, we may say that the "public" acceptance of both theories took still another half century. Curiously, the very phenomenon which brought final public conviction in the truth of the atom—namely, the atomic bomb—promises ultimately to induce public belief in that other great intellectual creation, the gene. As the biological consequences of high-energy radiation become clearer, it will become more and more difficult for anyone to ask seriously, "Are there *really* genes?"

The Rediscovery of Genetics

Simultaneous, independent discoveries are not uncommon in science, but there is no more remarkable instance of this phenomenon than the announcements of the "discovery" of genetics in the year 1900. Hugo De Vries, K. Correns and E. Tschermak each independently rediscovered the basic laws of genetics. Whatever moment of triumph each might have experienced in his discovery was soon spoiled by the bitter discovery that they had all been anticipated. That three men should in 1900 simultaneously make a discovery which one man had had very much to himself a generation earlier is an illustration of the truth that Galton has emphasized, that discoveries are most often made—and recognized—only when "the time is ripe."

The theory of heredity as Mendel had stated it was a highly *formal* one, *i.e.*, a theory that used abstract symbols (*A* and *a, R* and *r,* etc.) to refer to entities which were given no material meaning. Not many men, even in the brotherhood of science, like to deal with unembodied particles. There is, perhaps, a feeling that it's taken us long enough to get rid of ghosts and spirits of many sorts—why should we now introduce a new and equally ghostly "gene"? If there is a material particle, where is it, please? Something of this sort of feeling may have delayed the acceptance of genetics until it was possible to point to the material involved in heredity. This material had to be something that showed a high degree of constancy from one cell generation to another of the same species; it had to be passed from parents to offspring via the gametes (sperms and eggs); and—if Mendelian explanations were to be given a material meaning—it had to be subject to a process that in a formal sense was equivalent to the flipping of coins. Quite in ignorance of Mendel's work, a score or more workers were, during the last two decades of the nineteenth century, engaged in discovering just such a material mechanism within living cells. The behavior of this material was recognized by many researchers as being precisely what was needed to explain heredity, and so it was almost "inevitable" (if that word has any historical meaning at all) that Mendelism should be discovered around the turn of the century, as it had *not* been inevitable in 1866. Let us see what this material basis of heredity is, as we now know it.

The Great Fertilization Sweepstakes

Before beginning, it would be well to have some idea of the scale of the phenomena of heredity. For this we will use, as our measuring unit, the *micron* (symbolized by the Greek letter "mu," written μ). It takes 1,000 microns to equal a millimeter; there are a few more than 25,000 microns in an inch.

The organisms we are most familiar with are made up of many more or less independent living units called *cells*. Cells vary greatly in size, but it would not be too rash to say that a "typical" cell is about 25 microns in diameter—about one fourth as wide as a human hair. The human body contains, it has been estimated, some hundred million million cells. A most characteristic and constant feature of a cell is its "kernel" or nucleus, which is (to ignore variations) about 5 microns in diameter. Cells can reproduce by a process of splitting in two. Micro-surgical studies have shown us that the process of cell reproduction can continue indefinitely only in cells that have nuclei; the hereditary abilities of cells to bring about various biochemical reactions are determined almost entirely by the nucleus.

The analysis can be carried even further. Inside the nucleus there are tiny threads that can be stained. These threads are called *chromosomes*. They are not smoothly uniform in texture, but have bumps and constrictions in them, and they vary in length. It is possible to recognize individual threads, to name them, and study them. Thousands of hours spent look-

ing down microscope tubes have revealed that each species
of plant or animal has its characteristic number of chromosomes of constant size and shape: man has 46 (according to
Tjio and Levan, 1956), pea plants have 14, corn (maize) has
20. The cells of an organism are divisible into two sorts, those
that have the full number of chromosomes, called the *diploid*
number, and those which have only half as many, called the
haploid number. Most of the cells of the body are diploid:
these are the *somatic* cells ("body" cells). Only a small fraction of the cells are haploid: these are the *gametes*—*i.e.,* the
reproductive cells or germ cells: the eggs (in the female) or
the sperm cells (in the male). Human eggs and sperm contain
23 chromosomes each; the germinal nuclei of peas and corn
contain, respectively, 7 and 10 chromosomes each.

The difference between diploid and haploid cells is more
than one of mere numbers. Close examination reveals that
every one of the chromosomes in a haploid cell is different,
whereas in the diploid cell there are two chromosomes of each
kind. It is, therefore, more revealing to say that diploid cells
in humans contain 23 *pairs* of chromosomes, in peas 7 pairs,
and in corn 10 pairs. The specialized type of cell division
(called "reduction division") which produces haploid cells
from diploid ones, insures that each gamete gets *one and only
one* member of each pair of chromosomes. (Now we begin
to catch a hint of the penny-flipping mechanism of heredity.)

What a gene looks like, we still don't know. We know a
gene is very small—probably about 0.05 a micron in diameter; which is about four times too small to be seen with the
ordinary optical microscope, though we *should* be able to see
one with an electron microscope. We don't know what genes
look like, but there is a superabundance of evidence, converg-
ing from many different directions, that convinces us that
genes, whatever they are, are parts of chromosomes. Or put
in another way, each chromosome is made up of many hundreds of different genes. The mechanism that distributes the
chromosomes to the gametes necessarily distributes the genes
as well.

To see how this mechanism works in practice, let's take an
example from human genetics, and trace the distribution of
chromosomes and genes through the act of reproduction. In
doing so, we are admittedly going a bit beyond the *direct*
evidence available, for we do not know as much about the
chromosomes of man as we do about those of fruit flies or
corn plants. For our ignorance, there are various reasons:
for one thing, man is understandably reluctant to furnish his
chromosomes (that is, the cells of his body) to the biologist
for observation, so we don't have a large amount of reports

to draw on. For another, the chromosomes of most mammals (including man) are difficult to study; they are exasperatingly bunched up and tend to stick together most of the time. So most cytologists (students of cellular phenomena) avoid using mammalian cells for their studies. Nevertheless, there is enough indirect evidence to indicate that man is no exception to the laws of heredity that rule the rest of the living world, and so we will confidently indicate genes-in-chromosomes in humans, in order to understand the material basis for those hereditary differences that mean so much to human happiness.

Let's take the case of hyperdactyly—having too many fingers (6 or more per hand). The gene for this is a dominant gene, so a heterozygous person is hyperdactylous. Let us imagine that a man who is heterozygous for hyperdactyly marries a normal woman, and that they decide to have a child: what is the chance (probability) that the child will be normal?

First, let us *picture* what must be the situation with this man's genes. Our picture (Fig. 15) is not a realistic one, but an idealized diagram. All the diploid cells of such a man contain 23 pairs of chromosomes, of which one pair includes the genes for 5- or 6-fingeredness. We show only this pair of chromosomes, ignoring the other 22 pairs which, for the moment, are of no interest to us. The cells from which sperm cells are derived are also diploid: these are called "sperm mother cells." Each of the sperm mother cells divides in such a way as to produce haploid sperm cells which are numbered in the millions.

Now each sperm mother cell in our particular man is heterozygous for hyperdactyly. One member of the pair of chromosomes bearing the "fingeredness-gene" has the normal allele, the other chromosome of the pair (the "homologous chromosome") has the abnormal allele. Both chromosomes, of course, have many other genes as well, but we are not at the moment interested in them, so we will ignore them. Although no one has actually seen the "fingeredness-genes," we indicate them by drawing the normal allele as a figure 5 in the chromosome, and the abnormal allele as a figure 6 (not at all what genes look like, we are sure). Since the two types of alleles occur in exactly equal numbers in the sperm mother cells, the process of meiosis ("reduction division") will produce haploid sperm cells of the two types in exactly equal numbers. (However, sperm cells are delicate, and many die, so the *exact* equality will not long remain, but the numbers will continue to be *approximately* equal.)

The man's wife is normal, and can produce only one type

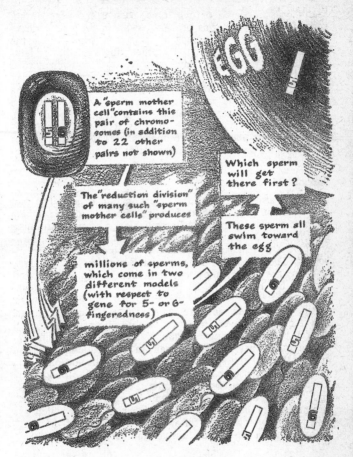

Fig. 15. The Fertilization Sweepstakes. How chance enters into the fate of a child.

of egg (with respect to this characteristic), an egg bearing the normal allele. What happens when mating occurs?

The man deposits approximately 300 million sperm cells in the vagina, of which about 150 million have the 5-finger allele, and about 150 million have the 6-finger allele. Now begins the great sweepstakes race that runs to completion somewhere in the world more than three times every second, every day, year in year out: 300 million violently wriggling sperm cells in search of one large, passive and very distant egg. Many of the sperms probably swim in the wrong direction; others, by the hundreds of thousands, perish along the way from exhaustion. Relative to their tiny size, the straight-line distance the sperms have to traverse is equivalent to a walk of eight miles for a man. Only a few thousand get any-where near the egg. And of these, *only one* penetrates the egg and thus effects fertilization, for once this happens the egg membrane becomes impenetrable to all other sperm cells. Which sperm cell gets there first? Is it one carrying a 5-finger allele, or one with the 6-finger allele? It is just a matter of chance, we say, and the chance, when the male is heterozygous, is fifty-fifty. Like flipping pennies.

Sex and Heredity

Chance also enters into the determination of sex. The fact that boys and girls are born in approximately equal numbers suggests that one parent is heterozygous for a sex-determining gene, the other homozygous. This is not quite the case, how-ever: rather than single genes, whole chromosomes are in-volved. The sex-determining mechanism works as follows:

There are 46 chromosomes in a human diploid cell, but they do not make quite 23 perfect pairs. Only 22 pairs are perfect pairs in both sexes; the remaining two chromosomes, in the male, differ, and are called X- and Y-chromosomes. The female, however, has two X-chromosomes (hence 23 perfect pairs). Although X and Y are perceptibly different in the male, they act like a pair in the reduction division process, half of the sperms receiving an X-chromosome, and half a Y-chromosome. All the gametes (eggs) produced by the female have an X-chromosome. For convenience, the X- and Y-chromosomes are called *heterosomes* ("different" chromosomes) in contrast to the other 22 pairs which are called *autosomes*. Let us follow the distribution of the chromosomes from one generation to another:

	Woman	Man
Diploid cells of 1st generation	22 pairs of autosomes + XX ↓	22 pairs of autosomes + XY ↓
Gametes of 1st generation	egg, with 22 autosomes + X	½ are sperms with 22 autosomes + X ½ are sperms with 22 autosomes + Y

Zygotes which
grow into
2nd generation

½ of zygotes have 22 pairs
of autosomes + XX   →females

½ of zygotes have 22 pairs
of autosomes + XY   →males

More briefly, XX individuals are females; XY are males. The system is a stable one that will produce nearly equal numbers of the two sexes in each generation, indefinitely. It is the fact that the sperm cells come in two different "models" that makes the difference in sex possible. We cannot, at present, tell a living X-sperm from a living Y-sperm; but this fact has not prevented more speculative minds from wondering whether we should not someday be able to treat the semen of a male and either destroy one type of sperm selectively, or separate the two kinds, thus enabling us to determine the sex of the offspring. It seems not too wild an idea. On a theoretical level it would be a rather exciting triumph. But would the discovery be a good one to make? If the means of sex control were freely available to all, one can easily imagine wild fluctuations in the fashion for having boys or girls at different times, with widespread and hardly predictable consequences.

The X- and Y-chromosomes differ in a significant way genetically as well as visually. For the most part, the genes present in the X-chromosome are unrepresented in the Y-chromosome, which seems to be almost a genetic blank. From this it follows that only a single "dose" of an X-borne recessive allele is enough to produce a phenotypic effect in the male, whereas the usual double dose is required in the female, which has two gene-bearing X-chromosomes. Consequently, a characteristic determined by a recessive X-borne allele crops out rather oddly in successive generations. Take ordinary "red-green color blindness," for example: everybody knows that it is commoner in males than it is in females. But the handicap has little or nothing to do with maleness in any important sense: the unequal distribution is merely caused by the fact that the abnormal allele—the allele producing color blindness—is a recessive allele that is borne by the X-chromosome. The Y-chromosome is blank with respect to this gene. Let's see how this allele will be transmitted through several generations.

Suppose a color-blind man marries a woman who is homozygously normal: what sort of vision will their children have? We can represent the color-blind allele by an asterisk after the X; the man's formula is therefore X*Y and the woman's XX. We predict their children in the usual way:

$$XX \quad x \quad X*Y$$

½ XX* (phenotypically normal females)
½ XY (completely normal males)

So all the children are phenotypically normal. What about the following generation? If we assume that their children mate with genotypically normal people—which are the commonest sort in the general population—then it is clear that the *boys* from the mating above will produce only completely normal offspring. For them, the fact that their father was color blind is irrelevant to predicting their offspring. With the *girls* from the above mating, the situation is different.

$$XX* \quad x$$

¼ XY (normal male)
¼ X*Y (color-blind male)
¼ XX (normal female)
¼ XX* (phenotypically normal female, but "carrying" the abnormal allele)

Only males—and only half of them, on the average—from such a mating are color blind. Notice the odd way in which this trait has popped up: the boys in the F_2 generation have inherited it from their grandfather *through their mother.* Who their father is does not matter, for this gene. This type of inheritance is sometimes called crisscross inheritance; it was first described in the early nineteenth century, but it was only an abominable puzzle until the development of genetics in the twentieth.

Color-blind females are rare, but they do occur. If a color-blind male (X*Y) mates with a heterozygous female (X*X), half their daughters should be color blind (X*X*). How often will this happen? To calculate this we use a very general principle of probability, often called the *Product Rule:* If the probability of a certain event's happening once is p, then the probability of its happening twice (concurrently, or successively) is p^2. For example, with one die, the probability of getting a 6 is $1/6$; with two dice, the probability of getting 6's on both at the same time is $(1/6)^2 = 1/36$. If the frequency of X* chromosomes in the general population of X-chromosomes is p, the frequency of color-blind males will also be p (since one dose of [*] is enough for males); whereas the frequency of color-blind females (X^*X^*) will be pp. In the American population about $1/12$ of the males are red-green color blind; about $1/144$ of the females should also be color blind. Studies indicate that their frequency is of this order of magnitude. Because of their "spotty" appearance in a pedigree, X-linked genes are easier to identify than auto-somal genes in an animal like man where employing the test matings of ordinary genetics is out of the question. As a result, we know of more genes in the X-chromosome than in any other human chromosome.

Inescapability of Chance

"Nature's book," said Galileo, "is written in mathematical language." As far as heredity is concerned, we see that the language is that of the theory of probability. It is a matter of chance whether a child will be a boy or a girl, whether it will have twelve fingers or ten, and whether it will be hemophilic or normal. The blood of a hemophiliac clots very slowly; as a result the slightest cut may endanger his life. Probably no hereditary distinction is so small as to be com-pletely without effect on the subsequent life of the child conceived. With so conspicuous a characteristic as hemophilia (which is due to a sex-linked gene), the reality of the con-sequences to the personal life of the possessor need not be argued. Such a characteristic may even be of historical im-portance. Queen Victoria was heterozygous for the hemo-philia gene. She was also very fertile. Through intermarriage of her children with the other royal families of Europe, the gene was spread from the Urals to the Pyrenees. Its existence in the royal family of Russia may have contributed to their downfall at the time of the Revolution. According to legend, part of the power of Rasputin was derived from his assertion that he could help the hemophilic crown prince; and one might suspect that the vacillating character of the Tsar may have been at least in part a consequence of the psychological stress imposed on a family afflicted with this hereditary defect. What has just been suggested is by no means historically certain, but it is worth saying to call attention to a neglected aspect of history, the historical effects of genetics.

It is a matter of chance—though the odds vary from character to character, and from family to family—whether a child will have hemophilia, crossed eyes, congenitally de-tached retina, scaly skin, hairy ears, webbed toes, short fingers, or be unable to smell hydrogen cyanide; whether it will suffer from diabetes, color blindness, muscular dystrophy, schizophrenia or varying degrees of mental incompetence; or whether it will enjoy an unusually high measure of intelligence, musical ability or fine muscular co-ordination. The development of some of these characteristics is also affected by the environment, but our ability to react to environmental influences is demonstrably determined by our genes. And what genes we get is always a matter of chance, the various probability values being determined jointly by the wisdom with which we choose our parents, and by the outcome of the Fertilization Sweepstakes that is blindly run at each human conception. Our lives are subject to the laws of the lottery from the moment we are only a gleam in our father's eye until death overtakes us. As willful human beings our hope is to eliminate the vagaries of chance where we can. Where we cannot, we must learn to live with uncertainty with some measure of grace.

7

Genes and Personal Decisions

WHEN Mendel's work was rediscovered in 1900, its importance was immediately recognized. In part, this was because Mendel now had a champion, William Bateson, who played for genetics the role T. H. Huxley had earlier played for evolution. Bateson "sold" Mendelism to his fellow scientists, and tirelessly explained it to the public at large. He was still explaining it during the First World War, when he contributed his bit to the defense of England by giving lectures on the subject to the troops in France. One wonders what the young men thought of it all, whether they caught even a little of the intellectual excitement behind the fractions ¼, ¾, ⅞, and ¹⁄₁₆; and whether they appreciated the splendid opportunity they were being given to develop their minds during their hours out of the trenches instead of degrading their bodies. History does not record. We do know, however, that Bateson, during one of his gay canters through a field of fractions, was caught up short when a soldier commented that *this Mendelism is just scientific Calvinism.* And so it is, the lecturer had to admit, with a shock of recognition. For seventeen years he had been busily occupied with the numbers game of genetics without once seeing what it all added up to: a rebirth, in modified form, of Calvin's doctrine of predestination, the belief that man's fate is determined for him at the time of conception, a determination that was (in Calvin's mind) irrevocable.

Genetics *is* a form of Calvinism—but it is Calvinism with a difference. That there is a sort of predestination at the time of conception is true: what genes an individual has is determined by what sperm unites with what egg. The genes of the gametes become the genes of the zygote, and (by repeated equational division) of all the cells of the adult body. In the formation of the next generation of gametes, chance enters in during the reduction division, in the assorting of the various alternative alleles, but the distribution must always be made from the genes available in the individual as a result of the earlier fertilization. Chance, operating within predestined boundaries, determines the possibilities of the succeeding generation.

Biological truth is richer than simple Calvinism. An example will help make the point. Among laboratory mice there are some animals that are very sensitive to noise. Put such a mouse in a metal tub and rattle keys against the side of the tub and you will cause the animal to go into convulsions and probably die. Susceptibility to such "audiogenic seizures," as they are called, is inherited. But one cannot say that a mouse of a susceptible strain is predestined to die of an audiogenic seizure, for it may never be exposed to the risk. Its death is not really predestined (not by genetics, at any rate); what is predetermined is its reaction to an environmental event that may, or may not, transpire.

The mice are worth following further. One can develop a strain that is practically pure for this type of reaction. Suppose we maintain such a strain in accoustically quiet surroundings, generation after generation: what will happen? The animals will, of course, live to a ripe old age without seizures. As generation succeeds generation, will the susceptibility to seizures disappear? *Not at all.* If, say, after twenty generations the colony should once again be subjected to raucous noise, convulsions and death will result just as surely as they would have at the beginning of the experiment. It is this sort of inevitable reaction that makes one regard genes as a kind of Calvinistic fate. It is probably because of this similarity that so many intelligent people reject genetics, consciously or otherwise; aware as they are of the many good effects that have come from revolutionary destruction of old ideas of caste and "divine right," they regard genetics as a dangerous counter-revolutionary movement. The impulse to reject is understandable. But if truth is our god, we must accept it even when unpleasant. We must also try to discern the lineaments of truth as closely as possible if we are not to be led astray by first impressions. We must study the gene more closely.

The Gene Becomes Subtle

The great physicist, A. A. Michelson, was once asked why he spent so much time determining the exact value of the velocity of light. In reply, he began by halfheartedly uttering some fashionable statements about the Value to Science, about Contributions to Knowledge, and so forth; but abruptly he interrupted himself, as his honesty got the better of his intentions, and laughingly said, "But the real reason is because it is such fun!" Few motives are more effective than this in getting the work of science done, and those fields of science that are the most fun generally advance the fastest.

Certainly this has been true of genetics during the first half century of its existence. Seldom has a science been more fun to develop. Probability theory holds a strange fascination for many minds, and in genetics men found a new science in which there was endless delight working with permutations and combinations, and in seeing the predictions beautifully verified in flies or corn plants: $\frac{1}{4}$, $\frac{1}{2}$, $\frac{3}{4}$, $\frac{7}{8}$, $\frac{9}{16}$, $\frac{13}{16}$, $\frac{15}{16}$ —there was no end to the fractions predicted and verified. It was a wonderful game.

But to play this game, it was almost necessary to be able to mate organisms at will, and one had to study only genes that were 100 percent determinative in their effects. It was because of the first need that most geneticists worked only with non-human organisms: and the second consideration caused them to work with only highly selected genes. Not all genes behave in a completely predictable way, even in a homozygous stock. Genes that produce only statistically predictable effects are often referred to, by the laboratory geneticist, as "bad" genes, meaning *bad for my work*—bad for the game of genetics. If you look through the published literature of the early period of genetics, you find few references to these "bad" genes; for the most part such genes were just thrown out of the game. Who wants to play with messy counters?

When we come to consider human genetics, however, such a cavalier attitude toward what is, is inappropriate, for the simple reason that we *are* human. The genes that contribute to epileptic seizures are "bad" genes in the laboratory geneticist's sense; but they are *bad* also in a humane sense, so we cannot ignore them, however esthetically unsatisfying the research may be.

Because of the difficulty of the work, much of human genetics has so far had to develop in partial independence of Mendelian theory. No one thinks for a moment that the genetics of human beings is fundamentally different from that of other organisms—in fact, year by year, we succeed in "mendelizing" more of the human data. But the facts of our heredity are so important to us that we must work as well as we can with the crude data even before we have succeeded in tying them firmly to theory.

The figures in Table I will give some idea of what we are up against. Here are listed various *congenital* defects, that is defects that are present at birth. Congenital abnormalities may or may not be hereditary. Congenital albinism *is* hereditary. Congenital syphilis is *not* (the child has merely been infected by its mother). Congenital blindness sometimes is, sometimes is not. What about the defects listed in the table? Are they hereditary? If they are, we might expect the figures shown in the right-hand column to correspond with one or another of the well-understood Mendelian probabilities, *e.g.*, 1 in 2, 1 in 4, 1 in 16, etc. Inspection shows few familiar figures. One of these is listed opposite "hyperdactyly." If we were told that one child of a family had too many fingers or toes, we could predict that his subsequent siblings would have a fifty-fifty chance of also having extra digits, for we know that hyperdactyly is caused by a rare dominant

TABLE I

Approximate incidence of selected congenital malformations, showing increase in risk for later children in a given family once it is known that one child of the family has the defect. (From Anderson and Reed, 1954.)

	Incidence in population	Risk figure for later siblings
All malformations	1 in 65	1 in 20
Central nervous system malformations (35%)		
Anencephalus	1 in 450	1 in 50
Spina bifida	1 in 375	1 in 25
Hydrocephalus	1 in 550	1 in 60
Mongolism	1 in 600	1 in 20
Muscular-skeletal malformations (25%)		
Harelip with or without cleft palate	1 in 1000	1 in 7
Cleft palate alone	1 in 2500	1 in 7
Hyperdactyly	1 in 1200	1 in 2
Syndactyly	1 in 2000	1 in 2
Clubfoot	1 in 1000	1 in 30
Congenital hip dislocation	1 in 1500	1 in 20
Cardiovascular malformations (20%)		
Patent ductus arteriosus	1 in 2500	1 in 50
Genitourinary malformations (6%)		
Hypospadias	1 in 1000	1 in 50(?)
Gastrointestinal malformations (3%)		
Tracheo-esophageal fistula	1 in 6000	less than 1 in 100
Atresia ani	1 in 5000	less than 1 in 100
Multiple malformations (11%)		

gene, and it is unlikely that both parents have the gene. Observation shows that the prediction is correct: the risk figure for later siblings is approximately ½. But what about the other risk figures listed: ⅐, ¹⁄₂₅, ¹⁄₆₀, etc.? What formal sense can we make of these? Not much. Plainly, more than "school genetics" is involved. Fortunately we can say something about the additional factors or principles that are probably involved in such ratios, principles for which there is adequate scientific evidence among non-human animals and plants whose reproduction can be experimented with.

First subtlety: *many different genes may have similar effects.* For example, there is a dominant gene for whiteness in chickens: there is also another gene for whiteness that is recessive. The experimenter who assumed that whiteness was always brought about by a single gene would be quite unable to explain some of the odd ratios obtained from different matings. Among humans, there is evidence that at least two different genes may produce diabetes, one being dominant, the other recessive.

Second subtlety: *two or more genes may have to act together* to produce a given condition. The ability to hear (among humans) is known to require both of two different dominant alleles, which may be called D and E. A person who has one or more of each of these, D-E-, can hear; all other genetic types are deaf (*e.g.*, dd E-. D ee and ddee). It is thus possible not only for two normal parents to have a deaf child (parents being, say, DdEE x DdEE) but also for two deaf parents to have a child who hears (*e.g.*, parents thus: *ddEE* x *DDee*). To those who do not understand genetics, such apparently contradictory results seem wholly mysterious.

Instances in which different genes have to act together to produce a normal structure or function are not the exception, but the rule. We know of biochemical functions that demonstrably depend on the coaction of as many as a dozen genes; the trend of genetic knowledge is such that we expect someday to find that almost all of the principal functions of the body require at least dozens, and maybe hundreds, of coacting genes. Whenever we have not yet identified the principal genes involved in a variable characteristic, it will be difficult for us to make simple sense of the "risk figures" that are produced by unidentified genes.

Third subtlety: *genes can kill.* When this happens, primary genetic ratios may be altered by the differential survival of the various genotypes. An interesting example has turned up in the silver-fox business. A generation ago a fox rancher in Wisconsin found among his standard silver foxes one animal with an interesting type of fur to which the name "platinum" was given. When this type was bred with the silvers, about half the offspring were silver, half platinum. Since silvers bred true, it looked as though platinum was caused by an ordinary dominant gene, say *P*. On this hypothesis, two platinum fox parents, if derived from mixed parentage, should produce among their offspring ¾ platinum and ¼ silver. But the prediction is not verified. If one breeds two platinum foxes and then counts and classifies the pups after they are weaned, one finds only ⅔ platinum with ⅓ silver. How come?

The answer becomes apparent when one observes the litters soon after birth. In the litters of platinum x platinum there are some foxes that are white. These die soon (always before weaning time), and the vixen, good housekeeper that she is, eats them. The primary genetic ratio is one of ¼ silver: ¾ platinum: ¼ white, which is modified by death of the homozygous platinum (white) to a ratio in the living adult foxes of ⅓ silver: ⅔ platinum. It is not possible to have a pure-breeding platinum strain.

Several points should be made in this connection. The platinum gene is of the sort usually called *lethal* or *sublethal* genes. The distinction between the two is not fundamental. If a gene kills before birth, it is called a lethal. Such a gene is "yellow" in mice, and "minor brachyphalangy" in man; both, when homozygous, kill their possessors in embryo. If the gene kills after birth, it may be called sublethal, particularly if it kills late. But where does one draw the line? Genes are known that have lethal effects at all periods of life, from the zygote stage to old age. Indeed, from a general point of view, one might say that everyone has lethal genes, but in some of us their effect is so slight that they take threescore years and ten to kill. The facts form a continuum, to which we must apply discrete terms as best we can.

It may seem strange that the white fox should die. Whiteness is not, by itself, a lethal characteristic: albinos, which owe their whiteness to a different gene, live. The important point is that a gene has many effects, and the superficial—*i.e.*, "surface"—effects from which we give the gene its name may be superficial in the metaphorical sense also, that is, of little basic importance. The platinum gene evidently modifies the biochemistry in such a way that various effects are caused, one of which is a change in fur color. The biochemical modification of the homozygote is so severe that it soon kills the pup. *How* the gene kills is a matter for further biochemical research.

The platinum gene raises a terminological question: Is it a dominant gene or a recessive one? With respect to coat color it is dominant; with respect to lethality, it is recessive (fortunately for the fox rancher's business). Clearly, it is purely a matter of convenience how one calls the gene; some genetical fence-straddlers like the term "semi-dominant."

Fourth subtlety: *the "penetrance" of a gene may be incomplete.* For example, the gene for Huntington's chorea, a disease characterized by involuntary jerking movements of the body, is unquestionably a dominant gene, and yet there are two features of its inheritance that require explanation: (1) in families born to a heterozygous parent and a homozygous normal parent, the affected offspring are not quite as common as simple Mendelian theory would predict; and (2) there are records of choreic individuals being born to parents neither of whom showed the characteristic. We "explain" both these observations by saying that the gene for Huntington's chorea has less than 100 percent "penetrance"; that is, that although it is a dominant gene—*i.e.*, a single dose of it is enough to produce the condition—nevertheless, heterozygous individuals do not always show the effect of the abnormal gene. It is as though the gene could not penetrate through to the soma. Hence the term "penetrance."

It is apparent that penetrance is not entirely satisfactory, as a concept. It has the smell of a term invented "to save the appearances," to save Mendelian theory from the threat of its exceptions. It clearly explains nothing. Can we, however, find an explanation for the facts that impelled us to invent the term? In many instances, we can. The incomplete

TABLE II

Progressive increase in proportion of individuals showing clinical symptoms of Huntington's chorea in a sample of 460 patients who eventually showed the symptoms. (Julia Bell, 1934.)

Age attained	Percentage showing Symptoms by this age
4	1
9	2
14	5
19	11
24	19
29	31
34	49
39	66
44	79
49	88
54	94
59	97
64	98
69	99
74	100

penetrance of Huntington's chorea is explained almost entirely by the variable period taken for the development of clinical symptoms. From Table II we learn that at age thirty-four less than half the people who will eventually be choreic are so. Suppose a genetically choreic individual who has not yet developed the symptoms has children (by a normal mate) and then dies before he himself is old enough to be choreic. Some of his offspring may eventually exhibit the disease, thus confronting us with what appears to be an anomaly: offspring affected by a dominant trait being born to unaffected parents. Anomalous—yet now completely explicable. The word "penetrance" can be given operational meaning, in the case of Huntington's chorea.

TABLE III

Relation of age of mother to various abnormalities that are congenital (but may or may not be hereditary). The frequency of the youngest age group is arbitrarily expressed as 1, and the others are stated relative to this figure. (From Stern, 1949, after Penrose, 1939.)

Mother's age	Frequencies of Nervous System Abnormalities	Frequencies of Mongolism
16-20	1	1
21-25	2.7	0.7
26-30	2.3	1.3
31-35	4.3	3.0
36-40	6.0	9.3
41-45	10.0	34.3
46-50	7.0	146.2
Number of cases	144	224

For other genes, other meanings may develop, Sometimes an abnormal condition may develop only if two different abnormal genes are present; if we are aware of only one gene, the *apparently* irregular expression of this gene we will attribute to "incomplete dominance." In other instances, the clinical expression of abnormal genes depends on certain environmental conditions that may not always be present. For example, Mongolian idiocy has genetic causes; but an important role in producing it is played also by environment —i.e., by the uterus, the environment of the developing embryo. Most Mongolian idiots are born to mothers near the end of their child-bearing period; the "penetrance" of the genes is very incomplete, particularly among young mothers (see Table III). What are the effective differences between the uterine environments of young and of older mothers? We don't know.

Fifth subtlety: *"variable expressivity."* How delicately the organism's potentialities are poised on the environment is shown by a wide variety of phenomena lumped under this term. The two different abnormalities, harelip and cleft palate, may be caused by identical genes interfering with normal embryogeny to different extents, simple harelip resulting from a minimum of interference. Males are more often affected, and more severely, than are females; in some sense that we don't understand, the male body is a different environment for the genes than is the female body. Identical twins may even be affected differently, indicating a hair-trigger sort of situation in development. (Both environmental and genetic factors are as nearly alike as can be in identical twins.) So delicate a hair trigger almost makes one wonder—in a moment of weakness—whether there was any wisdom in the old Norwegian law that forbade the hanging of hares in public view for fear that the pregnant women passing by might thereby be caused to produce children with harelips! The abnormality of hyperdactyly must also be delicately controlled, for not only does the number of extra fingers or toes vary among different affected individuals, but in a single individual the number of digits on the left appendages is often different from the number on the right.

Sixth subtlety: *environmentally caused defects may be indistinguishable from genetically caused ones.* The development of a human being is a complicated process. Each structure of the adult has its embryonic beginnings as one cell or a small group of cells called a *primordium.* Primordia are particularly susceptible to damage, and of course anything that injures the few cells of a primordium may destroy or greatly alter the normal adult structure that should grow out of it. Slight interference with the sensitive primordia of the hands may result in lack of hands, or in presence of webbed fingers, or in shortened fingers, or any of a number of other defects. The timing of the interference is all important in determining the result: each primordium has only a short period during which it may be easily affected. The same interfering agent, acting before or after this period, may be quite without effect. (Here we see another general explanation of the phenomena of imperfect penetrance and variable expressivity.) The interfering agent may be either genetic or environmental. In experimental animals a great variety of defects has been produced by treating pregnant mothers with different toxic chemicals, in various concentrations, and at various periods during the pregnancy. Many of these environmentally produced defects are—to the eye—indistinguishable from gene-produced defects; they are, therefore, called *phenocopies*. It is suspected that with continued trials we may be able to produce a phenocopy of almost every known genetic trait. The phenocopy, of course, does not breed like the genotype it mimics. A phenocopy web-toed animal breeds like a normal animal: its genes have not been affected—merely their mode of expression in the particular individual.

The consequences of accidental toxemias in human beings indicate that phenocopies occur here, too. We know that not all congenital defects are hereditary (*i. e.*, gene-caused); some of them—apparently the lesser fraction—are phenocopies. One of the best-proved agents for producing congenital defects is rubella, or "German measles." About 1940, Australia was so unfortunate as to suffer an acute epidemic of this disease, but the world was fortunate in that an unusually acute observer, a Dr. Gregg, was on the scene. He noted a fact which surely had long been true (though never before noticed), that a woman who has rubella during the first two months of her pregnancy is very likely to produce a defective child. The first month of embryonic life is the most sensitive period. The commonest defects in the offspring born of mothers who contract German measles are congenital cataract of the eyes (blindness), defective development of the internal ear (deafness) and imperfect division of the right and left chambers of the heart (resulting in "blue babies"). In other cases, the disease causes grossly abnormal brains, mongolism, or spontaneous abortion. Since this discovery, it has become common practice for humane obstetricians to induce abortion in patients who contract rubella in the first two months of pregnancy. (The human embryo, incidentally, at two months true age is only two inches long.) Where patient or doctor is a conscientious Roman Catholic, this mode of escape from the burden of fate is closed.

The "Heredity Versus Environment" Fallacy

In writing of phenocopies and genotypes I have carelessly written as if a defect were caused by genes *or* by the environment *either/or*. This is not true, of course. Every structure and function, normal or abnormal, is caused by the interaction of hereditary and environmental factors. We can often "get away with" such careless expressions only because some characteristics are completely indifferent to *existing* environmental variations (for example, albinism) or similarly indifferent to existing hereditary variations (an example of this is harder to find, but perhaps susceptibility to the common cold will answer). Many abnormal characteristics demonstrably depend on interaction of both heredity and environment. *Diabetes mellitus* exemplifies this principle well. The evidence that genes are involved is quite convincing, but only a small fraction of those who are genetically diabetic become so clinically. Diet and psychological factors are known to play a role in producing the diabetic condition among those who are genetic candidates for it. Similarly complex interactions of heredity and environment are found in what are called "epileptic seizures." The study of "brain waves" shows that epileptics can be differentiated from "normals," but that many unaffected persons have the epileptic type of brain wave. Apparently all persons with this type of wave are susceptible to epilepsy, but they will not, in fact, have seizures unless they are subjected to a suitable rigorous environmental stress. One recalls the history of the Russian novelist, Dostoevski, who became seriously affected with seizures after his prison wardens had pretended, with complete realism up to the last possible moment, that they were going to execute him. The "joke" was too much for Dostoevski, who undoubtedly had the genes for susceptibility to seizures. Others, of different genotypes, have survived equally grueling treatments without conspicuous damage. Viewing Dostoevski's life with a genetic bias, one might say, "He suffered from seizures because of his genes." Viewing it with an environmental bias, one could say, "His seizures were caused by his experiences." Both statements are partial truths. Dostoevski's genes were a sort of predestination for him—but only in determining his reactions to certain sorts of environments, which he might or might not encounter during his life. The predestination of genes is, in general, only a partial one, subject to some environmental modification.

Can I Accept Myself?

Genetic knowledge raises questions that are centuries old, but which many men in recent times had thought no longer valid. In old-fashioned language, the principal questions are two: (a) How can I find out my predestination? and (b) How can I accept it? We will take up the second first.

The acceptance of personal limitations is a problem that faces everyone; in a sense, it is independent of genetic knowledge, for a limitation must be accepted whatever its source. One's personal "talents," strengths, defects—call them what you will—play a role in the structuring of one's life analogous to the part played by the strength of materials used in constructing a building. They determine which of an infinity of designs for living are possible, which not. There is this important difference, however: whereas the strength of a building material is not influenced by what one thinks it is, the strength of a personal characteristic is. To an amazing extent, courageous refusal to accept an apparent limitation often brings about the displacement of the limit. By refusing to accept his stammering as an ultimate limitation, Demosthenes became a great orator; many a circus strong man has begun life as a sickly boy. On the other hand, the futile butting of ambitious heads against the stone walls of genuinely immovable limitations has produced personal tragedies without number. Such are the Scylla and Charybdis of the personal maturation process.

Genetics makes us aware of another facet of the problem, the acceptance of one's genetic limitations. It is a curious thing how we do not want to admit defects that are genetically determined—curious, because what can we be less "responsible" for than our genes? We didn't pick our parents. Yet the feeling of responsibility is there, perhaps because of an early psychological "identification" of the child with the parent. Whatever the cause, the issue of responsibility for ancestry is a minor one; the important responsibility is that for children. No one wants to produce a child that is seriously defective, yet every parent-to-be incurs this risk. The conscientious man would like to have some idea of the magnitude of the risk before embarking on parenthood. How can he determine it? In part, by assaying his own and his wife's personal qualities; but only in part, because of the notorious "hiding" ability of recessive genes. It is necessary to look also at one's ancestors. When one does, one is sure, sooner or later, to discover undesirable characteristics. How undesirable must the characteristic be, to influence one's decision? And how near must the ancestry be to affect the risk significantly? These are questions to which only probable answers can be given, and to give them requires the considerable technical knowledge found only among a new breed of professional men known as "genetic counselors."

Genetic Counseling: A Rare Commodity

Few married couples seek genetic advice before they have any children at all. The impelling circumstance is usually the appearance of one defective child. At this point, the disturbed parents want to know if the defect is gene-caused, and what is the risk in producing another child. With these questions, they usually turn to the family physician for counsel. Unfortunately, he is all too often unable to help them at all. The trouble lies not merely in the fact that the young science of human genetics is still only poorly advanced, but also in the fact that many, probably the majority, of the medical doctors are largely unaware of the genetical knowledg that is already available—unaware of both the principles and the facts. An all-too-common reply of the family physician (as Sheldon Reed, 1955, has pointed out) is a reassurance of the parents with the old bromide, "Lightning never strikes twice in the same place." The doctor's intention in saying this is clearly laudable: to take some of the burden of anxiety from the parents' shoulders. But the advice flies in the face of the facts in two different ways. First, lightning *does* sometimes strike twice in the same place; or to take a more appropriate example, if I get a zero on one spin of the roulette wheel, the chance of my getting a zero on the next spin is uninfluenced by the fact that a zero has just turned up, for the roulette wheel (to paraphrase the mathematician Bertrand) has neither conscience nor memory. Secondly, the fact that lightning *has* struck once in an unfortunate family is an indication that it is *more* likely to strike again in the same family than it is in some other family selected at random from the same population. This unwelcome truth is shown over and over by a comparison of the two columns of figures in Table I. The chance that a couple's first child will have a cleft palate in only 1 in 2,500; but if their child does have a cleft palate, the chance that the next child will also be so afflicted is 1 in 7, a very high chance, indeed. For clubfoot the risk figure rises from 1 in 1,000 to 1 in 30; for Mongolian idiocy, from 1 to 600 to 1 in 20; and so on. The physician who removes parents' anxieties at the expense of the truth plays with fire. It is hard to get any human being to accept an unpleasant truth that is irrevocable, but in the last analysis there is no security in denying the decrees of fate. At the very least, the unwise physician endangers the good name of medicine.

It must surely seem odd to the layman that physicians generally should be ignorant of genetics. The explanation is actually very simple. Genetics is a new subject. The medical-school curriculum has for over a hundred years been crammed full with essential studies. (There are few "electives" in medical school.) There are only three ways in which a new subject can get into an existing curriculum: by addition without increase in time, by addition with increase in time, or by displacement of an already-existing topic. The first choice is repugnant because medical students already study extremely hard—their weekly hours of unpaid work are nearly twice those of a paid union laborer. The second choice—addition made by increasing the years of medical training—is also repugnant. The recent action of Johns Hopkins University in decreasing the total number of years in medical and premedical training was taken in the belief that we have already come close to adding the last straw to the camel's back. The third choice—displacing existing topics in the medical curriculum in favor of genetics—would, to a simply logical and dispassionate observer, seem the best solution; but to hope for it is politically naïve. There are undoubtedly topics of the present medical curriculum that are less valuable to a doctor than genetics, but such dispensable subjects are taught by flesh-and-blood professors, who are only human if they seek to protect their invested interests from the threatened encroachments of unvested newcomers. Medicine is based on science, which changes, but the profession of medicine is a human institution and therefore is highly resistant to change. It is hardly to be expected that the centenary of Mendel's publication (in 1966) will see medical genetics established as a required course in more than a handful of medical schools, at most. Human institutions don't change that fast.

What about the premedical curriculum? Most students prepare for medical school for four years, commonly taking a bachelor's degree in biological sciences; cannot genetics be made part of the premedical curriculum? It can, and in many institutions it has been (though, as of 1956, only two out of eighty-five United States medical schools required a knowledge of genetics for entrance). With the aid of such courses, the medical ignorance of successive corps of doctors is lessening. On the debit side of the ledger, however, it must be pointed out that the introductory course in genetics, which is usually all that the premedical student has time to take, includes almost nothing of the special technical methods needed to study the genetics of human beings.

There are a few dozen medical doctors in the United States who, by one means or another, have made themselves proficient in human genetics. Being so few, they are hard to find. Many of the best trained men in this field are not M.D.'s but Ph.D.'s. Since, however, such a degree has less prestige in the eyes of the patient, most Ph.D.'s specializing in human genetics work with medical colleagues, or give advice only through medical correspondents. Of departments or institutes specializing in human genetics and prepared to give genetic advice, Scheinfeld (in 1956) could find only eleven in the United States (*see* Table IV). For a nation in which each

TABLE IV

Human Heredity Clinics. Taken from Scheinfeld, 1956, pp. 267-268. Where not otherwise specified, address inquiries to "Department of Human Genetics," at the institution named.

It is best that contact with the institution be made by the patient's physician.

UNITED STATES

Bowman Gray School of Medicine, Winston-Salem, North Carolina

Department of Zoology, University of Chicago, Chicago 37, Illinois

Dight Institute, University of Minnesota, Minneapolis 14, Minnesota

University of Michigan, Ann Arbor, Michigan

New York Psychiatric Institute, New York 32, New York

Ohio State University, Columbus, Ohio

University of Oklahoma, Norman, Oklahoma

University of Texas, Austin, Texas

Tulane University Medical School, New Orleans, Louisiana

University of Utah, Salt Lake City, Utah

Medical College of Virginia, Richmond, Virginia

CANADA

Hospital for Sick Children, Toronto 2, Canada

McGill University, Montreal, Canada

Children's Memorial Hospital, Montreal, Canada

---

year some 60,000 married couples find themselves confronted with the anxiety-engendering fact of a defective child, this provision seems hardly adequate.

Counseling: How Can the Truth Be Accepted

There is another side to the problem of genetic advice which we have not yet solved, but for different reasons. Given that the patient has found a competent adviser, and that his problem is one for which the facts are known, how does one advise him? (How, in fact, does one advise anyone about anything?) An actual case study will help make clear what the problem is. Sheldon C. Reed, of the Dight Institute for Human Genetics, was consulted about a couple who had produced a child suffering from *spina bifida* (incompletely formed spinal column) and hydrocephaly ("water on the brain"). The child was put into an institution. The mother was disturbed about not seeing her child and the parents wanted to know how serious was the risk of producing another defective offspring. After analyzing all the relevant facts, Reed wrote to the psychiatrist in charge (Reed, 1955, p. 62):

Reply "The chances are at least 1 in 10 and perhaps as high as 1 in 4 that the next conception will result in a malformation or a miscarriage. You, the psychiatrist, should convey this fact to the couple and make it clear that they must make the decision about another try."

Follow-up A few months later the psychiatrist reported, "The mother took the matter into her own hands and visited her defective child which gave her considerable relief and subsequent feeling of confidence. As a result of this, she and her husband were able to talk their problem through, and decided, despite greater risk than the average couple, but in the interest of having a family, that they would try once more."

Was the parents' decision *right?* Is a risk of 1 in 4 or 1 in 10 of bearing so grossly deformed a child low enough to justify producing more children? How can we decide? There is no accepted rationale for making such decisions. This lack is not confined to genetics, but is found wherever there is risk. Each American has about 1 chance in 5,000 of being killed by an automobile during any given year. Does this knowledge stop us from driving cars or walking across the street? Certainly not. Apparently we regard the advantages of using automobiles as sufficiently great recompense for the risk of being killed or injured by them. But suppose the risk were 1 in 500? Or 1 in 50? Or 1 in 5? It is evident that there must be some level at which we would say the risk is too great in comparison with the benefits. But at what level would we make this decision? We have no theory to tell us the correct answer.

This is one of the reasons why many genetic counselors believe they should not counsel at all, if "to counsel" means to advise the patient what he should do. "With rare exceptions," say Neel and Schull (1954), "we do *not* attempt to pass a judgment as to the advisability of parenthood. This is a decision to be reached by the family concerned." Professor Reed agrees. On the other hand, Dr. Franz J. Kallman, who is both a psychiatrist and a genetic counselor, strongly disagrees (1956). To tell a client cold-bloodedly that his chance of developing so fearful a nervous affliction as Huntington's chorea is 1 in 2, and that the chance that his child will have it is 1 in 4; and then to cast him adrift to make his own decision by himself—this, Kallman says, is the greatest psychological cruelty. He who has a genetic sword of Damocles hanging over his head is a disturbed human being; he needs psychological support and love—not statistics. (In passing, it should be noted that this need for human contact rules out advising by correspondence. The client who must find it in his heart to accept the decrees of fate will hardly do so unless the news is brought to him in face-to-face encounter. At this critical juncture of his life he requires warm human contact.)

The error of the "non-directive" genetic counselors is a simple one: they have failed to realize what it means to be a member of a *profession*. Ernest Greenwood has expressed the issues with especial clarity:

> A nonprofessional occupation has customers; a professional occupation has clients. What is the difference? A customer determines what services and/or commodities he wants, and he shops around until he finds them. His freedom of decision rests upon the premise that he has the capacity to appraise his own needs and to judge the potential of the service or of the commodity to satisfy them. The infallibility of his decisions is epitomized in the slogan: 'The customer is always right!' In a professional relationship, however, the professional dictates what is good or evil for the client, who has no choice but to accede to professional judgment. Here the premise is that, because he lacks the requisite theoretical background, the client cannot diagnose his own needs or discriminate among the range of possibilities for meeting them.

The client with a genetic problem is, in general, incompetent in two fields of knowledge: genetics and probability. The first needs no arguing. The second deficiency is not so obvious because many people are capable of making simple probability calculations, and of acting rationally on them when there is no psychological involvement. But when the individual is psychologically involved, his ability to make rational decisions may be seriously lessened. Many a young man has made a theoretical fortune playing the stock market *on paper,* only to discover that he can do nothing but lose money when he stakes a real fortune on his judgments and thus becomes emotionally involved. Some can pass the second, and real, test, but not many; the very existence of Las Vegas and Monte Carlo is evidence of the millions who are utterly unable to understand, *in their bones,* the meaning of probability. It is the professional duty of the genetic counselor to convey to his client the personal implications of a probability statistic. The counselor may, to secure acceptance of the truth, pretend to leave the decision up to the client, but this pretense is only tactical. The responsibility for really making the decision must rest on the shoulders of the professional.

Escape from Fate

To get married, to have children—healthy children—is considered the normal thing, almost a "right," in our society. Yet the odds against it, while small, are appreciable. In the United States, according to estimates of the National Research Council, 1 couple out of every 10 who desire children fails to produce them, try as they will. And of the children that are produced, 1 in 65 (nearly 2 percent) are defective at birth.

The probabilities of being thwarted by fate are not negligible. And the use of the old-fashioned word "fate" is really justified, for all evidence points to the conclusion that the majority of the cases of infertility and of congenital deformity, as well as the majority of spontaneous abortions, are caused by genes, about which we can do nothing.

We must accept our genes; but there is more than one way of accepting them. The predestination of genetics is not one of a single track to which we are bound, but rather is that of a field with more or less clearly discerned boundaries within which we must work out our lives. The individual who learns that he harbors deleterious genes that will probably cause his children to be defective, is not thereby condemned to produce a succession of heart-rendingly deformed children. He has a number of other options, each with its own advantages and disadvantages.

For one thing, it is obvious that he can avoid having children entirely. This can most certainly be done by observing strict sexual continence—most certainly, but by no means most pleasantly. "I would that all men were even as I," said the apostle Paul, who was content to remain celibate; but he knew they were not, and added, "But if they cannot contain, let them marry: for it is better to marry than to burn" (I Corinthians, 7:7,9). A biologist's view of sexual ethics is utterly different: were all men like Paul, there would soon be no men to be concerned about. Only those animals that "burn" with sexual desire can perpetuate their genes (including the genes for "burning") into succeeding generations. Ethical principles must be designed for such as these. To the biologist, the Pauline ideal is, at best, trivial; at worst, it borders on the monstrous.

For the married couple who face possible genetic tragedy, various paths are open. If they elect to produce no children of their own, how shall they achieve infertility? Two ways are suggested. They can either make use of one of the various scientific techniques known, in which case their sexual intercourse can be almost completely spontaneous; this mode of contraception, which permits emotional spontaneity, is, by some, called "artificial" birth control. The other way involves the inhibition of strong natural impulses, with the restriction of intercourse to days that are decreed by the calendar rather than by the emotions. Those who call scientific contraception "artificial" call the repressive mode "natural." The logic of this position comes in an unbroken line of descent from Tertullian, a Roman ecclesiastical lawyer of the third century A.D. Tertullian defined as "unnatural," and hence as morally wrong, the practice of circumcision, acting in plays, shaving the face, and the wearing of *dyed* fabrics. The last proscription gives the show away. Did Tertullian suppose that *undyed* fabrics grew on trees? The only consistency in seventeen centuries of polemics against the "unnatural" is the identification of *recent* technological advances as unnatural. One suspects that there was a time in the prehistory of man when the milking of cows for human food was looked on as utterly abhorrent. Indeed: to those who have the imagination to see the entire sequence of acts as if it had never been seen before, there is something decidedly "unnatural" in a man's manipulating a cow's mammary glands and then drinking the exudate, which was undeniably intended by nature for a suckling calf, and not for a grown man. . . . But then, it is dangerous to think logically.

It is possible, of course, to have children even if one does not produce them. The practical discovery of this elementary fact is surprisingly recent. A century ago unwanted children (if they were lucky) were thrown into an orphan asylum, while unwillingly childless couples accepted their plight as an unmodifiable decree of fate. Now, so completely is the idea of adoption accepted that the supply-and-demand picture is completely changed: there simply are not enough orphaned babies to meet the requests of would-be adoptive parents.

Parents who have produced a defective child of their own and have decided to obtain future children only by adoption will be chagrined to find that adoption agencies are very "choosy." They usually will not place a child in a home in which there is already a mentally retarded child, insisting that the atmosphere of the home first be made psychologically healthier by removing the defective child to an institution. Parents often find it hard to accept such an ultimatum: it seems cruel and unnatural to give up one's own child. But, in the long run, it is probably the kindest thing to do for the whole family, including the child. As Reed (pp. 92-93) points out, a mentally defective child in the family is

. . . a source of embarrassment to its sibs and will cause them to go elsewhere for social contacts. The retarded child is an invitation to improper sexual exploitation by ill-mannered neighbors or others.

Very frequently it will be the duty of the physician to convince the parents that the child would be better off in the state school than at home and to help with the procedures necessary to have the child admitted to the public institution. Even though the building may be old and crowded and the food scorned by Duncan Hines, the child will find himself among his equals and he will be able to compete with them, whereas in the home community he will be always either overprotected or cruelly rejected from social contacts. Children are more interested in satisfactory contacts with other children than they are in culinary fine points or the design of their bed spreads. To be sure, it is a little hard on the vanity of the parents to find that after a week or two their small retarded child no longer recognizes nor misses them, but it is fortunate that this does happen.

In the last few decades, yet another means has been employed to an increasing extent as a way of escaping a childless home, namely *semi-adoption*. If the parents are in some sense genetically incompatible, if the husband is sterile, or if the defective genes come from the male side, the married couple may decide that they would prefer to be half-parents, biologically speaking, rather than adoptive ones. For the wife to be fecundated by a man not her husband in order to produce a healthy family is a procedure that has probably been resorted to for thousands of years, to a small event. Where it has involved deception, the results have probably often been as unhappy as they were for Eugene O'Neill's Nina Leeds, who indulged in a "Strange Interlude" to avoid perpetuating the insanity in her husband's family. But even when consent has been mutual, the procedure has been a psychologically risky one.

The avoidance of disruptive emotional involvements has been made possible by that greatest of all practical developments of the last two centuries, the discovery of the technical separability of copulation and procreation. Just as it is possible to have copulation without the production of children, so also is it possible for a woman to become pregnant without sexual intercourse. It is a comparatively simple matter to impregnate a woman with semen from a man whom she has never seen and who is completely unknown to her (and to her husband). The procedure is, in its essence, completely impersonal. It has been called by various names: *artificial insemination* (which term has the disadvantage of raising the hoary old "artificial" vs. "natural" bugaboo), *transemination* (on the analogy of transfusion of blood), *therapeutic insemination,* and *semi-adoption* (in recognition that one member of the couple is the biological parent, only the husband being an adoptive parent).

How many babies have been conceived by artificial insemination no one knows, but the number so produced in the United States undoubtedly runs into many thousands. The most common reason for resorting to the procedure is sterility; but desire to avoid transmitting hereditary "taints" also plays a small role. Whatever the motivation, the procedure follows a common pattern. The knowing doctor, faced with a request for a transemination, "drags his feet" for many weeks to make sure that the request springs from a deliberate and mature decision on the part of both husband and wife. We all of us imbibe from the mores of our society so much in the way of superstitions and irrational attitudes toward parenthood, honor, adultery and other high-level, high-voltage abstractions, that it is no easy matter to view involuntary sterility or defective heredity in a rational manner. Only married couples who are unusually mature are fit to become parents of a semi-adopted child. It takes time to conquer the evil in one's mind. Hence the delaying tactics of the wise physician.

Once the decision has been agreed upon by both parents and the family physician, the couple is generally referred to a specialist in sterility problems, who carries out the artificial insemination. For many reasons, the locus of such activities is usually a large city hospital. One of the reasons is the desire for secrecy. A couple who have themselves worked through to the stage of maturity required for this procedure may feel no personal need for secrecy; but they are part of a larger, less mature society that may include, for example, prospective grandparents, who have probably passed the period of emotional growth. To spare the feelings of such as these (and hence, reflexively, of any children produced) deceptive silence is usually the better part of wisdom.

A large hospital is also ideal for the preservation of the anonymity of the donor of the semen. In one room of the large building, he can produce the required sample, which can then be carried to another part where the recipient is waiting. Methods of cold storage are now available so that the insemination can even be made at a much later date. Personal identification, and hence the possibility of emotional involvement, is completely avoided.

The criteria for selecting donors are of great importance. A donor must, of course, be in good health, both physically and mentally. It is important to check his family pedigree as carefully as possible with regard to possible genetic defects. For social reasons, it is desirable to choose a donor who resembles the husband in coloration and general body type. This seldom is difficult; the cliché, "Why, he looks just like his father!" will usually spring readily to the lips of unknowing relatives and friends when they are confronted with the *fait accompli*. (That the mother's face shows a momentary resemblance to Mona Lisa's will probably escape their notice.) In practice, most semen donations are made by medical students, for good reasons. Because of rigorous selection, they are above the population average in intelligence, health and stability; they have no irrational prejudices against the procedure; and they are readily available.

Are babies produced by transemination legitimate? Probably not, some jurists warn; but no decisive cases have been tried. A Canadian court at one time expressed the gratuitous opinion (it was irrelevant to the case in hand) that (1) the production of children was the primary aim of the marriage bond; and that (2) therefore conception without copulation was adultery. This led an English wit to point out that the same logic leads inevitably to the conclusion that copulation with contraceptives is not adultery, a view that not many courts are likely to accept. There the matter stands. The circumstances under which transemination is resorted to are such that it is not probable that a case requiring a decision will soon be brought before a court. Already the practice has been indulged in for more than half a century without significant litigation.

Attempts to pass legislative acts bringing the law into rational harmony with this new scientific development have so far failed. In the meantime, two different "gimmicks" have been proposed. Sometimes the parents adopt the child. This completely forestalls any possible charge of illegitimacy, but regional laws often make the procedure impossible or impracticable. Some districts require the consent of the biological parents; many require the naming of them. Both demands —which were devised before any legislator ever heard of transemination—make impossible the anonymity of the semen donor and the avoidance of publicity that are so desirable from a humane point of view. So the adoption procedure has been used very little. The other device is a procedural one. Most transeminations are performed because the husband is *believed* to be sterile; but since this is seldom a certainty, the attending physician can confound the legal quibblers by mixing semen from the husband with semen from the donor, and injecting the two together. Thus there is introduced a real doubt as to the paternity of the child. Scientifically, this procedure is rather ludicrous, but it has legal advantages. It may also have psychological advantages for the husband, who may not be completely reconciled to giving up the possibility of paternity. It takes only a very little wishful thinking to convince himself that he is the father after all. . . . Of course, where transemination is resorted to because of genetic defects on the husband's side, this mixed-semen procedure should not be used.

The medical jurist, Sidney B. Schatkin (1954), has predicted that the reaction of the law to artificial insemination will follow a pattern of evolution that has been shown in other legal adaptations to scientific advances, the stages being (successively): *perfect horror—skepticism—curiosity*—and, finally, *acceptance*. We should not, says Schatkin, become incensed at the inertia of the law; it is natural and proper that law should have its own mode of development.

> The lag between medicine and the law is not only inevitable but desirable. Too often scientific theories and practices fail to fulfill their promise. Were medical discoveries immediately reflected in the law, we would have not medical progress, but chaos. Science with impunity may reverse itself repeatedly; the law hardly ever.

How long will it be before the final stage—acceptance of transemination—will be reached? There is no theory of legal kinetics to tell us the answer, but if the history of contraception is any guide, the year 2000 A.D. will certainly have come and gone before the majority of the states will have adopted satisfactory laws. In the meantime, many high-minded married couples will, each year, produce thousands of children, conceived in this extra-legal fashion with the connivance of equally high-minded physicians. No better course is open to those of humane and tender feelings.

Paternity: Words and Emotions

The law mirrors popular beliefs, if not of the present generation, at least of the preceding one; if not of both sexes, at least of the males, who make the laws and who often reveal their own insecurity in their legislation. Back of the opposition to transemination lie centuries-old attitudes toward paternity, attitudes that are embedded in language. A man may say, "This is my child," and no one questions the meaning because the language is traditional. But what does it mean, really, to say, "This is *my* child"? "My" is a possessive. What does it mean, to "possess" a child?

There was a time when possession of a child was complete —as complete as the possession of a chair or a cow. The father could do whatever he wished with his property. That time is now well past. The modern father's rights include little more than the right partially to determine the education of his child. His rights are more in the nature of privileges— the privilege of observing the growing up of a child, the privilege of maturing himself as he vicariously faces for a second time the trials he more or less failed to pass during his own youth and adolescence. "This is my child" means, "this is my right to further psychological development." For this right, literal biological parenthood is, of course, an irrelevancy. An adopted child is as legitimate a voucher as a natural one.

But still, in the male, there is a gnawing question: If I procreate a child with my own semen, is it not more *mine* than if I adopt one, or allow my wife to use another man's semen?

Let's see what the facts are. First, it is an error to think of the semen as the essential agent of reproduction. In the reproductive act, a man may deposit as much as one sixth of an ounce of semen in his wife's vagina, but of the millions of spermatozoa in this donation only one fertilizes the egg. One spermatozoan is not very big: it weighs about 0.00,000,000,-000,02 of an ounce. The adult human weighs (say) 3,000 ounces. The maximum amount of substance that the father has contributed to his grown child is certainly less than one ten thousand million millionth of the total. In what sense, then, is the child *his* child?

There is, of course, a sense in which it is meaningful to say it is his child—it may look strikingly like him, and for good reason. Precious little of the substance of the child has come from the father, but that little is of critical importance. We should not, in fact, think in terms of substance, but rather in terms of *information*. The egg develops, through an incredibly complicated series of processes, into an adult that is distinguishable from all other adults. What determines the uniqueness of each human being? Genes, acting in conjunction with the environment. The fertilized egg has received half its genes from the mother, half from the father. Each gene can be thought of as a bit of information telling the zygote how to develop, whether to produce a long nose or a short nose, brown eyes or blue eyes, great intelligence or utter idiocy. What the father does contribute to his offspring is information, genetic information. And all this information, certainly 10,000 bits of it, and maybe as many as 100,000 bits, is packed into a tiny sperm's head which weighs not more than two hundred million millionths of an ounce. Great riches in a little room, indeed!

The father does, then, contribute significantly to the information that governs the development of the zygote. How unique is that information—how different is it from the information that might be contributed by another man chosen at random?

Every man has many genes—many bits of information. For most of the kinds of genes, a man is homozygous, that is, he has only one kind of allele. His genetic formula with respect to these genes we can represent as *AABBCCDDEE*

. . . , the formula continuing through several *thousand* different letters of the genetic alphabet. With respect to the genes for which a man is homozygous, his spermatozoa will be a correct representation of the man himself, *ABCDE* . . . —"like father, like son"—or rather, *like father, like spermatozoa.*

With respect to other genes, however, a man will be heterozygous, say *HhIiJjKk.* . . . For how many genes will a man be heterozygous? We don't know. The number of heterozygous pairs will vary from man to man, but it is hardly conceivable that this number will ever be less than a hundred. With respect to such genes, it is never true that the spermatozoa are like the father. Each sperm has one and only one member of each pair of alleles; so, of the various sperm types, possible (*e.g., HiJK; hIjk;* etc.) *none* are like the father. Even if we grant complete dominance with each pair of alleles, it would take only ten sets to reduce to less than one in a thousand the probability that one spermatozoan would be truly representative of the father's phenotype. With only twenty heterozygous pairs, the probability is reduced to less than one in a million. And with as many as one hundred heterozygous pairs (a conservatively low figure) the probability of a spermatozoan being "like" the father is vanishingly small. Only by seizing upon a few out of an almost infinite number of human characteristics can we persuade ourselves that a son is ever like his father. If one took the totality of differentia, without selection, the resemblance would be negligible indeed.

The genes possessed by a father are like a hand of cards. Each hand is unique. When it comes time for a father to pass genes on to his child, he does not pass on his whole hand, but only part of it. In this process chance plays a large role. Thus there is a not negligible probability that the hand that is passed on (the genes in the haploid spermatozoan) will be quite unrepresentative of the father's collection of cards. The haploid set of genes in a particular one of Mr. Jones's spermatozoa may, in fact, more nearly resemble what one would expect to find in a spermatozoan of Mr. Smith. If this spermatozoan reaches the egg first, the child may look more like the man next door than he does his own father, though his mother may have been as chaste as Susanna. Of all men, the true father is the one the child will most probably look like; but the chance that he will more nearly resemble an unrelated man in the same general population is almost as great.

As men come to appreciate the subtle principles underlying the fact of paternity, we can expect them to be less concerned with problems of "mine" and "thine" in the Fertilization Sweepstakes. Concern for the health and happiness of the children we are responsible for—morally responsible for, whether we are their biological fathers or not—may lead us to take steps to insure that the best possible spermatozoa are entered in the race, in utter disregard of emotionally charged possessive pronouns. It would be rash to assert that this trend, already slightly in evidence in our country, will necessarily increase, for that assumes that we will become ever more rational, which is certainly not self-evident. But if this does not come to pass in our own country, it very likely will in some other nation. The nation which behaves rationally will gain in strength. We will have to compete with it. Let us not forget that fact as we wrestle with the problems created by the conflict of tradition and rationality.

Genes and the Acceptance of Others

IN 1945, a young woman named Joan Barry sued the famous film comedian Charlie Chaplin for the support of her child, which, she maintained, had been sired by him. Blood tests were made of the three principals; Chaplin was type O, Miss Barry was type A, and the child was type B. These results meant, experts testified, that Chaplin could not be the father of the child. Miss Barry's attorney argued that no blood test is infallible, and argued so well that he succeeded in confusing enough of the jury (five out of twelve according to rumor) to produce a mistrial. A second jury was impaneled. This time the plaintiff had even better luck. In spite of the scientific evidence, Chaplin was declared to be the father and was required to pay for the support of a child that was certainly not his. . . . *Certainly?* Well, with as much certainty as we can reasonably expect in any legal matter. The chance that the child was Chaplin's was assuredly not greater than 1 in 10,000, and was probably much less. Few men would regard this as a high enough probability to warrant their being justly saddled with the support of an unwanted child.

The facts on which the scientific opinion were based are fairly simple, but involve some principles in genetics not known to Mendel. There are present in the red blood cells of all human beings some chemical compounds called the "A-B-O Group" of substances. Every human has either type A substance, or type B, or both A and B, in which case he is called an AB type; or neither, in which case he is type O. The presence or absence of these substances is determined by allelic genes, which are often designated by the same letters in *italics*, namely, alleles *A*, *B* and *O*. Blood type AB is produced by genotype *AB*, which means there is no dominance of A with respect to B. But both *A* and *B* are dominant to *O*, so genotype *AO* produces phenotype A, indistinguishable from that produced by genotype *AA*; similarly genotype *BO* produces phenotype B. The new element introduced by this gene is the existence of more than two alleles of the same gene, specifically three *A*, *B* and *O*. Since somatic cells are diploid, the cells of any one individual can contain at most two different alleles; a haploid reproductive cell can contain only one allele. Charlie Chaplin being of phenotype

O, must have been genotype *OO,* and hence capable of producing only one kind of sperm cell, namely *O.* Miss Barry, who
was of phenotype A, could have been either *AA* or *AO* genotypes; but only in the second case could she bear, as she did,
a B-type child. So she was *AO.* Her child could be type B, only
if the father had a *B* to contribute; the father must have been
B or AB type. Chaplin was O. The jury's decision was quite
erroneous. One suspects that the defendant's well-known and
self-admitted amorous peccadillos, or perhaps his political
deviations, had more influence than the scientific evidence in
determining the verdict.

It is a rather striking fact that blood tests have proven so
useful in determining parentage, inasmuch as there are so
many old sayings that attribute great importance to blood in
heredity, *e.g.,* "blood will tell." However, this meeting of
science with folklore is scarcely more than coincidence. Blood
is no more charged with heredity than any other body tissue;
but blood cells can be gotten with a minimum of discomfort
to the individual, and so we test their chemical characteristics
rather than that of other cells, which could be obtained only
with greater difficulty and pain.

How Science Threatens Law

One inherits many characteristics that conceivably might
be used to deduce parentage: height, body build, color of
skin and hair and vocal characteristics, to name only a few.
In everyday life we remark on resemblances between child
and parent in these characteristics; but few of them possess
the properties necessary for use in courts of law. Many of
them, for instance, are easily modifiable by the environment.
Hair and skin may be darker and lighter depending on ex-
posure to sun (not to mention bottled chemicals). Training
can modify innate patterns of movement and gesture. Characteristics that vary in a continuum (*e.g.,* hair color) are difficult to classify objectively. The blood group substances, by
contrast, are either present or absent—no ifs, ands or buts.
They are completely unaffected by environmental factors; even
a blood transfusion cannot change them. They are a sort of
"chemical fingerprint." (One might, it is true, almost completely replace the blood cells of an AB person with O-type
corpuscles; but in a few days' time, newly made AB corpuscles
would be detectible in the blood stream, and the O corpuscles
would steadily disappear as they underwent the process of
aging and death common to all red blood cells. In six months'
time no demonstrable O cells would remain.)

One important aspect of all "paternity tests" needs emphasis: namely, that they are not truly paternity tests, but

Charles Robert Darwin (1809–1882). (Bettmann Archive.)

HMS *Beagle*. The Darwin Expedition in the Strait of Magellan.
(Bettmann Archive.)

The study in which the *Origin of Species* was written.

Erasmus Darwin (1731–1802), evolutionist and grandfather of Charles. (Bettmann Archive.)

Robert Waring Darwin (1766–1848), physician and father of Charles.

Charles Darwin, in 1849, ten years before the publication of the *Origin of Species*.

Charles Lyell (1797–1875), tactful geologist and great friend of Charles Darwin.

Alfred Russel Wallace (1823–1913), whose independent discovery of the theory of Natural Selection spurred Darwin to publish his work. (Gernsheim Collection, London.)

Joseph Dalton Hooker (1817–1911), Darwin's most intimate friend. (Portrait by George Richmond.)

Francis Galton (1822–1911), cousin of Charles Darwin and proponent of eugenics.

Popular travesty of Darwinism, showing alarmed flunky announcing "MR. G-G-O-O-O-Rilla." (Bettmann Archive.)

T. H. Huxley (1825–1895) in his mature years. (From T. Hamilton Crawford, after a painting by John Collier. By permission of the Museum Galleries, London.)

H. J. Muller (1890–   ), geneticist and discoverer of the mutagenic effect of X rays. (Courtesy *Life* magazine. Copyright 1955 Time, Inc.)

Sewall Wright (1889–   ), who has given us the picture of evolution in a world of some ten thousand dimensions. (Lewellyn Studio.)

Sir Ronald A. Fisher (1890–   ), distinguished
modern statistician, who has done much to advance the mathematical theory of evolution.
(Lafayette Photo.)

J. B. S. Haldane (1892–
    ), co-discoverer of the
Haldane-Muller Principle.
(Wide World Photos.)

(Johann) Gregor Mendel (1822–1884), an Augustinian monk, whose experiments with peas revealed the laws of heredity. (Plaque by Daniel Milton.)

rather, they are "non-paternity tests." Only if a test *excludes* a man as a possible father should the result enter into a juryman's thinking (and then it should be decisive). Had Chaplin's blood type been B, it would only have meant that he *might* have been the father of the Barry baby—as might many millions of other males of blood types B or AB. The New York state law governing blood tests, a model of such laws, specifically says that the results of the laboratory tests can be received as evidence in court *only* when definite exclusion is established. When the accused is not excluded by blood tests, the court is no better off for the evidence than it would have been had genetics never been discovered.

However, there is a very real possibility that with the passage of time this situation may change. At present, we know about a dozen different sets of inheritable blood groups, among which are the ABO, MNS, Rhesus, Kell, Duffy and Lutheran. (This last is not a religious factor! It was named after the man in whom it was first found.) With the ABO set alone, only about 18 percent of men falsely accused can be exonerated. Using all the tests, about 60 percent can be eliminated as possible fathers of a given child. Even the latter percentage certainly is not great enough to consider the tests as ever establishing positive paternity. But, with the passage of time, we will probably discover more genetically determined biochemical substances. As the probability of excluding falsely accused men rises to 80, to 90, to 99 percent, will our attitude toward the tests change? What if we some day have such a battery of tests that we can exclude falsely accused men 99.99 percent of the time—what then? If it can be said in court that, of men selected at random, only one in ten thousand would have the proper blood groups to be a possible father of this child—and that the accused *has* such a set of blood groups—may we not then decide that the man on trial is scientifically convicted beyond a *reasonable* doubt? Or, if a one in ten thousand chance is thought to introduce too great an error, what about one in a million, or one in ten million? Where will we draw the line? We see in this problem but another instance in which progressive science threatens traditional law. For centuries, the law has taken cognizance of the idea of proof "beyond reasonable doubt," without once defining the limit of *reasonable*. With the quantification of doubt made possible by genetics, the law may someday have to define, in exact mathematical terms, what constitutes "reasonable doubt."

Dimensions of Individuality

In the preceding chapter we were concerned with such

hereditary characteristics as harelip, water on the brain, Mongolism, deafness and epilepsy—all spectacular and interesting, but, in a way, misleading when we consider them at such length. They might lead us to suppose that heredity is concerned mostly, or most importantly, with the spectacular, with the highly abnormal. This is quite false. Most gene effects are small and produce little difference in viability or vigor. The blood-group genes are examples in point. The abnormal, with which genetic study traditionally begins, is rare. Overweening concern with the abnormal is the result of our usual fascination with the bizarre, coupled with the observational principle that it is easier to discover and study a great variation than a small one.

Without question, by far the most numerous hereditary differences among human beings are the ones that produce effects of extremely low adaptive significance. Nevertheless, the mere fact that such small hereditary differences exist in abundance is of the greatest importance in human affairs, as we hope to show. First, however, it will be worth while to present a hodgepodge of genetic characteristics to give some impression of the immense variety of genes affecting the human species.

Some people can curl the sides of the extruded tongue upward to form "O"; others cannot. The difference is genetic. Some people can taste "PTC" (phenylthiocarbamide), describing it as bitter; others cannot; a few report it as sweet or salt. Again, the difference is determined by genetics, and is independent of a general ability to taste. Some can smell hydrogen cyanide gas ("odor of bitter almonds"); some cannot. This hereditary difference, which is probably of little importance to us most of the time, might, in some industries, be a matter of life or death. Do you have hair on the second joint of your fingers? This is a matter of genes. Drooping eyelids (ptosis), the Mongolian fold to the eye, left-handedness, the various patterns of baldness, a white flare of hair at the back of the head, one kind of night blindness, ordinary red-green color blindness, the susceptibility of the skin to sunburning, the skin's susceptibility to freckling, and the color of the unexposed skin itself—all these individual characteristics are determined by genes. Does your urine smell of methyl mercaptan shortly after eating asparagus? Again, there's a gene for it; some people don't have this gene, and urinate inoffensively. Or perhaps you are one of those rarer people whose urine is red after eating beets? Genes again.

Such are only a few of the gene-controlled differences that are known to exist. They have been chosen on the basis of relative triviality. They are not very important (so far as we know) in terms of the basic problems of biological survival, though some, by affecting the individual's image of himself in social contexts, may produce widespread and subtle effects on human relations. (The world is not the same to a twenty-five-year-old man who is completely bald as it is to his hirsute contemporaries. For a bald woman, the world is still more different.)

De gustibus non est disputandum—there is (that is, there should be) no disputing tastes. What a wise old saying this is, and yet how often it is honored in the breach rather than in the observance! A. F. Blakeslee once made a mass survey of PTC tasters and non-tasters by setting up a booth at a national science convention, and testing all co-operating passers-by. Of more than 6,000 tested, he found that 65 percent reported PTC as bitter, 21 percent as tasteless, 5 percent each as sour and salty, 2 percent sweet, with the remainder holding out for such complex tastes as "rhubarb" and "cranberries." Almost more significant were individual reactions to the whole idea. Many a person who tasted PTC as bitter could not really believe that others could not taste it, or that they found it sweet or salty. When a married couple differed in their reactions, a spirited altercation would sometimes develop, the wife perhaps accusing her husband of deliberately contradicting her just for contrariness' sake, or the husband doubting the sincerity of his wife's report. For centuries, we have said that there's no disputing tastes, but have we really believed it, deep down inside? Each of us thinks of himself as the normal type, and supposes that everyone who is not like himself is "abnormal." This supposing is at such a deep level that we do not verbalize it; we may not even be aware of it. We are only beginning to see how wrong we have been.

The importance of innate differences in tasting has been obscured by the fact that experience is important in determining our likes and dislikes of foods. No one will deny that experience plays a role in the liking of an Eskimo for blubber, of a Chinese for old eggs, or of an African for toasted grubs. But there is increasing evidence that experience alone does not determine our food preferences. The greatest mass of evidence for this point of view has been brought together by Roger J. Williams, biochemist at the University of Texas, and one-time President of the American Chemical Society. Williams has written three books on the subject of human differences and their significance, *The Human Frontier* (1946), *Free and Unequal* (1953) and *Biochemical Individuality* (1956). It is his contention that there are immense deeps of human individuality of which we, at present, know scarcely the surface; that there are real differences of the most subtle sorts in the ways in which we see the world and in which we react to the world. Discovering, describing and studying these differences will require the utmost in analytical subtlety, in imagination, and in objectivity. "I always find it uncanny when I can't understand someone in terms of myself," wrote Freud in 1882, and thereby he revealed a serious weakness in the approach of most psychoanalysts to the problem of human differences—the feeling that that which is "different" is uncanny, and not natural. True, it is uncanny when *you* report that saccharine tastes sweet and *I* that it tastes bitter. Those who find saccharine sweet are the more common, but by what logic does that make them more normal? This chemical is not one that is encountered in a state of nature, and we are not "naturally" selected for our reaction to it. We just happen to differ. We must learn to accept one another.

That real differences between human beings are considerable and common is so recent an idea that there are no journals devoted to publishing studies of this sort. The data available are widely scattered, and (for the most part) are found as incidental parts of papers devoted to other subjects. Only in Williams's books can one find anything like a synthesis. I have, in what follows, borrowed freely and shamelessly from them.

It is difficult to get studies of human diversity published in scientific journals. (Why? . . . This is a most pregnant question.) Among the more interesting of the unpublished studies cited by Williams are those of Arthur L. Fox, the chemist who discovered the PTC taste difference. He has recently carried out a large-scale survey of the food preferences of people as correlated with their reactions to the pure chemical substances PTC and sodium benzoate. Of those who found PTC bitter and benzoate salty, 82 percent liked sauerkraut, the remainder disliking it; but of those who found both pure substances bitter, only 26 percent like sauerkraut, 23 percent disliking it. That leaves about 50 percent of this latter group in the "no comment" group. In general, the group that found both pure substances bitter was characterized by a large number of indifferent responses to such "controversial" foods as sauerkraut, buttermilk, turnips and spinach. By contrast, of those who found only the PTC bitter, an average of 97 percent reacted strongly (positively or negatively) to each of the test items. It would be difficult to argue that training plays a significant part in establishing these correlations.

To some, saccharine is sweet, to others bitter. Quinine is not bitter to all. Mannose, galactose and a number of other sugars are not sweet to everyone; indeed, ordinary table sugar, in 20-percent strength, cannot be tasted by some children. Six people out of 10 report that water has a peculiar taste (sweet?) after eating artichokes, the others denying this. Individuals vary, qualitatively or quantitatively, in their reactions to creatine (abundant in meat), sodium and potassium chlorides, hydrochloric acid and cascara. Most of these reactions are innate. How many are hereditary we do not yet know: the whole field of investigation is just being opened up, and work is proceeding at a snail's pace, for reasons that will presently be noted.

First, however, it is desirable to show that significant individual differences are not confined to matters of taste, but extend to (and are derived from) the fundamental biochemical reaction patterns which vary from person to person, and which are only to a minor extent modifiable by the environment. In Table V will be found a listing of only a few of the many characteristics for which significant individual variations have been proved. In reading this table, we must keep constantly in mind this important fact: *only "normal" people are included in these measurements.* (Inclusion of those labeled "abnormal" would, of course, extend the range considerably.) Also it must be emphasized that the samples on which many of the data are based are small. This fact would invalidate many generalizations, but not the one we wish to establish here, namely that human variation is great. It is a universally accepted statistical principle that increasing the size of the sample will increase the range of variation. Our present conclusions are, therefore, conservative.

The key statistic is recorded in the last column. From this we see that some normal adults have a heart rate (admittedly influenced by training) which is 2.3 times as great as that of other normal adults; that the red-blood-cell count of new babies varies by a factor of 1.6, the white-blood-cell count by 3.3. The red cells, remember, are essential for carrying oxygen, the white cells for combating disease organisms. Blood platelets, which are needed in the blood-clotting process, are 4.6 times as numerous in some adults as they are in others who are equally "normal." Phosphate, which plays a key role in all the dynamic chemical processes of the body, varies by a factor of 1.9; protein-bound iodine, important in the functioning of the thyroid gland, which in turn affects the general vigor of all bodily reactions, varies by a factor of 3. Acetylcholine, a basic chemical in nerve reactions, varies by a factor of 16; the enzyme arginase by 4.2; the enzyme phosphatase by almost 11. And two glands that are known to have great effect on behavior, the thyroid and the gonads, vary by factors of 6.2 and 4.5, respectively. And so on, and on.

The inescapable conclusion of such data is that what we

TABLE V

Variability of "Normal" Healthy Human Beings

Data abstracted from Roger J. Williams, Biochemical Individuality, New York: Wiley. 1956. For documentation refer to page cited in Williams.

Item No.	Page Citation in Williams	Item Measured	No. of Individuals in Sample	Factor of Variation
1	28	Heart beats per minute, adult	182	2.3
2	33	Red blood cells per cu. mm., 1 week old	15	1.6
3	33	White blood cells per cu. mm., new born		3.3
4	33	Blood platelets per cu. mm., adult		4.6
5	35	Volume of paranasal and frontal sinuses, children		20
6	50	Phosphate concentration in blood		1.9
7	50	Sodium concentration in blood corpuscles		3.3
8	53	Protein-bound iodine conc. in blood	402	3.0
9	52	Acetylcholine conc. in blood plasma		16.0
10	55	Glycine conc. in plasma		6.7
11	56	Vitamin A conc. in blood		15.0
12	71	Arginase enzyme, conc. in blood		4.2
13	70	Plasma alkaline phosphatase conc. in blood	600	10.8

14	72	Serum amylase conc. in blood		>320
15	81	Thyroid glands, weight		6.2
16	87-8	Gonads, adult weight		4.5
17	87	No. of ova in female at birth		13.3
18	88	Androgens, conc. in adult male urine		11.0
19	108	Alcohol, minimum intoxicating percentage in blood		
20	110	Mercuric chloride, min. conc. for producing skin irritation	1000	8
21	125	Minimum perceptible movement, peripheral vision in 20-20	35	>100
		individuals	28	42
22	125	Relative amount of oxygen in blood at 44,800 feet elevation	8	1.4
23	136	Daily dietary intake of table salt		15
24	137	Daily dietary calcium needs, adult	19	4.6
25	147	Vitamin D requirement, children		>25
26	152	Vitamin B$_1$ requirement	15	4

NOTES

Where the number in the sample is small, a larger sample would undoubtedly show greater normal variability.

It is known that there is individual constancy over a long period of time for Items 5, 12, 13, 14, 15, 16, and

19. Probably at least some of the others show individual constancy, but this is not a matter of record.

Where selection is biased, the bias is probably such as to minimize variability, as in item 22, the measurements of which were carried out with Air Force candidates, a highly select sample.

call "the normal man" is largely a figment of our imaginations. Human beings vary naturally and innately over a far wider range than we ordinarily suppose. And since our suppositions lead to actions and attitudes, error is a serious matter. How can we reasonably expect Mr. A and Mr. B to act like some median stereotype if the thyroid and sex-hormones in the blood stream of one are 10 times as great as in the other? How can we reasonably expect all men to have the same safe-driving records, when, even among men with "normal" vision, some are 42 times as good as others in detecting movement in the periphery of the visual field? Is it reasonable to expect the same "philosophy of life" in two men, when the blood stream of one has 10 times as much of the basic energy-releasing enzymes as are present in the blood of the other? And how can we reasonably demand that all children partake of a "normal" diet, when the vitamin B_1 requirement varies at least fourfold, and the vitamin D requirement at least eightfold? Left to themselves, children will select enormously different diets, and it may be that some of their apparently bizarre selections bespeak a sort of unconscious wisdom of the body. (In passing, it should be noted that experimental animals allowed a free-choice diet sometimes exhibit such body-wisdom, sometimes do not.)

The Russian novelist, Turgenev, once remarked that "a man is capable of understanding anything—how the ether vibrates and what's going on in the sun—but how any other man can blow his nose differently from him, that he's incapable of understanding." Yet this is what we must bring ourselves to understand. We must understand and learn how to live with people who differ in many ways: in nose-blowing, in sexual conduct, in ability to handle high-speed machines and meet emergencies, in liking for physical activity, in resistance to systematic poisons, in diet preferences and diet requirements, and—in the most general sense—in taste. *De gustibus non est disputandum* we piously say. But the way to avoid disputes is not by denying real and ineradicable differences. Dispute must somehow be avoided even though we make full and frank acknowledgment of human differences. We must, in a deep sense, accept our humanity, our *variable* humanity. In the past we have not been notably successful in this, and the least successful have been the theologians, the moralists and the political scientists who have, with rare and uninfluential exceptions, built their systems to fit only some fictitious "normal" Man, and then wondered why *men* did not behave like *Man*. We will never solve the moral problems of men until we accept, in our bones, the insights of the biologist and the geneticist.

Before we can do that we must find out first why we have resisted the truth so strongly. We must uncover the noble motives of our errors.

The Heavy Hand of Equalitarianism

"We hold these truths to be self-evident . . . that all men are created equal . . ." Perhaps few words in the last century and a half have been so productive of good and evil as these words in the American Declaration of Independence. *All men are created equal . . .* What does this mean? If it means what it literally says, few statements are so false. There are overwhelming odds against even two men being created equal. Genetic equality must be the rarest of accidents, a phenomenon hardly fit to be an axiom for a political system.

Curiously enough, one can argue with some plausibility that the assertion of human equality may have been in part an accident of rhetorical polishing in the writing of the Declaration of Independence. Before the Declaration there was the Virginia Declaration of Rights, from which many of its ideas were drawn. In this earlier document there occurs the phrase "all men are by nature equally free and independent." What this means exactly is not altogether clear, but certainly it is a much less objectionable statement. To say that all men are "equally free" is not nearly so unbiological as to say that they are "equal." The slight difference in rhetoric covers a world of difference in meaning.

But, it is often objected, when we say all men are equal, we don't mean biologically equal—we merely assert our intention of treating them as equals before the law. If this is the meaning, well and good; but it is the words men remember and the words don't say "legally equal." If we attack the phrase "all men are created equal," the defense reactions that are evoked lead us to believe, as hinted in the preceding chapter, that we have here laid bare what Plato would have called a "noble lie"—a statement which is false in fact but which will (it is believed) lead to praiseworthy consequences if it is not questioned publicly. What are these praiseworthy consequences?

First, there is the matter of the legal procedures the fiction of equality leads to. These, for the most part, we must praise. Social power is a force that easily makes unto itself a cybernetic system with positive feedback; power naturally begets power until (unless legal sanctions are imposed) it is all but impossible for a weak man to obtain justice. The assertion of equality in the eyes of the law breaks the cybernetic system and insures judgment on merit. It may be ludicrous to assert that a genius and a moron are equal, but we need not worry about the outcome of so doing. The genius should be able to take care of himself without the aid of positive feedback.

Perhaps the most ardent support of equalitarianism has come from those personally involved in social service and philanthropy. The human degradation that constantly confronts a social worker would be difficult to face day after day if he suspected that manipulation of the environment would be powerless in the face of genetic predetermination. Frank acknowledgment of the social worker's *prejudice*—the word is used correctly—against heredity is found in a statement made a generation ago by a director of a New York training school for social work:

> The notion of biological heredity and of innate capacity, as a determining factor, would have a paralyzing effect upon the young social worker, faced as he is with problems of maladjustments of various kinds. Without the hope and courage which the theories of social causation and social control give, no one could long endure social work.

To this one can only reply with Thomas Mann's courageous words, *A harmful truth is better than a useful lie.* If social work cannot find a firmer foundation than a noble lie, then so much the worse for it. A biologist, viewing the whole structure of social work from the standpoint of evolution, would suspect that such an institution acts as a selective agent for gathering together an unusually large aggregation of people who are notably capable of self-deception. It is rather interesting to speculate on the revolution that would take place in social work if geneticists were put in charge of it for one generation.

Where Lies the Burden of Proof?

One of the principal arguments of the equalitarians has been what we may call the "burden of proof argument," which may be stated approximately thus: Since we don't know, in any particular instance, whether two men are equal or not, should we not, as a matter of principle, assume their equality until we are proven wrong? Should not the burden of proof be placed on him who asserts inequality?

There may have been a time when this argument rang true: but no longer. We know too much about heredity and individual differences now. We know that life is a kind of game of cards, and that sexual reproduction is a shuffling process that redistributes these cards each generation, according to certain fixed rules. The deck is a large one—ten thousand cards, at least. Even with the restrictions of the meiotic process the chances of any two people getting the same selection of cards

—genes—is vanishingly small. That this idea is correct is shown by the phenomenon of skin transplantation. For a skin transplant to be acceptable it must be of the same genetic constitution as the tissues beneath it and the blood that feeds it. Skin transplantation is successful only when host and donor are the same. When one person's skin is transplanted to another, it always sloughs off in a few weeks, as we would expect if all people are different. There is only one exception to this generalization (and it strengthens rather than weakens the argument of the anti-equalitarians): identical twins. Such individuals, who arise from the subdivision of a single fertilized egg, have the same genes and can exchange skin transplants. In fact, such an operation has been used on at least one occasion to prove identicalness of twins in a case of accidentally interchanged children.

If "burden of proof" is to be based on probability, it is clear that we should always assume inequality, until we are proven wrong. In any case, we will not be thoroughly satisfied with any position until we have more facts. We need now to return once more to the question: *Why don't we know more about human genetics?*

Impediments to Genetic Knowledge

The usual excuses for the poverty of positive knowledge about human genetics are (1) the youth of genetic science, and (2) the technical difficulties in verifying human genes. Both excuses are valid, of course. Genetics, practically speaking, is only a bit over a half century old; and it is hard to prove genes in a species in which the number of children per family is so small, the time between generations so great, and in which matings cannot be made at the will of the experimenter. All this is true, but it is only part of the story. Statistical techniques have been devised for bypassing some of the methodological roadblocks, and these are being used to an increasing extent. But looking back over the past five decades one cannot help feeling that there has been more than a little dragging of feet, that researchers have fled all too willingly to the tempting refuge of the *Drosophila* laboratory, rather than expose their unconscious wishes to the threat of unwelcome truths about human nature. The first half of the twentieth century, like the first half of the nineteenth, was a time during which a scientific subject was crying to be heard but was laboring under a taboo. In the nineteenth, the subject was evolution; in the twentieth, it was human inequality. If we listen to the literature of the earlier period, we hear the whisper, *All life is one and man is an animal;* but much louder comes the censor's voice: *Don't say it!*—

don't say it! Erasmus Darwin spoke the truth prematurely; his words were squelched by an unorganized conspiracy of silence that lasted fifty years. Then Robert Chambers tactlessly said what everyone knew in his bones was true. He was chastised and sent to his corner like a bad boy. But the unwanted truth could no longer remain unsaid; it echoed around the walls of the prim chambers of the Victorian mind despite all brave attempts to smile it out of existence. Finally Charles Darwin shouted the truth and the world moved on to a new, and more truthful, adjustment to reality.

All men are, by nature, unequal—this is the censored truth of our century. We are as afraid of the consequences of admitting this truth as the Victorians were of the consequences of admitting that men are animals. Yet surely history will ultimately show that, in both instances, the consequences are good and compatible with human decency.

Some of the impediments to the study of individuality are economic. For one thing, it costs a lot more to determine the limits of normal variation than it does to make a few measurements, calculate an average, and call it "normal." Again, consider the matter of mass production: it presumes unitary "Man," and largely ignores individual variation. The standard seat, the standard bed, the standard diet—all these are favored by economics. In a day when our things were hand-crafted it was as easy to make the exceptional as it was the average; with mass production all this is changed. Only the "average man" gets a fair break. The rest of us have to make do, in a commercial world that tries to pretend that we do not exist. And yet we who are exceptional are, in fact, Everyman. As Williams (1957) has pointed out, if we define the normal for any variable characteristic as that portion of the range that includes 95 percent of the population, and then demand normality in all of 10 different independently varying characteristics, 40 percent of the population is "abnormal." If we include 15 such characteristics in our consideration, 53 percent of the population is "abnormal." If 100 characteristics are measured, 99.4 percent of the population will prove to be "abnormal" with respect to one or more of them. And human beings vary in many more ways than a hundred. Paradoxical though it sounds, almost everyone is abnormal.

We have been speaking of characteristics that vary in a continuous way, of such things as height, weight, intelligence and reaction time. The rareness of the "normal" becomes even more pronounced when we consider entities that vary discontinuously, as do the blood-group factors. (One has either A, B, AB or O type blood—there are no intermediates.) If we define as "normal" that blood that has the commonest type with respect to each and every one of the nine best-known blood-factor systems, then we discover that less than 1 percent of the population has "normal" type blood. Plainly, "normality" has little useful meaning now that we appreciate the individuality of blood. Yet in the early days of blood transfusion, this assumption was oh-so-naturally made, often with lethal results to the patient. In the *Journal of the American Medical Association* for 1907 there is an account of a transfusion that terminated fatally in spite of the bland assurance of the attending physician that he tested the "serum of the patient's blood against the red cells of a normal individual." *Normal* individual indeed! We are appalled now at such an account, but is not the attitude of that physician perfectly excusable in one who believes in the "normal"? How many cruelties must we not still be perpetrating in matters in which the phenomena are less well understood than blood, and where our failures are less obviously signalized than they are in transfusion-death!

Like the maladroit tailors in the land of Laputa, we daily cut our cloth to fit that almost nonexistent creature, the "normal" man. The fiction of normality survives the truth that contradicts it because the assumption acts as a "self-fulfilling prediction." The way it works may be easily shown.

Although it is not widely known among the laity, scientists not uncommonly throw away embarrassing data. For example, a scientist who wants to measure a table as accurately as possible will do so by measuring several times and then taking an average of his figures. But suppose, when he sits down to do the arithmetic, he discovers these recorded figures: 39.71, 39.67, 39.68, 39.73, 49.72. Should he just average them all? Obviously, the last figure is suspect. A good and honest scientist will, in fact, throw it out and average only the consistent figures. In effect, what the scientist asks himself is this: "Which is more probable: that the figure 49.72 (a deviant of about 10.0) is a natural deviant in measurements correctly made, when the usual deviations from the average are only about 0.05—or that the figure 49.72 is quite erroneous, perhaps because I wrote 4 instead of 3 in the tens' place?" Of the two probabilities, the latter seems much greater, so the scientist discards the highly aberrant figure. Few sensible men would do otherwise. Probability is our guide to wise action.

But is it legitimate to apply a similar procedure to measurements made of many different human beings? There is in the research literature an account of a study of the lipid (fat) content of blood of 67 healthy human beings, a study carried out by a reputable team of workers. In reporting their data they point out that: "Subject 24 showed a total lipid content so far above the range of all the other subjects that it appears consistent with the probable truth to consider that he had a lipemia from some undetected metabolic abnormality. On the other hand Subject 67 showed a total lipid content much below the range of all others. We have accordingly considered these two subjects as probably abnormal with respect to their lipid metabolism and have omitted their data from the calculations and from the graphs." Though there is a formal similarity of this procedure with that of the scientist measuring a table, there is a real and important difference. With the table, the presumption of a unitary, material object of constant length is the sort of thing a "reasonable" man can accept. With human beings, however, the existence of a non-material but unitary "normal man" is precisely the question at issue. It is only by throwing out the unusual measurements of healthy men that we create that which we assert—the fictional "normal man." This is what we mean by a "self-fulfilling prediction." The situation is least bad when the authors report their procedure, as the above experimenters did. There are undoubtedly many instances in which this is not done, or in which the entire study is left unpublished because it does not "fit" established ideas of the "normal." Williams (1956, p. 58) attests to one such.

Perhaps nowhere has valuable data on human variability been discarded with such abandon as in the research laboratories of the drug houses, and for the best of economic reasons. Every practicing doctor knows that patients differ enormously in their reactions to drugs. Williams (1956, p. 111) has reported a study made of the effects of morphine on 29 healthy students. Nausea was produced in 18, sleep in 16, drunkenness in 9, dizziness in 13, itching in 9, and indistinct speech in 7. The pattern of reactions is seldom the same in two individuals, and the quantitative sensitivity varies over a wide range. Yet morphine is one of that minority of drugs that have survived competition in the doctor's armamentarium for a long time because their effects are *relatively* predictable—relatively, that is, with respect to the vast majority of drugs which show even greater variability in their effects on individuals. Of this great number of drugs we hear very little because, obviously, they are not suited to a medical practice which uses the working hypothesis of "normal man" as a guide to treatment. A drug which elicits, say, 20 different reactions, and none of them in more than 10 percent of the population, is going to find little favor with the practicing physician. It will be even less welcomed by the drug manufacturers, who are in business to make money. The large drug houses have research laboratories that are constantly trying out hundreds of new chemical compounds. The majority of them are judged, as we would expect, to be useless medically, and one of the reasons for eliminating a potential drug is variability in its effects. Commercially understandable as this attitude is, it has been unfortunate for the advance of knowledge. The variability in drug response mirrors deep-seated biochemical variability of human beings; this variability is undoubtedly, in most cases, hereditarily determined. Drugs that have individually variable effects should be wonderful test-reagents for determining the dimensions of personality. By testing many people with a large number of drugs we should be able to discover correlations of "personality"—a very subjective concept—with objectively determinable drug reactions. Such a scheme of personality assessment would be far superior to the presently used questionnaires, Rorschach test, etc., for the simple reason that it would not be possible for a clever and knowing person to fake answers. Samuel Butler, a contemporary of Darwin, anticipated "a time when it would be possible, by examining a single hair with a powerful microscope, to know whether its owner could be insulted with impunity." It now seems unlikely that the microscope will suffice, but it does seem most probable that Butler's dream will one day be achieved through the study of the biochemical profiles of men. But before we can do this we must realize the opportunity that the despised drug "idiosyncrasies" offer us, grasp it, and pull ourselves upward to a new understanding of humanity. It almost makes one weep to think of the large amount of revealing data that has been thrown away by research laboratories of drug houses because the observations did not point the way to commercial gain.

Knowledge Versus Power

Genetics was born into a world in which the "environmentalist" has been increasing in power as never before—a world saturated with the idea of progress, a world in which the continuous existence of frontiers and space to expand in has made plausible the idea that men can accomplish anything if only the environment is suitably manipulated. The "hereditarians"—those who believe that heredity sets real and important limits to what men can do—have, in a sense, been competing with the environmentalists for public support. And for the most part, the hereditarians have been losing the business.

You are dissatisfied with your place in the world? "Ah," says the environmentalist, "your deficiencies are caused by the defects in your education. These can be remedied. *Hire me and I will cure you.*"

And what has the hereditarian to offer in competition? "Your deficiencies," he says, "stem from your heredity, which is past mending. *Hire me, and I will give you understanding.*"

Is it any wonder that it is the environmentalist who gets the business? Who wants mere understanding, when power is offered instead? Certainly not the majority of the people, as is shown by the relative popularity of the religious revivalist and the psychiatrist. "Are you sick of yourself?" asks the revivalist, who then promises, *Hire me and I will save you.* To which the psychiatrist counters, *Hire me and I will give you understanding.* Millions flock to the revivalist's tent; only dozens enter the psychiatrist's door. Discouraging? Immediately, yes; but in the long run, perhaps not. We who embrace science think—hope—believe—that Ernest Renan's calm faith may in the end prove justified: "Pray remember that no truth is ever lost, that no error ever strikes root." Genetics may yet come into its own. When it does, men will discover that it is only by knowing the truth about themselves—knowing all their strengths and weaknesses, both those that are remediable and those that are past change—that they can adjust their individual environments to meet the needs of their individual natures. In the long run, only by knowing and acknowledging the truth is self-fulfillment possible.

"If a man does not keep pace with his companions," said Thoreau, "perhaps it is because he hears a different drummer. Let him step to the music which he hears, however measured or far away." This the individual owes to himself. To others he owes an equal privilege, which he can easily give on two conditions: (1) that he is psychologically secure and at peace with himself, so that he need not indulge in that form of aggression called equalitarianism; and (2) that he freely allows the evidence of the inequality of men to enter his mind. It is an irony of logic that equalitarianism, though it may proceed from the best of motives—to *allow* freedom to the individual—in fact, in practice, has a natural tendency to decay into a dogma that *demands* equality of taste, of performance, of ideals, *i.e.,* that demands that *others* be like *me*—or rather, like my image of myself. Equalitarianism readily degenerates into a powerful pressure for conformity that takes no cognizance of the different drummers men hear. The contrary belief, that men are really different, supports and fosters individual freedom.

9

Mutation and Sex, Generators of Variety

A fundamental characteristic of a gene is its great stability. A given allele (say the *O* allele of the ABO blood group) reproduces itself true to type, cell generation after cell generation. Only very occasionally will it "make a mistake" and produce a different allele (say the *A* allele, or the *B*). When it does, we say a *mutation* has occurred. On the average, the probability of a mutation at a given gene locus is about 1 in 100,000. That is, all the spermatozoa of a man of blood type O will carry the *O* gene, except for about 1 sperm in every hundred thousand, which will have a different allele. The hereditary mechanism is first of all conservative; only secondarily, and on a small scale, does it introduce novelty.

Novelties are needed, however, if we are to study heredity, and the early days of genetics were devoted principally to looking for new novelties, new mutations. This was slow work. Natural mutation was exasperatingly slow. For many years, attempts to speed it up by artificial means apparently failed. We are sure now that they did not all fail, but that the means of finding the mutants were too crude. Then in 1927, H. J. Muller, one of the cleverest of the geneticists, devised an exceedingly sensitive test for mutations, and with this he showed that X rays greatly increase the rate of mutation in fruit flies. Since then, many other species have been tested and the mutagenic (mutation-producing) effect of X rays has been verified with all tested, without exception. Some rather unusual chemicals (*e.g.,* nitrogen mustard) have also proven to be mutagenic. Probably more important, it has been found that many kinds of high-energy radiation *e.g.,* alpha, beta and gamma rays, and neutrons, are also mutagenic. Most newly produced mutations are bad—why, we shall see subsequently. In medicine, in industry, and in the practice of and preparation for war, we are producing ever more high-energy radiations. We cannot but wonder: Are we seriously affecting man's genetic heritage by our production of more radiation and radioactive waste products? Let us see what the general picture is.

Can Genetic Damage Be Proved?

In 1946, shortly after the explosion of the atomic bombs over Hiroshima and Nagasaki, there was appointed one of the most unusual commissions ever to be set up: the Atomic Bomb Casualty Commission, a field agency of the United States National Academy of Sciences. One of the principal jobs of this commission was to try to determine the genetic effects of the bombs. A sensible-enough assignment this appeared to be, on the surface, yet it was a foregone conclusion—known to every geneticist in advance—that: (1) the bombs undoubtedly caused genetic damage, (2) the commission would fail to find evidence of such damage.

These statements raise arresting questions. How do we know Fact 1? How can we be so sure of Fact 2? If Fact 2 is true, is Fact 1 to be relied on? If the assignment was certain to fail, why embark on it?

The last question should perhaps be answered first—it involves only politics. We *had* to appoint the commission. We Americans were the ones who had done the damage, who had subjected civilians to a devastating, destructive force the like of which had never before been known. As a matter of decency we had to at least face what we had done, to study the results as carefully as possible. We had to appoint the commission, even though some of its assignments were doomed to failure. And failure was what its genetic investigations ended in. The commission's reports, issued many years later, when shorn of numerous and justifiable qualifications, add up to just what had been expected: no provable significant genetic effect of the bombing; nevertheless, a firm belief that such effects had been produced.

How can these diverse statements be reconciled within the framework of a genuinely critical science? In the interest of posterity we must see how.

Radiation and Posterity

Early attempts to arouse the public to the genetic dangers of radiation met with an opposition, the vigor of which was not to be explained by the purely intellectual issues involved. Men who insisted that atomic bombs endangered all mankind were openly accused of sympathy with the enemy. The reasons for these accusations are part of the history of post-World War II anti-intellectualism, but we will not go into them here. Disbelief in the genetic danger of radiation was not confined to uneducated people. Many medical men were also skeptical. As late as 1950, a much-revised medical manual, widely used by physicians, had this statement in it:

"Many geneticists believe that there is danger of gene altera-
tion in later generations if men and women who have been
temporarily sterilized by radiation are allowed to have children. No concrete evidence to support this theory is yet
available."

To a biologist this assertion is an astounding example of
misplaced conservatism. What would we think of a medical
manual that published this statement: "Many biologists believe
that if a living man is dropped, without a parachute or other
supporting device, from an airplane flying over rocky terrain
at 42,000 feet, the man will be killed. No concrete evidence
to support this theory is yet available." Such an assertion is
true, in a narrow technical sense—there is no *concrete* evidence, if by that we imply a record of a particular event of
this sort. Yet who could perform the experiment in good conscience, excusing himself from blame by saying that "no concrete evidence" was available to him beforehand? The point
is, there is a whole fabric of evidence that supports us in the
belief that a 42,000-foot drop to jagged rocks would be fatal,
and we act confidently on the basis of this large body of general knowledge, without demanding the "concrete evidence"
of a particular experiment. So it is also with the belief that
radiation causes genetic damage in human beings. Here the
lack of "concrete evidence" is not because the experiment of
irradiating men and women has not been carried out, for it
has—many times. The lack of evidence is due rather to the
fact that, by their very nature, most genetic changes are very
unlikely to be detected in less than three generations' time in
human beings—and this only if first cousins marry. We have
only recently become aware of the danger and begun to think
we should keep the necessary records. There has not been
time enough to carry out the necessary genetic tests. Unless
we discover new and more sensitive methods of detection of
genetic damage, it will be yet another fifty years or more before we have "concrete evidence" of radiation damage to the
human germ plasm. In the meantime, we must make our decisions on the basis of experimental data from other animals
and plants—and such data we have in great abundance,
derived from the study of many scores of species. All the data
substantiate the following important generalizations:

1. Mutation has been found to occur naturally in every
species that has been studied with adequate genetic techniques.
The over-all rate of mutation varies from species to species,
and, indeed, sometimes from race to race within a species.

2. High-energy radiation causes mutations in all species.
No exception has ever been found.

3. It is practically unimportant whether a mutant allele is

a "natural mutant" or an "artificial mutant," *i.e.*, one induced by man.

4. Mutation is always a highly localized phenomenon within a cell. The mutation at each gene locus is independent of changes that may take place at other gene loci in other cells, in the same cell, or indeed, within the same chromosome. Gene mutation results when a particular chromosome is "hit" by a high-energy particle (quantum of radiation).

5. What particular mutation will occur when enough of a mutagenic agent is brought to bear on a cell is unpredictable, though (experience shows) some mutations are more probable than others.

6. Each gene is capable of existing in many different allelic forms. The mutation rate for each conceivable change (from one particular allele to another particular allele) is a constant.

7. There is, at present, no perceivable principle that determines what a particular mutation rate will be. The relation between "opposite" mutation rates (*e.g.*, the rate for normal-to-hyperdactyly allele, and the reverse) follows no rule.

8. The genetic effects of discontinuously administered irradiations seem to be strictly cumulative. That is, the genetic damage caused by, say, 50 roentgens of radiation is the same whether given all at once or subdivided into smaller doses administered over a period of time. (Damage to somatic tissues, *i.e.*, nonreproductive tissues, is often not so strictly cumulative: repair processes may undo some of the damage between irradiation.)

9. There is no known threshold below which damage does not occur. Half the dose, half the damage; one tenth the dose, one tenth the damage, and so on. We can hardly speak of a "safe" dosage; we can only hope to agree on a permissible one.

10. Mutability under radiation varies from species to species. Mice are about 15 times as sensitive as *Drosophila*. (We suspect that man is more like a mouse than he is like a fruit fly.)

11. Most new mutations are recessive to the "normal" or "wild" type from which they were derived.

12. Mutations with small phenotypic effects occur more commonly than those with large.

13. Finally, and most important: with very, very rare exceptions, most new mutations are harmful to the organism affected by them.

In the face of a great mass of highly consistent evidence, those who would deny the human danger of high-energy radiation can do so only by implying that man is not a part of nature. "But isn't man different from other animals?" some may say. Yes, man is different, if by "different" we mean that this remarkable animal is able to form elaborate intellectual concepts, to conceive of death and the future and to let his conceptions alter his instinctive reactions to present stimuli. But in his primitive corporeal manifestations he cannot usefully be distinguished from "the animals," *i.e.*, the other animals. Shakespeare or Shylock, he has, like them, eyes, organs, dimensions and sense; he is warmed by summer and cooled by winter; and he is injured by disease and hurt by weapons. Among these weapons are those we call the mutagenic agents. By his intellect, man is able to do what no other animal can —to increase the activity of such agents; but, once loosed, mutagenic substances and emanations exert their effect impartially on all organisms, human or infra-human. The peculiar humanity of *Homo sapiens* is no direct shield against what we have the conceit to call his "inhuman" actions. We have no direct measure of the mutability of human germ plasm, but we have no reason to think that it is at all exceptional. The burden of proof lies on those who suggest that it is.

Direct Proof of Damage

It should now be clear why the commission found no clear-cut evidence of genetic damage among the survivors of the atom blasts in Japan. Suppose that the (diploid) genetic formula of a normal individual be represented thus:

$$AABBCCDDEE \ldots \ldots$$

Verifiable experience with other organisms tells us that the atomic radiation undoubtedly produced many gene mutations in the population, most of them recessive. Suppose that, after the bombing, the reproductive cells of a certain Mr. Kimura were altered so that he now produced some spermatozoa which had the following haploid formula:

$$aBCDE$$

Suppose that Mrs. Kimura had had her reproductive cells altered, too. Since there are many gene loci—at least 10,000 in human beings—it is unlikely that Mrs. Kimura's genes would have been altered in the same way. We may represent her new type eggs as:

$$ABCDe$$

With sperm and egg of the types indicated, the zygote will be:

$$AaBBCCDDEe$$

Notice that it is homozygous for neither of the new recessive mutants; consequently, the child that it will develop into—the first generation after the bombing—will be "normal."

What about the second generation? It is very unlikely that this offspring will happen to marry someone who contains either the mutant a or the mutant e, consequently the results of the bombing are very unlikely to show up in the second generation. (Brother-sister mating among the first generation offspring would have a reasonably good chance of producing some mutation homozygotes, but this is an uncommon type of reproduction in all human societies.) Only if some of the first cousins in the second generation marry is there a reasonably good chance (far less than fifty-fifty, however) of revealing in the third generation a mutant that was produced by the atomic irradiation more than fifty years earlier.

This is not a nice state of affairs, from a human point of view, and geneticists are naturally casting about for ways of proving and detecting genetic damage earlier. One of the more promising studies is that of William L. Russell, of Oak Ridge. Experiments were carried out with mice subjected to neutron radiation. Russell proved a radiation effect in the first generation, the demonstration depending on two assumptions justified from other experiences: a) Even "recessive" mutants have a slight effect on a heterozygote, the effect being measurable as a shortening of life, if in no other way; b) The spermatozoan is almost entirely composed of genetic material, consequently any effect of the spermatozoan on the life of the zygote may, with only a small margin of error, be attributed to its genes.

What Russell did was this: Male mice were exposed to neutron radiation of varying intensities. They were mated to females, 19 to 23 days later. The females had not been irradiated. Any shortening of life in the offspring of such a mating could reasonably be attributed only to the sperm, and most probably to new mutant genes in the sperm. From the findings recorded in Table VI, it is apparent that there is a

---

TABLE VI

Length of life in the offspring of male mice exposed to neutron radiation 19-23 days before mating. Deaths before weaning age are excluded. Radiation source screened, reducing gamma radiation to less than 10% of total. (From W. L. Russell, 1957).

Total Dose to Father (In rep)	Number of Offspring Studied	Mean Length of Life of Offspring (In days)
0	103	792
31	50	754
71	5	699
118	22	723
136	8	688
186	2	756

general shortening of life of the offspring with increasing irradiation of the father. This is just what we would expect if the irradiation is producing mutations, and is not easily explainable in any other way. (The irregularities in the relationship are to be attributed to the small scale on which the experiment was run, as recorded in the second column. It is to be hoped that a larger-scale experiment will be performed in the future. In the meantime, we must be content with this one.)

Neutron radiation is measured by a unit called the "rep" ("roentgen equivalent—physical"). On the average, Russell calculated, 1 rep of irradiation administered to the father shortened the life of the offspring mouse by 0.61 day. If the same relative shortening of life takes place in man—and of course we don't know that it does—1 rep administered to a human father would shorten his son's life by 20 days. *If* this is true—*if*—then total body irradiation has greater effect on length of life of the offspring than it does on the individual himself, for studies made of the occupational hazard of X rays to roentgenologists indicate that 1 roentgen (approximately equal to 1 rep) shortens the recipient's life only about 2.5 days. We stand greatly in need of more facts. The relationship indicated is, however, the sort that geneticists have long known to be true, namely that the germ plasm is far more sensitive to radiation damage than is the soma. When the medical man has finally decided what is, from his point of view, a "safe"—*i.e.*, an acceptable—radiation level, the geneticist will undoubtedly insist that this standard be reduced still further in the interests of posterity.

Why Most Mutations Are Bad

Uniformities in nature always need accounting for. That mutations are almost always bad for the organism is a remarkable uniformity. Some might regard it as evidence of the existence of a personal devil, but we want an explanation of a more operational sort. What is the explanation?

The explanation can be simply given in terms of a picture of a well-adjusted machine. Suppose, as one biologist once put it, you had a finely adjusted racing car, and you stood ten paces from it and fired repeatedly at it with a shotgun: how likely is it that you would improve its performance? Certainly not very likely. Admittedly, a shot *might* nick the carburetor slightly, improving its adjustment. But it would plainly be much more probable that your shooting would damage the machine. So it is with a living organism, which is a far more delicately adjusted mechanism. High-energy radiation or unusual chemicals alter the genetic substance in ways that are purely random as far as the organism's needs are concerned. Most such alterations will certainly be for the worse in a machine that is already finely adjusted to the demands of its environment.

But how did the living machine become so finely adjusted? Was it not by a process of mutation and selection? Yes, certainly. *But is this process at an end?* Certainly not: but remember that the types of mutations we see now (even when we speed up their production artificially) we see repeatedly; they must have occurred repeatedly in the past. For an animal like man, the physical environment has probably not changed significantly during the last hundred thousand years. During all this time mutations—millions of millions of them—have occurred, each specific kind many times. Those mutations that are best for man in his environment, having already occurred many times, have already been incorporated into the species by natural selection. The great majority of new mutations have, at all times, been eliminated by the same process. It is extremely unlikely that we should in one short lifetime (even with the aid—aid?—of mutagenic rays) observe a new and *good* mutation that has never before occurred in any part of the world during some three thousand lifetimes.

But suppose the environment changes? That alters the situation. When we make DDT a part of the environment of houseflies, we alter the selective value of some of their alleles: the allele or alleles that make for DDT-resistance, which were of no value to the flies in their natural environment, are now of positive selective value. Whenever mutation produces one of these alleles, the new allele has a better chance of survival than the allele we formerly called the "normal" allele. In the new environment, the new allele is "good." But, of course, *most* new mutations are still "bad."

If there is a change of environment, is it advantageous to

speed up the mutation process? Here is a really difficult question, which plainly is entangled in many other questions having to do with rates of change, with the costs of waste, etc. The questions involved, though taking the form of qualitative questions, can be answered, if at all, only by quantitative considerations. We are not yet in a position to give an answer. We can say this, however: that undesirable though mutation may be from a humane but shortsighted human point of view, it is in the long run the primary creator of hereditary novelty on which the process of evolution depends.

Is Sex Necessary?

Mutation creates novelty; sex preserves it, and even augments it. That this is so was not at all obvious until comparatively recently. Fleeming Jenkin supposed that a new hereditary variant would be "swamped"; his error stemmed from the "paint-pot" theory. With the coming of Mendelism, it was seen that a particle could not be diluted out of existence, but a new danger was feared. Since a new mutant is generally recessive, is there not a danger that it will be replaced in time by its dominant allele? This sounds like such a reasonable supposition, and yet it is completely wrong, as was shown in 1908 by the mathematician, G. H. Hardy, and (independently) by the physician W. Weinberg. The methods they used were mathematical, but their conclusions can be reached by purely verbal means.

What do we mean when we say that allele A is dominant to allele a? Just this: that when both alleles are present together in an individual, the phenotype reveals only the presence of A. In the sex cells of this heterozygote (Aa), both alleles are present in equal numbers. Meiosis plays no favorites in distributing the alleles to the gametes: a gametes are as numerous as (and no more so than) A gametes. Dominance, then, is a phenomenon of development, not of heredity in the strict sense. A dominant gene will *not* tend to replace a recessive gene. If one gene tends to replace another, it will be because it has greater selective value, regardless of whether it is dominant or recessive.

Sexual reproduction plays the role of a shuffling mechanism. The two unlike alleles that are brought together in one zygote as a result of the sexual act are, in the process of preparing for sexual reproduction in the next generation, separated again to be reshuffled with other alleles from other individuals. There is great loss of individual genes (think of the 300 million spermatozoa released in each copulation), but the risk of loss (or preservation) for each gamete is strictly proportional to its frequency, and so the sexual process tends to maintain the status quo with respect to the frequencies of all the gene-alleles. Life is a sort of game of cards in which each of us is given a hand derived jointly from the two parents. The deck is a big one: instead of only 13 different denominations of cards (1, 2, 3 . . . K, Q, A) there are in the neighborhood of 10,000; these are the gene-loci (the ABO-locus, the hemophilia-locus, etc.). Instead of only four different suits (spades, hearts . . . there are often a half-dozen or more alleles (A_1, A_2, etc.), which are, unlike the suits, *not* equally common. The rules of the game specify that each gamete must contain one card (and only one) of each of the 10,000 denominations; a zygote will contain two of each. Within these restrictions, the sexual process is a randomizing process that insures that all the suits (alleles) will be passed on from one generation to another. This is, in effect, what the Hardy-Weinberg law says.

Sex tends to preserve novelty (mutant genes); it also creates novelty in the form of new combinations of genes. If an individual of genotype *AaBbCcDd* mates with one who is *aabbccdd* there will be produced (if enough offspring are born) children of a total of 16 different genotypes (*e.g.*, *Aabbccdd*, *AaBbccdd* . . .), all but two of which are completely new and owe their appearance to sex.

Could new combinations of genes not appear without the help of sex? Yes, they could, but only with much greater difficulty (*i.e.*, with much less probability). An asexual organism can evolve markedly new genotypes only by simultaneous mutations in the same organism, or successive mutations in the same family line. If any of the intermediate genetic combinations are of negative selective value, they probably will not survive long enough to permit the appearance of the great variety of hereditary types that sexually reproducing species produce so readily. As H. J. Muller remarked in 1932, only the geneticist can answer the hoary old question, "Is sex necessary?" *Not necessary,* he answers, *but very convenient.* The world would be a much more stable, much more monotonous world without it—and we need think only of genes to say this. The variety-generating capacity of sex is of positive value to the species that enjoys it.

10

Eugenics: Is Man Part of Nature?

WITH our account of mutations and the genetic threat of atomic bombs we have brought ourselves face to face with one of the most crucial questions facing man at the present time, namely, how shall man deal with himself as a biological organism, subject to biological laws? The question is timely, but not new. In its genetic aspects, beginning attempts were made to answer it almost a century ago, shortly after the publication of the *Origin of Species*. The answers did not gain general acceptance and the question is still before us. Recent developments in genetics make the outlines of an answer clearer than they were a generation ago. We shall examine these recent developments a bit later. But before we do, it is desirable to review the early approaches to the question, to see what false starts were made and why. Only so can we understand the emotion that envelops the problem now.

Is man a part of nature? When we ask this question we imply that we can divide, dichotomize, the world into two entities, *man* and *nature*—but that having done so, we then doubt the dichotomy. Such ambivalence has periodically come to the surface throughout man's intellectual history. Atoms and void, mind and body, organism and environment—these dichotomies are centuries old, and their validity is no more certain now than it was two thousand years ago. First we make progress by assuming a dichotomy; then by asserting its contrary. And what is Truth? We don't know. Pressed to the wall by critics obsessed with a striving after consistency, we may have to invent a learned-sounding verbal escape. "Complementarity," Niels Bohr softly says; more stridently a Hegelian will speak of "dialectic." The motivation is the same: to preserve the richness, the mystery and the fruitfulness of the real world when our freedom is threatened by orderly system-makers.

Is man a part of nature? The learned men of the Western world during most of the Christian era have asserted that, in important respects, man is not part of nature, that he stands a thing apart from those entities and processes that can be studied by rational means. The man-nature dichotomy was felt to be a necessary foundation stone of revealed religion and established society; any attempt to modify the distinction was regarded as subversive of moral order. That was why there was an immediate rejection of Darwin's hint that man's distant past was co-terminous with that of the apes and all other living beings. That man's future development might also be a *natural* one was (and is) even more shocking.

Is man a part of nature, or is he not? Out of more than two million different species of plants and animals, man alone can ask that question, and thereby he shows that he *is* something special, a being who, in some sense, stands outside of nature. But his ability to verbalize and his delight at ringing the changes in concepts have in the past led him to create an overly homocentric universe, which it has been the task of scientists, from Galileo to Freud, to correct. When an error is discovered, the first correction of it that is offered is not always entirely correct (a gross understatement!). As we approach more and more closely to man himself and to our own times, it may be expected that the errors in recently developed views deriving from science will be greater. Our present interpretation of the meaning of the facts of heredity and evolution for man's future is undoubtedly not entirely correct, but we can work our way to truth only through error. Always the most fruitful errors to study are the most recent ones, for these are the errors that we ourselves would very likely make, had not our immediate intellectual ancestors been so obliging as to make them first. The most suggestive errors in the applied side of genetics are subsumed under the name of "eugenics," a complex of doctrine that is not, however, wholly erroneous. In determining our present position, it will be useful to trace the approximate path we followed in getting to it.

Galton and the Founding of Eugenics

Eugenics may be defined as the science of genetics applied to man himself; it has in view the improvement of the species in a biological sense, or at any rate, the minimizing of forces that might cause a deterioration in the genetic quality of man. The fundamental theorem of eugenics is this: *Man's political actions have genetic consequences.* "Political" is interpreted in the broadest sense to include all things having to do with public policy, whether ordinarily called social, religious, or "political" in a more narrow sense.

The first extended discussion of eugenic ideas was published by Francis Galton in a popular British magazine in 1865, the same year in which Mendel orally presented his theory of heredity to the Natural History Society of Brünn. Galton assumed that what we describe as "talent" in human beings is subject to the laws of heredity (whatever these might be) just as physical characteristics are; and that men of great talent would pass on at least a part of their endowment to their children . . . *if any*—for Galton called attention to the fact that all too often the man of talent has no children, as a result of an error in social organization: Said he:

> Many forms of civilization have been peculiarly unfavorable to the hereditary transmission of rare talent. None of them were more prejudicial to it than that of the Middle Ages, where almost every youth of genius was attracted into the Church, and enrolled in the ranks of a celibate clergy.

But we need not go back to the Middle Ages, or restrict the discussion to the Roman Catholic Church to find instances of the genetically unfavorable effects of public policy. We need look no further from home than our own time to find an instance of man's "unnatural" and dangerous meddling with nature:

> Every animal, before it is of an age to bear offspring, has to undergo frequent stern examinations before the board of nature, under the law of natural selection. . . . [But] one of the effects of civilization is to diminish the rigour of the application of the law of natural selection. It preserves weakly lives, that would have perished in barbarous lands.

The implication is all too clear: since medicine works contrary to natural selection, and thus allows the breeding of weakly individuals, will it not, as generation succeeds generation, produce a breed of men ever more dependent upon the ministrations of medicine? Is not this short-term blessing a long-term folly?

In the light of the principles of evolution, our task is twofold, said Galton: to encourage the breeding of the better elements of the population, and to discourage the breeding of the poorer. The former has come to be known as the program of *positive eugenics,* and the latter as that of *negative eugenics,* though Galton did not coin the word "eugenics" until 1883, thus adhering to an almost universal rule that brain children are conceived and brought to birth long before they are christened. Of the two aspects of eugenics, Galton thought the positive was the more important. Near the end of his life, writing in 1905, Galton envisioned a society in which a "suitable authority" would issue "eugenic certificates" to the young people of greatest genetic worth, who would thereupon be given special economic concessions, enabling them to marry earlier and have more children, thus raising the average quality in the population. The need for a greater number of superior men and women in society was, in Galton's view, critical.

> The average culture of mankind is become so much higher than it was, and the branches of knowledge and history so various and extended, that few are capable even of comprehending the exigencies of our modern civilization; much less of fulfilling them. We are living in a sort of intellectual anarchy, for the want of master minds.

Master minds . . . this sounds strangely familiar . . . *Superman:* that's it, isn't it? It probably is. The present-day comic-strip character comes from Bernard Shaw, and (as the biometrician Pearson pointed out) Shaw got his Superman from Nietzsche, whom we know was interested in Galton's work. Galton to Nietzsche to Shaw to the comic page (and we should not forget Houston Chamberlain and Adolf Hitler). Nothing is so contagious as ideas; and no contagion so much altered in the transmission.

Who was this Galton who fathered such an infective fantasy? Was he, like Nietzsche, a neurotic misanthrope? Or, like Shaw, a posturing iconoclast? The largest-scaled application of a eugenic program—or rather, a travesty of eugenics—was carried out in Nazi Germany by men of the most distasteful character, sadists who, in the name of Nordic superiority, killed, sterilized or tortured tens of thousands of innocent people. Was Galton such a beast? Quite the contrary. Francis Galton was one of the mildest, kindest and most gentlemanly of aristocrats. Considering the fact that the greatest opposition to Galton's ideas has come from the camps of the Communists and Socialists, perhaps the most convincing evidence of Galton's personal goodness will be a quotation from a noted Fabian Socialist. Beatrice Webb, in recalling the members of an informal group of discussants known as the "X-Club," wrote that

> . . . among these scientists, the one who stays in my mind as the ideal man of science is, not Huxley or Tyndall, Hooker or Lubbock, still less my guide, philosopher and friend, Herbert Spencer, but Francis Galton whom I used to observe and listen to—I regret to say without the least reciprocity—with rapt attention. Even to-day I can conjure up from memory's misty deep, that tall figure with its attitude of perfect physical and mental poise, the clean-shaven face, the thin compressed mouth with its enigmatic smile, the long upper lip and firm chin, and as if presiding over the whole personality of the man the prominent dark eyebrows from beneath which gleamed with penetrating humour, contemplative grey eyes. Fascinating to me

was Francis Galton's all-embracing, but apparently impersonal, beneficence.

He was, by all accounts, a remarkable concatenation of nearly all the traits that cultured men of his time (if not of ours) regard as admirable. *Trustworthy, loyal, helpful, friendly, courteous, kind, obedient, cheerful, thrifty, brave, clean and reverent*—the roster of his qualities is that of the Boy Scouts (save, possibly, the reverent, for he once wrote a statistical study of the efficacy of prayer, concluding that it did no good). Such a man, of course, seldom attracts the attention of our novelists or biographers; their "realism" is not so catholic as to include excellence. Galton was too "good" to be interesting to a Faulkner or a Caldwell or a Steinbeck— or to the myriads of readers whose psychic hungers they feed.

Galton was very much "for" the uncommon man, the man of talent, the man of genius. Unlike the later supporters of the Nordic myth, who were themselves very un-Nordic (remember what Hitler and Goebbels looked like), Galton personified the very traits he admired. At the age of one he knew his capital letters; a half year later he knew both alphabets. He could read at two and a half, and sign his name at three. A few days before he was five years old he wrote as follows to his sister: "I can read any English book. I can say all the Latin substantives and adjectives and active verbs besides 52 lines of Latin poetry. I can cast up any sum in addition and can multiply by 2, 3, 4, 5, 6, 7, 8 and 10. I can also say the pence table. I read French a little and I know the clock." One who visited him when he was almost seven reported that he could repeat a page by heart after reading it twice over. At eight he commenced the study of Greek.

His education, however, included more than mere booklearning. His father was a successful Quaker businessman, who believed that a child should learn early to be self-reliant. With this end in view, he once sent his son, at the age of seven, on a journey by himself. His destination was two days away by stage coach, with several changes to be made, and an overnight stay at an inn to be secured. The seven-year-old boy successfully passed the test. (He did not know that his father had also dispatched a servant who trailed him to make sure that all was well.)

Perhaps it was from such early experiences that he acquired a taste for the career in which he made his first reputation, that of an explorer. His school education paralleled Darwin's in many respects: for the most part it was desultory, segmented, dull and profitless. Like Darwin, he started to be a doctor, and like him, he abandoned that career when he found that he was to be independently wealthy, setting off (in his case) on a solo tour of Europe at the age of eighteen. One thing led to another and he presently found himself in Africa, where he spent many years in exploration, opening up some regions never before visited by white men. To those who love exploration and who can read prosaic accounts empathetically, Galton's descriptions are still fascinating, but they are not for the superficial thrill-seeker, for there are few "adventures" in them. "Adventures" are the sign of the incompetent explorer, and Galton was nothing if not competent. Lack of water, poor food, unfriendly and even threatening natives—all these Galton took in his stride. Considering his frequently exposed situation, one wonders at his getting out alive and can find no other word to account for his success than "character"—which, of course, doesn't explain it at all. The qualities of the Boy Scout were in daily demand, and he had them. But even he could occasionally fail, as appears from the following autobiographical account of his attempt to secure a necessary travel permission from Nangoro, a native king in central Africa:

> I did much to make myself agreeable, investing Nangoro with a big theatrical crown that I had bought in Drury Lane for some such purpose. But I have reason to believe that I deeply wounded his pride by the non-acceptance of his niece as, I presume, a temporary wife. I found her installed in my tent in negress finery, raddled with red ochre and butter, and as capable of leaving a mark on anything she touched as a well-inked printer's roller. I was dressed in my one well-preserved suit of white linen, so I had her ejected with scant ceremony.

King Nangoro refused the permission Galton so much wanted. Perhaps the virtues of a Boy Scout were not quite enough.

At about the age of thirty, Francis Galton gave up travel (except for yearly trips to the continent), married a schoolmaster's daughter and settled in London, living in one house for fifty years. His life from this time on was that of a wealthy dilettante. But his accomplishments were of no mean order. Besides such small items as the invention of the first supersonic dog-whistle, he developed stereoscopic maps, various instruments for weather recording, and contributed the idea of the "anti-cyclone" to meteorology. He made many contributions of the art of anthropometry—the measurement of man—as an outgrowth of his interest in the differences among races. His most notable practical idea was that of using fingerprints for individual identification. His first studies of fingerprints were made in the hope that they would prove useful in differentiating races. They did not, being correlated with nothing. But he noticed that they were completely individual, and he developed a means of classifying them and urged that they be used in police work.

A man's failures are often as revealing as his successes. Galton's career included two major failures: one of them connected with the mind of man, the other with his heredity. The first, first. Galton had a passion for measuring everything: the boringness of sermons as indicated by the number of fidgets in the audience, the number of brush strokes required to paint a portrait, and the relative number of pretty girls met on the streets of different British cities (Aberdeen had the lowest prettiness coefficient). He even once measured the exact dimensions of a notably steatopygous African beauty queen—though the operation was carried out from a properly Victorian distance, using surveying instruments. If there is a single thread that runs through his life, it is that he wanted to get the Measure of Man. After he had done a fairly thorough job of getting man's physical measure, he turned his attention to the mind. He discovered that there were great differences, for example, in the way that different people conceive the numbers, some assigning them to one sort of irregular mental space, others to others, and some to none at all. Some people think in terms of images, while others apparently do not. As he plunged deeper into his inquiries he discovered that people make some very odd, *i.e.*, "illogical," associations of things, one person describing the number 3 as a "treacherous sneak," another as a "good friend," and another as a "female companion" to the number 2. This seemed very curious, and Galton, by introspection, found that even *his* mind (certainly a model of a modern English logical machine) had some strange things in it. The results of his investigation gave him, he said,

> . . . an interesting and unexpected view of the number of the operations of the mind and of the obscure depths in which they took place, of which I had been little conscious before. The general impression they have left upon me is that which many of us have experienced when the basement of our house happens to be under thorough sanitary repairs, and we realize for the first time the complex system of drains and gas and water-pipes, flues, bell-wires and so forth, upon which our comfort depends, but which are usually hidden out of sight, and with whose existence, as long as they acted well, we had never troubled ourselves.

Clearly Galton caught a glimpse into the underworld of

the mind which Freud and Jung later laid bare. He hints that what he found was not pleasant to a well-bred mind, but he is reticent as to details.

"It was a most repugnant and laborious work," said Galton, "and it was only by strong self-control that I went through my schedule according to program"—*i.e.*, according to the original program, before he had any conception of the plumbing of the mind. But he did not devise a new attack based on the glimpse he had just had. In Pasteurian phraseology, his Victorian mind was not prepared for the accident of Freud.

Galton's second failure, in the study of heredity, is of a different sort. His interest here was a logical outcome of his eugenic beliefs. Obviously his position would be on sound scientific ground only if it could be shown to mesh with the principles of heredity—and what were these? By what means was talent passed from one generation to another? In his attack on this problem, Galton quite unconsciously accepted the implications of common speech about heredity ("half-bloods," "quarter-breeds," etc.) and produced a theory of blending inheritance, quite mathematical, but basically incorrect. His life and work present a significant contrast with that of his exact contemporary, Mendel. Of these two men, both mathematically minded, the Englishman (whose I.Q. has been estimated, post mortem, at over 200) was undoubtedly the more brilliant, yet the great discovery of genetics was made by the Moravian monk who could not even pass his teacher's examination. Plainly, even in the intellectual realm, intellect is not enough. Where it is a question of escaping the conceptual tyranny of Bacon's "idols of the market place"—the beliefs that are rigidified by language itself—the outcast, the impoverished, and the lonely man sometimes has an immense advantage over the accepted, "well-adjusted" man of wealth.

But we must not despise intellect. A good mind may, for want of inner freedom, fail to solve the problem it attacks, but it is almost sure to come up with something interesting or useful. Galton failed to crack the riddle of heredity, but he did produce the concept of the "correlation coefficient," a statistical tool that has been used ever since. He started the important English school of "biometry," or statistics-applied-to-biology. His concern with the problem of heredity bore fruit, even if not quite of the desired kind.

Nature Versus Nurture: A Logical Quagmire

No historian of ideas has yet devoted his attention to the eugenics movement. This is a pity, for a livelier bunch of participants it would be hard to find: biologists, sociologists, psychologists, militarists, pacifists, Socialists, Communists and conservatives have joined in the melee with fervor, if not with discretion. Since the issues are so humanly important, it is difficult to view the fracas with objectivity. But he who succeeds in doing so should have a tale to tell that will have more than a little humor in it. Lacking a definitive history, we must, for the present, be content with some broad generalizations of the course of eugenic thought from 1865 to what one may, with considerable accuracy, date as the end of the Galtonian epoch, 1932. This general picture will be presented by contrasting some eugenic doctrines with the rebuttals subsequently offered to them.

The notable family argument. The argument for the reality of biological inheritance from the existence of families of conspicuous talent or eminence is certainly an old one; Galton gave it new life by a careful cataloguing of families of many different sorts of eminence in his *Hereditary Genius* (1869). A more recent study is Paul Bloomfield's *Uncommon People* (1955). Looking over these family trees one can hardly fail to be impressed: it is hard to believe that it is entirely accidental that Lord Shaftesbury, the philanthropist, Anthony Eden, Winston Churchill, Henry Fielding (the novelist), and Bertrand Russell all trace their ancestry to one George Villiers in the sixteenth century. (We do not even mention the almost innumerable noble relatives in this kinship, headed by the present Queen of England.) Galton himself was part of a kinship that included the Wedgwoods of pottery fame, Erasmus Darwin (his and Charles Darwin's grandfather), and the great naturalist; the line has continued to the present day, producing several first-rate scientists as well as Ralph Vaughan Williams, the composer. Through marriage it has now joined with the Keynes's, through Maynard's brother Geoffrey, a distinguished scholar and bibliophile. Then there is the Bach family of Germany, musicians of importance for two hundred years. (In Erfurt, Germany, the very word "Bach" became a common noun meaning *musician.*) And the Bernoullis of Switzerland, who produced four really distinguished mathematicians during two generations. . . . So one can go, on and on. Unfortunately, this sort of evidence is most impressive to those who are already convinced (the "hereditarians") and seems scarcely more than diverting anecdote to those of opposite persuasion (the "environmentalists"). (*See*, for instance, sociologist C. H. Cooley's early criticism of Galton.)

One basic criticism of the notable family argument is that it suffers from an unknown statistical error. Even *if* there were no hereditary factor at all (in either the biological or the social sense), among the many existing families a few would be expected to be outstanding *just by chance*. The logic behind this statement can be seen by thinking of throwing ten coins simultaneously: if this is done enough times, there will be a few throws that will consist of all heads or all tails. In the case of the coins, we can calculate how often this rare event will happen by chance: about one time out of 512. But with families, how can we calculate the chance expectancy, to see if the observed frequency is greater?

Furthermore, says the environmentalist, I don't assert that chance alone is involved: besides the non-chance factor of biological heredity there is the factor of social heredity, which has two aspects: transmission of know-how, and the passing on of advantageous position. You must admit that children whose last name was Bach had some remarkable instruction in music in the home; and the name of Rockefeller is not exactly a handicap if you have a hankering for banking or finance.

But, retorts the hereditarian, you forget that socially inherited position is of very little use unless there is ability, too. You forget about all the rich men's sons who never amount to much. . . . But that could just as well be regarded as evidence against biological inheritance, is the reply.

But you should read the detailed histories of the men in distinguished families: then you will see that most of the individuals achieved fame in spite of great personal disadvantages. . . . But what is a disadvantage? Remember that Benjamin Franklin said, "To be thrown upon one's own resources is to be cast in the very lap of fortune." And Carlyle remarked that "for one man who can stand prosperity, there are a hundred that will stand adversity." The challenges of life are subtle.

To the hereditarian, close study of the lives of great men leads to a strong feeling of Fate, of an inexorable force moving men from within toward their external destiny. Speaking of the Bernoullis, E. T. Bell has remarked:

No fewer than 120 of the descendants of the mathematical Bernoullis have been traced genealogically, and of this considerable posterity the majority have achieved distinction— sometimes amounting to eminence—in the law, scholarship, science, literature, the learned professions, administration, and the arts. None were failures. The most significant thing about a majority of the mathematical members of this family in the second and third generations is that they did not deliberately choose mathematics as a profession but drifted into it in spite of themselves as a dipsomaniac returns to alcohol.

Perhaps, replies the environmentalist: but what do you mean by "in spite of themselves"? Are we, like Galton, to shut our eyes to the insights of Freud? The human psyche is, of all things, the most deceptive.

Historically, the argument was "won" by the environmentalists, for various reasons. First, there was the matter of the type of evidence: the best of the hereditarian's case can be only in terms of genes and chromosomes and enzymes and statistical tests of significance. These highly technical matters are not to be understood easily. The environmentalist, by contrast, does not have to bother with technical details: his appeal is pretty directly to the heart. Just as Galton's argument had appealed to the "common sense" of an aristocratic nineteenth century, so later sociologists appealed to the "common sense" of an equalitarian twentieth. How thoroughly the environmentalists carried the day among intellectual groups is apparent when we note that as late as 1950 the United Nations affiliate, UNESCO, put out an authoritarian "Statement on Race" which had as one of its leitmotifs a quotation from Confucius: "Men's natures are alike; it is their habits that carry them far apart." Unless this statement is quoted significantly out of context (which it probably is) one can only say that it is inconsistent with the general corpus of Confucian writings, and factually naïve even in the fifth century B.C.

The genetic viewpoint has been largely missing from informed lay thought in our century, and for this the geneticists are largely to blame (if "blame" must be placed). In educational institutions, trained geneticists have, in large part, confined their teaching activities to a small segment of the student population, the budding specialists in biological research. Outside these institutions, geneticists have been largely silent, generally avoiding contamination by eugenics societies. William Bateson, the Huxley of Mendelism in England, wrote in 1919: "I never feel Eugenics is my job. On and off I have definitely tried to keep clear of it. To real Genetics it is a serious—increasingly serious—nuisance diverting attention to subordinate and ephemeral issues . . ." Bateson's standoffishness has been followed by most other professional geneticists. By way of defense, we can point out that this attitude has probably been a good thing for the development of the academic discipline of genetics. It has allowed genetics to develop by its own internal logic during the critical formative years, when great harm could have come to both its direction of development and to its public reputation through a premature attempt to apply incomplete results of pure investigation.

The Eclipse of Eugenics

The eugenic movement started by Galton came to a fairly clear-cut end in 1932. This is not to say that the eugenics societies founded in England and the United States did not continue beyond this time, for they did, but their effectiveness was much diminished. Organizations are, of course, almost immortal. (For an apposite example consider the Greenback Party which was founded in 1874: it was still nominally in existence in 1948, polling just 6 votes out of a total of more than 48,000,000 cast in the Presidential election.) After 1932, the eugenic movement seemed in danger of undergoing a similar downward evolution, for various reasons.

For one thing, many eugenicists had suffered from the same delusion as many of the prohibitionists, namely the belief that law molds sentiment. The truth is quite the opposite: *sentiment molds law*. The ill-advised enactment of a law prohibiting the sale and use of intoxicating beverages in the United States put back the cause of temperance by several decades—and promoted disrespect for law as well. Sentiment was too far behind law. In a similar reformist mood (and at approximately the same time) eugenicists succeeded in pushing eugenic laws through the legislatures of more than two thirds of the states. These laws had not, fortunately, the compulsive character of the prohibition law: they merely *permitted* negative eugenic measures—the sterilization of the markedly incompetent— under closely supervised conditions. (No positive eugenic laws have ever been seriously proposed in the United States.) But even this faltering step was too much in advance of popular sentiment, and as a result, the eugenic laws of most of our states have been a dead letter for many years.

That the idea of eugenics has not been welcomed by the general populace is probably an indirect effect of its failure to excite the intelligentsia. Like the idea of prohibition it has seemed too simplistic an idea, one that ignores too many of the complexities of this rich life of ours. Many thoughtful people who have read Galton have been repelled by his bland assumption that his world—the Victorian world—was the best of all possible worlds, and that the peaceful, law-abiding, conservative, satisfied and thoroughly rational Victorian man was the best of all possible men. In acknowledging that there actually exist some men who prefer adventure to a settled life, Galton wrote:

> Luckily there is still room for adventure, and a man who feels the cravings of a roving, adventurous spirit to be too strong for resistance, may yet find a legitimate outlet for it in the colonies, in the army, or on board ship. But such a spirit is, on the

whole, an heirloom that brings more impatient restlessness and beating of the wings against cage-bars, than persons of more civilized characters can readily comprehend, and it is directly at war with the more modern portion of our moral natures. . . . As the Bohemianism in the nature of our race is destined to perish, the sooner it goes, the happier for mankind. . . . By this steady riddance of the Bohemian spirit of our race, the artisan part of our population is slowly becoming bred to its duties. . . .

William Bateson, who in championing Mendel had unseated the Galtonians in the field of genetics in England, attacked them with equal vigor for the narrow view they had of the aims of eugenics. Galton's castigation of "Bohemianism" aroused the ire of Bateson, who was a friend of the "Bloomsbury set" and who had a sufficiently discerning appreciation of art (a blind spot for Galton) to enable him to amass a collection of contemporary paintings that was worth a small fortune at the time of his death, though he bought with a poor man's purse. Bateson wrote:

> It is not the eugenists who will give us what Plato has called divine releases from the common ways. If some fancier with the catholicity of Shakespeare would take us in hand, well and good; but I would not trust even Shakespeares, meeting as a committee. Let us remember that Beethoven's father was an habitual drunkard and that his mother died of consumption. From the genealogy of the patriarchs also we learn—what may well be the truth—that the fathers of such as dwell in tents, and of all such as handle the harp or organ, and the instructor of every artificer in brass and iron—the founders, that is to say, of the arts and the sciences—came in direct descent from Cain, and not in the posterity of the irreproachable. Seth is to us, as he probably was also in the narrow circle of his own contemporaries, what naturalists call a *nomen nudum*.

Thus he touched the Achilles' heel of the eugenic argument: When we say we want "superior people," we mean superior *in what respect?* In physical and mental health? (The mother of Nobel Prize winner J. J. Thomson could not find her way from her home to a railway station "not very many yards away.") In "social adjustment"? (What of those distinguished jailbirds, Cervantes, Bunyan, Thoreau and Gandhi? The "fittest" in the phrase "survival of the fittest" is defined by the environment. If, for human beings, we modify that environment by consciously adopted eugenic devices, we—mere humans—define what is "fittest." How shall we do that?

For many, the problem was simple: the fittest to reproduce were simply those who had prospered most in our society.

The wealthy American capitalist, Chauncey Depew (1922), told the guests at great dinners and banquets that they who had come to New York and risen to the top were the fittest, the ones of "superior ability, foresight and adaptability." Explicitly or implicitly, this was the assumption of most contemporary eugenists. Then came 1929.

Almost overnight the climate of opinion changed. Bankers and captains of industry, formerly regarded as the paragons of wisdom, now were charged with undivided responsibility for the Depression. "Capitalist" became an insulting epithet; to be a member of "the People" was to be one of the chosen (though one could hardly say, *select*). In such an intellectual atmosphere the eugenic position was precarious.

The effective end of Galtonism came in 1932, when the eminent geneticist, H. J. Muller, made a speech before the Eugenics Society in New York that, in the words of a contemporary observer, Bentley Glass, "just about finished the activity of the Eugenics Society." Muller, greatly acclaimed for his discovery of the mutagenic effect of X rays five years earlier, did not pull his punches. His arguments set an important part of the pattern for anti-eugenic arguments for the next two decades. For that reason they are worth quoting at some length.

Eugenic deals cannot now be achieved, said Muller, because our capitalistic system produces the wrong motives of individual action.

> In the first place, it is undeniable that the profit system leaves little place for children. In general, they are not profitable investments: their cost is excessive, the dividends from them are uncertain, they are likely to depreciate in value, are practically non-transferable, and they do not mature soon enough. . . . For the great masses . . . each extra child commonly means more intensified slavery for the parents. . . . And as the status of the middle class sinks, the parents hesitate to rear children with lesser privileges than they.
>
> How much can eugenic considerations weigh in determining the actions of people under these conditions? . . . Is it to be wondered at that a census of eugenists themselves has disclosed an appalling failure to reproduce themselves, despite the fact that they are maximally steeped in their own doctrines?

This last was an especially telling point: it is almost symbolic of the eugenic position that Francis Galton, the originator of the argument and the brilliant epitome of the ideal eugenic type, died childless.

Muller went on to discuss problems connected with the differential fertility of the various social classes. It had long disturbed the eugenists to observe that the butcher, the baker and the green-grocer's boy had more children than the doctor, the lawyer, the lord and lady. With few exceptions, wherever statistics were available, they showed an inverse relation between position in the economic and social hierarchy, and fertility. But should this concern us, asked Muller? It seemed highly probable, he said, that differences between economic classes are caused by environmental differences in opportunity. (Thus had the most influential social scientists preached for the last forty years.) Moreover, he asked, who prospers in our society?

> Are the characteristics which now lead men to rise, economically, those which are the most desirable, from a social point of view? It could at least as well be maintained that the dominant classes tend to have the genetic equipment which would be least desirable in a well-ordered social system, since they have been selected chiefly on the basis of predatory, rather than truly constructive, behavior. A study of the lives of many eminent financiers confirms this. The 'respectable' captains of industry, military leader or politician, and the successful gangster are psychologically not so far apart. The high-minded, the scrupulous, the idealistic, the generous and those who are too intelligent to wish to confine their interests to their personal monetary success, these are apt to be left behind in the present-day battle.

It would be wrong, he said, to embark on a eugenic program now because the dominant class would try to see to it that society produced more captains of industry who "could see us through bigger and better depressions," as well as predatory sportsmen, "slapstick and slush artists," and "safe and sane scientists to invent better poison gas." No, he said, we are not yet ready for eugenics.

> Only the impending revolution in our economic system will bring us into a position where we can properly judge, from a truly social point of view, what characters are most worthly of a man. . . .
> Thus [he concluded] it is up to us, if we want eugenics that functions, to work for it in the only way now practicable, by first turning our hand to help throw over the incubus of the old, outworn society.

The following year, 1933, H. J. Muller became the Senior Geneticist at the Institute of Genetics of the Academy of Sciences of the U.S.S.R.

11

Liberalism and the Specter of Competition

The truth that is suppressed by friends is the readiest weapon of the enemy.

—ROBERT LOUIS STEVENSON

THERE was a time when educated men supposed that myths were something of the past—quaint, irrational fairy tales believed in by our credulous and superstitious ancestors, but not by us, oh dear no! (*We believe only facts,* we said.) Now we know better. We know now that every man, no matter how rational he may aspire to be, leads a life that is governed in its most significant aspects by myths—myths that he believes all the more strongly because he is unaware that they are myths. In fact, at the moment when a man becomes aware of a guiding myth, the myth dissolves, and his new-found wisdom is but retrospective. (And in the decay of the dying myth a new myth is spawned.)

For the Western world, during the second quarter of the twentieth century, the most widespread and powerful of all myths was the Myth of the Soviet Utopia, to give it only one of many possible names, none of which is wholly satisfactory. It was a myth of a kingdom of heaven that was usually either distant in space: the actual Soviet Union, many thousands of miles away—or distant in time: the coming classless society of Communism triumphant. A few starry-eyed true believers found their heaven right before them as they visited Soviet Russia (though usually not for long). For the others, the enduring distance of the mythic utopia, whether in time or space, did not in the least diminish the intoxication of it. Like the early Christian's kingdom of heaven it was more real than daily bread.

Myths die hard. This is probably more true now than it ever was in "primitive" times. In our Gargantuan world almost everything we believe, we believe on hearsay—the hearsay of press and radio. Never have men had to govern their daily lives so largely by faith, by the faith that there is truth in the stories about millions of people thousands of miles away. It cannot be otherwise. Therefore it is not to be wondered at—indeed, it can be defended as a manifestation of rationalism—when modern man occasionally disbelieves a particular report about those millions of people thousands of miles away. (Millions of Russian peasants are being killed for non-cooperation, American newspapers said during the 1930's. *Just capitalistic propaganda,* retorted the liberals. *What is the evidence? Nothing but hearsay. I see no dead peasants.*) Hearsay, always weak, is doubly so when it conflicts with a beloved myth. (To argue that the myth also is based on hearsay is to miss the point.) At all times, from the earliest days of the Russian Revolution on, there was ample evidence that the Bolshevik heaven bore a striking resemblance to our concept of hell, but the signs were compulsively ignored. As early as 1920, the philosopher, Bertrand Russell, spelled out the nightmare qualities of the Russian dream in terms that he never needed to revise in the light of later facts. For his pains and his honesty Russell was quietly ousted from his position as the philosophic spokesman of the liberal elements. (Since he was patently unfit to speak for the conservatives either, he was henceforth a philosophic man without a party. This position may not be the most comfortable of all positions, but for a living philosopher it has its advantages.)

Myths die segmentally, for one fraction of the true believers at a time. The myth of the Soviet Utopia had its first dying for some at the time of the Spanish War. Here, for the first time, large numbers of European and American liberals were brought face to face with their god, who proved to be made of clay from head to foot. Another segment became disillusioned when the Soviets signed a "ten-year" non-aggression treaty with the Nazis in 1939. (It lasted less than two years.) Others lost faith when the eastern colossus attacked tiny Finland. The latest defection from the ranks of the bemused came with the rape of Hungary in 1956. This was perhaps the last disillusionment; the few true believers left after Hungary are probably so highly selected for myopia that no evidence can shake their faith. Only death will decimate their ranks.

For the scientific segment of the population, the denouement came in 1948. One must be careful not to exaggerate the importance of the event: it was not nearly so searing an experience as that undergone by militant American liberals during the Spanish Civil War. Scientists, as a group, are perhaps more commonly a-political than are most intellectuals. (For this they are damned from both the right and the left.) Nevertheless, there had been a *small* band of able scientists who had subscribed to the Soviet myth. This group was particularly influential in England, where it included such men of genuine distinction as the embryologist, Joseph Needham, the physicist, J. D. Bernal, and the geneticist, J. B. S. Haldane. That an embryologist or a physicist should take seriously the claims of Communism is perhaps no more surprising than that a machinist or a miner should: the relation of the myth to their vocational assumptions is by no means obvious. But that a keen student of genetics and evolution should subscribe to an ideology which denies the very fundamentals of his science is evidence of the immense power of subconscious myth.

Haldane was not alone among geneticists in embracing the delusion. In our own country the myth was accepted by a scientist of at least equal stature, H. J. Muller, who, as we have seen, renounced the capitalistic world and fled toward the eastern mirage in 1933. Haldane, at least as late as 1950 (perhaps much later), still clung to the myth—as he could easily do, living in the freedom and security of semi-capitalistic England; Muller, who had the advantage of having lived for a while in the holy land itself, was soon cured of his delusions. Once in Russia he quickly realized that his principal personal problem was escaping the heaven he had fled to.

When Muller left the United States, it was not with the immediate intention of taking up residence in Russia. However, external circumstances drove him faster than he had planned. He left the United States in 1932 on a Guggenheim fellowship to do research at the Kaiser Wilhelm Institute in Berlin. In 1933, Adolf Hitler came into power, and Muller moved on to Soviet Russia, accepting a position as senior geneticist at the Institute of Genetics of the Academy of Sciences. There were many distinguished geneticists in Russia at this time, doing excellent work. Genetics was benefitting from the Soviets' generosity toward the sciences, but genetics was, by its very nature, an especially dangerous science to support. As J. B. S. Haldane said in 1932—before he joined the Communist party:

> The test of the devotion of the Union of Socialist Soviet Republics to science will, I think, come when the accumulation of the results of human genetics demonstrating what I believe to be the fact of innate human inequality becomes important.

Muller had not been long in Russia before he discovered that the U.S.S.R. was undergoing that test of devotion to science—and was failing it. In 1932, G. A. Levitsky and N. P. Avdoulov were sent to labor camps. When the most distinguished of all Russian geneticists, N. I. Vavilov (who had studied with Bateson in England), appealed to Stalin, these men were re-leased—temporarily. Then B. S. Chetverikoff, W. P. Ephroim-son and L. P. Ferry were banished to Siberia. The last named, together with I. J. Agol, were the first geneticists to be put to death, in 1935. In 1937, S. G. Levit met the same fate, as did (probably) Avdoulov. In 1939, N. A. Iljin joined the ranks of the martyrs; in 1942, the roster was swelled with the names of Vavilov and G. D. Karpechenko. We mention only the more distinguished men whose fate is known with a consider-able degree of probability. Many others simply disappeared.

All the Soviet geneticists, whether working with human problems or studying the chromosomes of garbage-flies or making hybrids between cabbages and radishes, ultimately felt the heavy hands of a monolithic state fearfully tighten around their necks, but it was the workers in human genetics who suffered first. The Medicogenetical Institute of Moscow in the early 'thirties had started a program of investigation of iden-tical twins that promised to be of the greatest value. Identi-cal twins, remember, are twins with the same sets of genes. When such twins are separated at an early age and raised in different environments, any differences in character that may develop can properly be ascribed to environmental dif-ferences. Such separations occur occasionally, by accident, in our part of the world; in a totalitarian country like Russia the separation might be brought about deliberately, as an experi-ment. Suspecting (whether rightly or not) that such a state might carry out such experiments on a large scale, geneticists outside Russia awaited the reports of the Moscow Institute with great interest. In 1934, the results of studying some 1,000 pairs of identical twins were released. They were devastating to the Communist line: they showed an overwhelming impor-tance of heredity. The truth was intolerable. The Medico-genetical Institute was soon disbanded. Levit, its founder and director, confessed his ideological error and was liquidated.

Now it happened that at about this time the Soviet Union was preparing to be host to the 1937 International Genetics Congress, a congress that is held once every four years. The threat of free speech was obvious. Russia demanded an agree-ment in advance that no papers dealing with the heredity or evolution of *Homo sapiens* would be presented by any dele-gate. The demand was, of course, rejected, and Russia refused to invite the congress. The last-minute refusal caused a delay of two years before the rescheduled meetings could be held in Edinburgh. It was by then not very international. The Rus-sian delegates, en masse, were refused permission to leave their country. Hardly had the meetings begun (on the twenty-third of August, 1939) before the German delegates were called home by their government. The invasion of Poland and the beginning of World War II took place on the first day of September.

Lysenko

We have only begun the story of the Russian rape of biology, but we cannot go on until we retrace our steps a bit to introduce the Hamlet of the piece, T. D. Lysenko, the guiding genius behind the purges of science from 1936 to 1948. To most of the world he was completely unknown until the startling revelations of the 1948 trial, but a few Westerners knew of him earlier. Among these was a distinguished English plant breeder, S. C. Harland, who in a radio broadcast in 1948 told of his first impressions of Lysenko, whom he had met fifteen years earlier:

> I was invited to visit the Soviet Union in 1933, and Vavilov took me on a tour that lasted nearly four months, not only to the main experiment stations of Russia proper, but also far into Central Asia to Tashkent and beyond that nearly to the Chinese frontier. In Odessa we went to see a young man named Trofim Lysenko, who Vavilov said was working on the vernalization or treatment of seeds in order to secure earlier maturity or greater productivity. I interviewed Lysenko for nearly three hours. I found him completely ignorant of the elementary principles of genetics and plant physiology. I myself have worked on genetics and plant-breeding for some thirty-five years, and I can quite honestly say that to talk to Lysenko was like trying to explain the differential calculus to a man who did not know his twelve times table. He was, in short, what I should call a biological circle squarer. Vavilov was more tolerant of Lysenko than I was. He said the factors of the environment had never been adequately studied by anybody; that we ought to explore the environment; and that young men like Lysenko who "walked by faith and not by sight" might even discover something. He might even discover how to grow bananas in Moscow. Finally Vavilov said that "Lysenko was an angry species", and that as all progress in the world had been made by angry men, let Lysenko go on working. It did no harm and might sometime do good.

For his tolerance Vavilov paid the standard Russian price. Within five years' time he was deposed as President of the Academy of Sciences, to be replaced by Lysenko. In 1940, Vavilov was arrested and sent to Siberia. Sometime, probably in 1941 or 1942, he died. When the Academy of Sciences of the U.S.S.R. celebrated its 220-year jubilee in 1945, the name of its former President, N. I. Vavilov, was not included on the list of living or recently deceased members.

With the wisdom of hindsight, we see now that we should have recognized what was happening to Soviet science by 1936. In this year there was held a national genetics congress, for which the stage was cleverly prepared by Lysenko, who was carefully coached by the Marxist philosopher, Prezent. As the English geneticist, C. D. Darlington, tells us:

> Propaganda at all levels from the daily press to the scientific journal, and in all directions, practical and theoretical, political and philosophical, was brought to bear on genetics. A large and popular audience, to the number of 3,000, was marshalled in the conference hall. With this planned organisation Lysenko and his manager launched their attack. They presented their arguments on a correct philosophical and canonical basis which made experiment unnecessary; which was fortunate, for the experiments adduced were without controls, without definitions, and without numbers. In a word, they had no scientific meaning. Before a meeting suitably packed with party men these shortcomings proved to be no disadvantage. H. J. Muller, the leading foreign exponent of the philosophy of the science, replied to the charges that had been brought against genetics, but the official report omitted his remarks. The Lysenko-Prezent program in 1936 was an almost entire success. At the end the chairman was fully convinced, and a resolution was passed that in the future genetics and plant breeding were to conform with dialectical materialism.

The following year Muller, thoroughly disillusioned, left the Soviet Union. Did he shout his disillusionment from the housetops, and was he listened to respectfully? Of course not: this is not the way of love grown cold: nor would he have been listened to. He belonged to that most ignored of all classes of the 'thirties, the left-wingers grown wise. (Only much later did the "I was a Communist" literature flourish.) Neither liberal nor conservative wanted to hear from such a man. What it meant to belong to this then-select group can perhaps be most clearly realized by reading the essays of George Orwell, another liberal who became wise too soon. Not until much later did Orwell come into his own, with the publication (in 1949) of *Nineteen Eighty-four*. Muller spent a similar period in spiritual exile after his flight from Russia, filling various minor academic posts until the administration of the University of Indiana, with what looked like spectacular foresight, made him full professor in 1945, just one year before he was awarded the Nobel Prize.

In the meantime events in Russia had assumed the familiar pattern. In 1939, a purely Russian genetics congress was held

in Moscow. The Lysenko forces dominated this, singling out
for heavy personal attack Vavilov, who had been so unfortunate as to be named the President of the International Congress at Edinburgh that Russians were not permitted to attend.
On the ideological side, a clear-cut line was drawn between
despicable "Mendelism-Morganism" and holy "Darwinism-
Michurinism." A word is in order regarding these labels. The
emotional content of them for Communists was terrific, as one
can appreciate by reading the verbatim reports of this and
subsequent Russian congresses. The phrase Mendelism-Morganism clearly filled the comrades with loathing. Mendel was
a particularly splendid whipping boy, because he had been a
monk, a most repulsive form of humanity in Communist eyes.
But Morgan—why should the name of T. H. Morgan induce such bile? Could it be that T. H., the geneticist, was
confused in the minds of the ignorant with J. P., the capitalist?
As for Michurin, here was a name we would never have heard
of had it not been for Lysenko. Michurin was an uneducated
Russian plant breeder of very minor importance. He had two
great virtues: his anti-scientific superstitions fitted Lysenko's
needs; and he was dead. He was eminently fitted for Soviet
sainthood, and a saint he was made. This gave Lysenko a
banner he could fight under, thus creating an illusion of personal modesty. . . . And Darwin? Here was a strange historical quirk—that a capitalistic thinker should be a god of
anti-intellectual "workers." This strange Assumption was
made possible by Darwin's failure to penetrate the mystery of
heredity. As we have told earlier, when Darwin failed to
achieve the insight of Mendel, he resorted to a theory that
was essentially a modified Lamarckism. It is this Darwin, the
confused and stumbling Darwin of the *Variation of Plants
and Animals,* rather than the much more scientific and rigorous Darwin of the *Origin,* that Lysenko paid reverence to. It
was the only great name in Western science that could by any
means be twisted to give support to Lysenko's childish and
unsupported theories.

The Second World War imposed a truce in the genetics battle. After the war, the rise of chauvinism in Russia strengthened Lysenko's cause greatly. The widespread belittling of
foreign innovators suited his campaign perfectly, and Lysenko soon made it clear that only by following the footsteps
of the Russian Michurin could one be a true Soviet scientist.

1948

On July 31, 1948, Academician T. D. Lysenko opened the
meetings of the V. I. Lenin Academy of Agricultural Science
with a long summary of "The Situation in Biological Science,"

as he saw it. To discuss Lysenko's beliefs as if they were scientific questions would be to mistake the nature of science itself. It is a cardinal rule of scientific procedure that an assertion shall be backed up with detailed accounts of the experiments on which it is based—the materials used, the environmental conditions, the methods of observation, the observations themselves, the methods of analysis—to mention only the broad categories of a scientific report. Lysenko, in twenty years of controversy, presented no such reports, in spite of repeated requests from scientists both within his own country and outside. His statements are simply pronouncements, issued *ex cathedra*. They are not a part of science, and cannot be discussed as if they were. How can we analyze data that are not given? How can we repeat experiments that are never described?

This would be quibbling if Lysenko were to say only what everyone knows is true, but this is not the case. He asserts some most remarkable things, which there are sound reasons to doubt. Consider the following:

(1) Lysenko claims he can convert one species into another, quickly and suddenly, by environmental pressure. He can convert, he says, hard (spring) wheat into soft (winter) wheat. These two wheats are different *species,* as different as jack rabbits and cottontails. He says:

> When experiments were started to convert hard wheat into winter wheat it was found that after two, three, or four years of autumn planting (required to turn a spring into a winter crop) *durum* becomes *vulgare,* that is to say, one species becomes converted into another. *Durum* wheat with 28 chromosomes is converted into several varieties of soft 42-chromosome wheat, nor do we, in this case, find any transitional forms. . . . The conversion of one species into another takes place by a leap.

To such a claim one can only reply that nothing like this has ever been observed by Western scientists in any experiment that was properly controlled, though the opportunity to make such an observation has been more than ample. Where proper controls have *not* been maintained, the observation has several times been reported. Robert Chambers, the author of *Vestiges,* claimed that oats could be thus changed into rye. The explanation of all such magical species transformations is quite simple, and completely Darwinian: natural selection operating on mixed seed.

(2) Lysenko claims he can hybridize plants by vegetative grafts. This is contrary to thousands upon thousands of experiences in the rest of the world. From his reports, which

are inadequate as usual, it is apparent that he did not establish proper controls, or use genetically pure strains, or guard sufficiently against contaminating pollen. Some of his results might be explainable by periclinal chimera formation or by virus infection. These are highly technical matters that we need not go into here; it is enough to note that Lysenko has simply baldly asserted that there are no such things as chimeras, and that virus is a concept that is not acceptable to Soviet biologists.

Lysenko rejects the theory of probability and the use of statistics in scientific studies. Quantum physics, life insurance, testing of grain samples, evaluation of manufacturing procedures, prediction of weather, design of artillery fire patterns, design of telephone circuits, and the testing of hypotheses everywhere—all these depend on probability and statistical theory, explicit or implicit. "We biologists do not want to submit to blind chance. . . . We maintain that biological regularities do not resemble mathematical laws," says Lysenko. One can only view this defensive rejection of mathematics with pity, contrasting it with what the wealthy bourgeois, Charles Darwin, said much earlier: "I have deeply regretted that I did not . . . understand something of the great leading principles of mathematics, for men thus endowed seem to have an extra sense." Lysenko, the proletarian, is unable to muster such humility. He seeks to destroy what he cannot understand.

Such are the credentials of the man who appeared before the Lenin Academy to destroy Soviet genetics. His treatment of "The Situation in Biological Science" has been published in English on several occasions. It may be found in Zirkle's book *Death of a Science in Russia,* from which excellent collection of original documents and critical analyses much of what is included here has been taken. In summary it may simply be said that Lysenko's presentation shows less understanding of the nature of genetic evidence than an American college student has after the first month of a genetics course, although the Russian sibyl had had twenty years to prepare himself. It is not just genetics that he fails to understand: it is all science. He cites with approval a statement of Michurin that his conclusion—Michurin's, that is, but Lysenko's also by imputation—constitutes "a principle which we bequeath to the naturalists of future centuries and millenniums." Shade of Hitler's Reich of a Thousand Years! Nothing like it is known in real science. One searches in vain in the literature of Western science for statements of this degree of modesty.

The concluding sentences of Lysenko's address are most significant:

> V. I. Lenin and I. V. Stalin discovered I. V. Michurin and made his doctrine the property of the Soviet people. By their great fatherly attention to his work they preserved the wonderful Michurin doctrine for biology. The Party and Government and I. V. Stalin personally are constantly looking after the further development of the Michurinist doctrine. For us Soviet biologists there is not a more honorable task than the creative development of Michurin's doctrine and the introduction of the Michurinist method of investigation of the nature of development of living things into all our activity.
>
> Our Academy must foster the development of Michurinist doctrine as taught by the personal example of solicitous interest in I. V. Michurin's activity on the part of our great teachers V. I. Lenin and I. V. Stalin. (*Tremendous applause*)

In retrospect the threat of this peroration seems plain enough, but it is a most remarkable fact that no less than seven speakers rose to the defense of "Mendelist-Morganist" biology in the subsequent sessions. True, their defenses were hedged in by protestations of political orthodoxy and careful disclaimers of heresy, but defenses they were, nonetheless. It is not for us who live in a many-times-freer world to question the courage of these men. They were genuinely courageous. And they all paid the price.

How foolhardy they had been became immediately apparent when, at the end of the week, T. D. Lysenko arose to address the meetings again. He began:

> Comrades! Before proceeding to the concluding remarks, I consider it my duty to declare the following.
>
> I have been asked in one of the memoranda as to the attitude of the Central Committee concerning my paper. I answer: the Central Committee of the Party has examined my report and approved it.

The ovation that followed was described thus in *Pravda* the next day: "This communication by the President aroused general enthusiasm in the members of the session. As if moved by a single impulse, all those present arose from their seats and started a stormy, prolonged ovation in honor of the Central Committee of the Lenin-Stalin Party, in honor of the wise leader and teacher of the Soviet people, the greatest scientist of our era, Comrade Stalin."

Immediately after the session several of the erring scientists drafted letters of recantation. George Zhdanov wrote to Stalin saying, "I consider it my duty to assure you, Comrade Stalin, and through your person the Central Committee of the Communist Party of the Soviet Union, that I have been and remain an ardent Michurinist. My mistakes [were] due to inexperience and immaturity. I will correct my mistakes with deeds."

P. M. Zhukovski, speaking to the Lenin Academy, said, "Let the past which separated us from T. D. Lysenko (true, not always) pass into oblivion. Believe me, that today I make a Party step and appear as a true member of the Party, *i.e.*, honorably" *(applause)*.

From S. I. Alikhanyan: "It is important for us to understand that we must be on the same side of the scientific barricades as out Party and our Soviet science."

Finally, Professor A. R. Zhebrak said, "Since it is the sacred duty of the scientists of our Country to keep in step with the entire nation, . . . to fight the vestiges of capitalism, to aid the communistic education of the workers and to advance science continuously forward, then I, as a member of the Party and a scientist of the people, do not want to be considered a renegade. . . . I want to work within the framework . . . propounded by . . . Michurin."

An editorial in *Pravda* put the matter even more succinctly. How, asked the writer, had the scientists come to fall into the ways of error? The answer was simple: it was because they "forgot the most important principle in any science—the Party principle." Patently, the basic issue was not one of science (as we understand the term) but of partisan politics. Once this truth was spelled out in the U.S.S.R., science laboratories were rapidly purged of dissident thinkers, even, of course, of the majority of those who had recanted after Lysenko's revealing speech.

In a society of other-directed men, failing to get the togetherness signals until the eleventh hour is apt to be fatal.

Lamarckism—The Evidence

Politics, not science, was the arena in which Lysenko operated. But he borrowed from the language of science, thus leading fellow travelers outside Russia into thinking a scientific question was at issue.

Lysenko's principal thesis is simple Lamarckism—the "inheritance of acquired characteristics," as it is usually summarized. A passage from Lamarck's *Philosophie Zoologique* (1809) will serve to illustrate the idea:

The bird of the water-side that does not like to swim and yet needs to go to the water's edge to secure its prey is continually liable to sink in the mud. Now this bird tries to act in such a way that its body should not be immersed in the liquid, and hence makes its best efforts to stretch and lengthen its legs. The long-established habit acquired by this bird and all its race of continually stretching and lengthening its legs, results in the individuals of this race becoming raised as though on stilts, and gradually obtaining long, bare legs, denuded of feathers up to the thighs and often higher still.

The structural modifications the individual acquires in his lifetime, says Lamarck, are preserved in reproduction, to be further modified the next generation, this modification in turn to be passed on to the offspring. Thus, generation by generation, heredity is warped by the environment in a useful way. It may be, as Charles Darwin suspected, that Lamarck got this idea from the French translation of Erasmus Darwin's works, but this is not the only possible explanation. The idea that individual modifications may be inherited is actually many centuries old; Lamarck may merely have lifted it from folklore and used it to explain biological adaptation.

Are "acquired characteristics inherited"? The phrase in quotation marks is not unambiguous, and Western apologists for Lysenko made strenuous efforts to exploit the ambiguity. The English physicist, J. D. Bernal, said that Western genetics asserted the "dominance of unalterable inheritance." Bernal speaks rubbish. Mendelian genetics, from the time of its rebirth in 1900, has recognized that heredity is, from time to time, altered by mutations; and Muller, in 1927, proved that the environment can produce mutations. His proof was limited to the mutagenic effects of X rays. Since then, more sensitive tests have shown that mutations can also be produced by salts of heavy metals, by odd organic chemicals like mustard gas, by ultra-violet rays (in those organisms where the germ cells are near enough to the surface to receive them, which man's germ cells are *not*), and even by sudden changes in temperature in some cold-blooded forms. Acquired characteristics *are* inherited—*but not in the Lamarckian sense.* In modern terminology, the Lamarckian concept asserts that a change in the environment necessarily produces a mutation that is better adapted to the new environmental factor. This is not true. The mutations that are produced by X rays, mustard gas, lead salts or temperature shocks bear no useful relation to the environmental agent. Mutation is a random process, random in relation to environmental demands and the organism's needs. Mutation is not directed by need. Natural selection, operating on a vast supply of mutations, most of which are bad, is the directing agent. Literally thousands of experiments give the lie to Lamarck.

Even before the mutation process was understood, the

inheritance of acquired characteristics had been written off as an improbability. Microscopic anatomical studies during the latter half of the nineteenth century showed that the segregation of germ cells from the other cells of the body ("soma") takes place during the embryonic phases. Thereafter, the only "communication" between germ plasm and soma is by means of dissolved chemicals. In material terms, the Lamarckian idea would assert that the enlarged biceps of a professional weight-lifter would produce some sort of chemical that would travel in the blood stream of the sperm-producing cells in his testes, where the chemical would cause a particular mutation at a particular point of a particular chromosome that would result in his son's having larger muscles to begin with. Put so specifically, Lamarckism borders on the incredible.

However, the incredible is sometimes true. We want a direct experimental test. One of the neatest of such tests is that reported by W. E. Castle and J. C. Phillips in 1909. These men took a female albino guinea pig, removed her ovaries, and replaced them by the ovaries of a black female. Subsequently, this animal was mated to an albino male. *The offspring were black.* In other words, the ovaries, though completely surrounded by the tissues of an albino host, were behaving true to their own genotype, uninfluenced by any hypothetical Lamarckian substance the host tissues might be producing. (In passing it should be remarked that it was surprising—and fortunate—that Castle's and Phillips's experiment worked. Tissues transplanted from one animal to another usually do not "take hold," unless the animals are identical twins. However, some glands, including the ovaries, seem to be less subject to immunological rejection; and Castle and Phillips were using highly inbred strains, so their animals were close to being identical twins.) Similar experiments have been carried out by other geneticists, using various animals and various combinations of genes, always with the same results: the intimate environment of the host tissue does not directively alter the germ plasm of the implanted gonads.

Lamarckism has been most tenacious in the psychological field. Learning and instinct are great mysteries. Where there is so much that is not understood at all, it is only natural to be tolerant of outlandish ideas like Lamarckism. The great Russian physiologist, Ivan Pavlov, at one point in his work on conditioned reflexes, thought he had detected the hereditary transmission of learning, and so reported, orally, in 1923. Subsequently, more extended work convinced him that he had been in error, but his first report had started a snowball that would not stop. William McDougall, a psychologist, took up the cause and during the last fourteen years of his life produced an unparalleled set of ill-designed and tortuously analyzed experiments purporting to prove the inheritance of acquired learning. It was bad science, as T. M. Sonneborn (1931) has clearly shown. (It is of more than a little interest to note that it was as a collaborator in this work of McDougall's that J. B. Rhine, the celebrated exponent of extra-sensory perception, was introduced to the methods of science.) Sonneborn's analysis was on a purely logical basis, however, and could not—in the eyes of practical scientists—be as convincing as an experimental checking of McDougall's work. But when almost everyone is convinced that there is nothing in Lamarckism, who will be so self-sacrificing as to devote several years of his life to carrying out experiments that will in all probability result only in "negative findings"? Such results seldom bring scientific immortality; and scientists, like all men, do not willingly give up the chance of glory. Fortunately, there were a few altruistic workers who did check McDougall's work experimentally, first F. A. E. Crew, and then W. E. Agar and O. W. Tiegs. The latter two began their work in 1932 and continued it without interruption for twenty-two years, producing an exhaustive set of beautifully designed experiments, meticulously carried out and faultlessly analyzed, all of which add up to one simple conclusion: *Lamarck was wrong.* Those who are interested in seeing the method of science at its finest can hardly do better than read Agar, Drummond and Tiegs's paper of 1948—the very year of Lysenko's political triumph.

The Siren Qualities of Lamarckism

Few things are more disturbing to the layman than continuing disputes in science. To the scientist, science is non-authoritative. To him who is not a scientist, science is inescapably but another authority. Authority is effective only when it speaks with but one voice. How can the layman feel wholly satisfied with the majority of scientific opinion that says *Lamarck is dead,* when from time to time, even after a century and a half, someone asserts his resurrection? Or, to change the image, surely "where there's so much smoke, must there not be some fire?"

Yes . . . perhaps so: but the fire is in the hearts of those who sing Lamarck's praise. The problem is not biological but psychological: why, in spite of the complete lack of repeatable experiments in its favor and in the face of a large mass of negative evidence, does Lamarckism remain so tempting a refuge from rationality? This is the only fruitful basis on which the doctrine can still be discussed. However impotent

Lamarckism may be in explaining biology, the examination of the history of the doctrine reveals much of the nature and aspirations of mankind during the past century,

It is a significant fact that few scientists took Lamarckism seriously until after the *Origin of Species,* which was published exactly fifty years after the *Philosophie Zoologique.* Then gradually the interest in Lamarck reawakened. In part, the interest was historical: how far back could the idea of evolution be traced, and who were the intellectual godfathers of Charles Darwin? Another part was less pretty: many praised Lamarck in the hope of denigrating Darwin to their own personal advantage. The most conspicuous of these during the nineteenth century were Samuel Butler and St. George Mivart. Both of these men were intensely proud and personally ambitious far beyond their small abilities. Darwinism was a burr under their saddles. Efforts aimed at personal aggrandizement often produce, it must be admitted, some good byproducts. Some of the criticisms put forward by Butler and Mivart were keen and fruitful. Their principal shortcoming was a complete lack of perspective of the whole of evolutionary theory. They—particularly Butler—started a rumor that Darwinism had been tried and found wanting, a rumor that has been passed down through the writings of Henry Adams, Henri Bergson and George Bernard Shaw to the Jacques Barzun of our day. The rumor has lived its life almost exclusively within the literary tradition, a stream of thought that has been, unfortunately, to a large extent cut off from the scientific world which should nourish it. To the biologist it seems not too far from the mark to say that even the most modern theory of evolution is only an extended footnote to the *Origin.* A scientist who denied Darwin would be guilty of a gaucherie comparable to that of a literary man who maintained that there is really little of literary worth in the writings of Shakespeare. True, Darwin is not the last word in science; but neither is Shakespeare the final insight into human nature. He who fails to honor either genius for his positive accomplishments inevitably attracts the speculative psychiatric eye to himself.

As we read the apologetic writings of Western Communists and fellow travelers at the time of the Lysenko affair, we become keenly aware of another source of opposition to Darwinism and genetics: a deep distrust of the social consequences of acknowledging the correctness of scientific views. Bernal, for example, has rejected Mendelian genetics because (in his view) "it leads directly to the reactionary justification of aristocracy in eugenics and ultimately to race theories, the oppression of colored races and the bestialities of the Nazis." This is, of course, an argument from consequences, a species of polemic cannon that has been leveled at evolutionary theory from the day of the Reverend Mr. Sedgwick's review of *Vestiges* down to the present. *We must not believe in evolution and genetics, for such belief will degrade us.* Some asserted that such belief would necessarily destroy all belief in gods and hence take away all reason for moral action, resulting in spiritual anarchy. Because of the consequences, they said, we must not even consider the evidence.

Yet, *a harmful truth is better than a useful lie,* as Thomas Mann has said. Why better? Surely we do not desire harm? No: but the history of science—indeed, the history of all creative thought—shows that time after time a new truth, which has at first appeared dangerous and ugly, has in the end proved to be both useful and beautiful. Some argue that we would have been better off had we never left the garden of Eden. Perhaps; but once we have discovered a new truth, our two options are to acknowledge the truth or to repress our knowledge of it. Psychology has shown clearly enough the evils of repression. We must acknowledge the truth and go ahead to explore its implications. To do so is an act of faith in science, faith in the future, faith in the essential goodness of truth. Bernal, competent physicist though he is, is in a real sense not a complete scientist. He lacks faith and courage to accept all truth.

One of the central truths of biology is that man is an animal. Not *only* an animal, of course, for no one would deny the genuine novelty that results from his ability to speak and deal with abstract concepts; but in most of his functions he is an animal and as such is subject to the basic laws of life. In the nineteenth century, men of religion repeatedly denied man's animal nature, for fear of the consequences. It is of more than passing interest to see Communists taking the same position in the twentieth century. After news of the Lysenko trials reached this country, H. J. Muller publicly resigned his corresponding Membership in the Academy of Sciences of the U.S.S.R. The Academy responded with a diatribe in which this significant passage occurred: "The development of society is subject not to biological laws but to higher social laws. Attempts to spread to humanity the laws of the animal kingdom are an attempt to lower the human being to the level of beasts." Thus did Communism, the historical opponent of religion, once again show that it, too, as Bertrand Russell realized as early as 1920, is really a religion. The scientist's faith in truth is not shared by the true Communist of our time.

The corrosive effect of suppressing acknowledgment of the

truth is clearly shown by the tragic case of Paul Kammerer, the first Communist scientist to insist on the inheritance of acquired characteristics. He was a Lamarckian for noble reasons, of course. "If acquired characteristics cannot be passed on," said this Viennese zoologist, "then no true organic progress is possible. Man lives and suffers in vain. Whatever he might have acquired in the course of a lifetime dies with him. His children and his children's children must ever and again start from the bottom." This is a cry from the heart, and we are not surprised when such a man claims to have performed numerous experiments leading to Lamarckian results. There were curious features about a number of these claims, but one in particular attracted attention. In a toad of a species that normally has light-colored thumbs, Kammerer claimed that he produced. by environmental means, inheritable black pads on the thumbs. The English geneticist, William Bateson, publicly questioned the evidence in 1919 and asked to see the specimen. Kammerer refused. An acrimonious dispute ensued, but the experimenter was adamant. Finally, in 1926, the American, G. K. Noble, succeeded in examining the preserved specimen in the presence of Hans Przibam, the director of Kammerer's institute, and found that the dark color of the thumbs was caused by artificially injected ink. Upon the publication of Noble and Przibam's denunciation, Kammerer wrote to the Moscow Academy of Sciences saying, "I am . . . not in a position to endure this wrecking of my life's work, and I hope that I shall gather together enough courage and strength to put an end to my wrecked life . . ." and killed himself. He had embroidered upon the truth. But his intentions were surely noble.

The Real Enemy: Competition

Through the anti-genetic literature of the Communists, as through much of Soviet literature, there runs a thread that is only dimly visible but of prime importance to Communist ideology: fear and hatred of competition. Occasionally it is explicit, as when Lysenko said, "after a deep and comprehensive investigation I have come to the conclusion that there exists no intra-specific struggle but [only] mutual assistance among individuals within a species." The belief that it is possible to escape competition has its roots in orthodox utopian literature. However much the various utopias may differ, almost without exception they sketch a world in which competition is at an end: food is available for the taking, clothes are disbursed from a common wardrobe, no one competes in buying or selling—or in politics, for either all rule all or (probably more significantly) there is an all-powerful, perpetual dictator. A yearning for an end to competition has been a most significant part of the personality of the utopia-makers. The matter deserves more psychological attention than it has yet received.

Can competition be eliminated? A biologist has something to say about this. Competition can be put into a broader framework, that of the struggle for existence, using this phrase, as Darwin did, "in a large and metaphorical sense," to include both the literal struggles of individuals with one another, and the figurative struggles of individuals to extract a living from the physical environment. *It is certain that the struggle for existence cannot be escaped.* In times of exceptional prosperity, there may be an apparent suspension of the struggle for a while, but this is only a temporary matter. Organisms, if they are to exist continuously in a world of variable risk, must necessarily "tend" to increase geometrically, as Malthus put it. (In mathematical language, the reproductive potential is an exponential function with an exponent necessarily greater than unity.) But the environment is finite. From this, the struggle for existence necessarily follows.

The struggle for existence may take various forms. Under very rigorous conditions, the struggle may be almost entirely against the elements. The twisted cedar near timber line competes perhaps not at all with other living things: its only problem is to withstand the buffeting of the elements, maintaining a tenuous roothold in the rocks and spreading out its photosynthetic surface to catch as much of the sun's energy as it can without being blown from its moorings. Its struggle for existence is with the non-organic world. At the other extreme are the inhabitants of a tropical rain forest, where (for example) 99 seedlings out of 100 may be crowded out of existence by competition among themselves.

It is often useful to subdivide the concept of competition into two sorts: interspecific and intraspecific. Interspecific competition is competition between different species and includes such activities as predation, parasitism and competing for the same food; it is competition in a large, loose sense. Intraspecific competition is competition in a narrower, stricter sense: it is the struggle of individuals of the same species for the same sort of food or *Lebensraum*.

It is a basic axiom of biology that the *struggle for existence cannot be escaped:* it can only be altered in the form it takes. Under severe climatic conditions Arctic lemmings may be "struggling" largely with the severe weather for their existence; under somewhat better conditions, their numbers may be kept in check by Arctic foxes and snowy owls—an example of interspecific competition. Under still better conditions it is the rivalry of lemming with lemming for food that is decisive: intraspecific competition. The example illustrates the general rule that as a species becomes increasingly "successful," its struggle for existence ceases to be one of struggle with the physical environment or with other species and comes to be almost exclusively competition with its own kind. *We call that species most successful that has made its own kind its worst enemy*. Man enjoys this kind of success. Intraspecific competition may be as crude as cannibalism or infanticide, as "romantic" as chivalrous jousting or dueling, or as subtle as Stephen Potter's "one-upmanship," but it all has the same end in view: the securing of advantage to one's self at the expense of one's neighbor in a world that is not, and cannot be, large enough for the continuously "successful" species. No activity of man is without competitive uses. Even tact is a competitive weapon. From a humane point of view, we may prefer one weapon to another, but let us not deceive ourselves as to their ultimate effect. We are at one with the rest of the living world: either we must struggle with other living species, or we must compete with ourselves. Having subdued the rest of the living world—even, for the most part, the disease organisms that lay low so many proud kings of the forest—we have no choice but to compete with ourselves. This is the specter that haunts Communism. This is the specter that haunts most of what has been called "liberalism" in the past century and a half. This is the demon that cannot be exorcised by verbal incantations of "brotherly love," "co-operation," "togetherness," or—that marvelous invention of Marxian apologists—"socialistic competition." (The phrase is never defined, of course, but is shrilly insisted to be quite unlike the evil competition of the Darwinian or capitalistic worlds.)

The biologist who looks at social affairs cannot but reach the conviction that here, too, the principle of the inevitability of competition is observed. Consider, for instance, one of the most conspicuous of men's attempts to do away with competition, the labor-union movement. Few can read the tribulations of laborers in the early nineteenth century without being moved by pity for these wretched pawns of insensitive industrialists. Labor was but a commodity to be dealt with in a strictly economic fashion, "economic" being interpreted in the narrowest way. It is doubtful if the most intelligent "planner" could have devised a kinder solution to the wretched problem than the labor-union movement that actually developed, pockmarked though its history was with lawlessness, violence and bloodshed. The aim of the movement was to put an end to the competition of laborer with laborer in the labor market, to see to it that a mere surplus of labor did not drive wages down to a subsistence level through the unregulated operation of the Ricardian scheme. The labor-union movement was ultimately successful: but did it put an end to competition? Not at all! It merely changed the locus of the competition, and the pay-off. Now laborers compete with all non-organized groups—office workers, farmers, scientists, clergymen and artists—for shares in the general wealth, to the disadvantage of the non-unionized groups. And if all men were unionized, would this put an end to competition? Certainly not: the competition would take some other form, perhaps for offices of power and wealth within the union to which everyone belonged. It might be polite and lawful competition, or it might be vicious and corrupt, but competition it would be.

No activity of man is without its competitive aspect. Even the activities involved in what Matthew Arnold has taught us to call "culture"—painting, sculpture, music and writing—have their competitive uses. Each youth as he matures casts about for an occupation, trying—overtly, or at a hidden mental level—one after another until he finds his vocation. How does he recognize a "calling"? In part, perhaps, by esthetic means, or by logical analysis; but probably only in small part. To a far larger extent than most young men probably realize, one's occupation is chosen on the basis of a subconscious estimate of one's competitive position in the field. After choosing an occupation, one rationalizes its importance to the whole body politic so as to magnify one's self in the larger competitive scheme. Perhaps it is psychologically essential that he who is choosing a calling not know his own motives. The greatest rewards are reserved for those who feel a force larger than themselves, outside themselves. If they knew to begin with that the "call" came really from within, they might never paint pictures, build bridges, study protozoa or write books. This is the surmise that psychiatry has planted in the mind of "rational" man. (There may be some kinds of truth that cannot be faced at first without a disintegration of the self. If this is so, "truth" then takes on new meanings undreamt of in "objective" science. It is for the future to unravel the implications of the psychiatric surmise.)

"The pen is mightier than the sword"—this statement was surely made by a man who was clumsy with the sword but clever with the pen, a man who wished to gain with the cultural weapon the competitive advantage that he could not possibly achieve with the more primitive one. He wished to change the rules of the game—in his favor. In a restricted but real sense even "culture" is only an extension of the means of competition. (Though saying so is not to damn it.)

We can never eliminate competition. We can only change the rules of the game, and the pay-off. Competition is to be found in the subdued and pious Quaker meeting just as surely as it is on the bloodiest of battlefields. The devices of love may be found in its arsenal side by side with weapons of steel. Our problem is not to avoid the unavoidable—competition—but to choose our weapons. In seeking the means that are most commensurate with human comfort, pleasure and dignity we cannot necessarily trust first impressions or traditional moral standards. We will need the deepest insights of psychology and anthropology to enable us to choose well.

Ideas: Infection and Recovery

There is yet one more aspect of the Russian experiment that a biologist would like to point out. We can regard erroneous ideas as infections with which a people may be seized and from which they may recover. There are certain principles connected with bacterial infections that seem to have a parellel in the ideological field.

Ideally, a disease infection leads to a critical illness, during which the defense mechanisms of the body are mustered; a phase during which these mechanisms gain the ascendency over the invaders (if we're lucky); followed by a nearly complete immunity to the disease. This is the ideal situation. Sometimes, in some people, the course of events is different. The disease organism may never cause a sharply defined, critical disease state, and the host may never muster vigorous defence measures. Instead, a condition of uneasy and unstable truce may exist between parasite and host for months or years, to the great discomfort and harm of the host. There is reason to think that rheumatic fever is this sort of disease condition.

The ideological disease of denying competition has, in its most virulent form, produced Communism with its dream of the classless society. In its most virulent form, it has produced the fever of Soviet Russia. But is that country now the site of the most serious infection with this ideological error? Suppose, to use the device invented by Ernest Renan, we imagine the "Man from Mars" being given this assignment: to ascertain which state is at the present time most truly communistic in spirit, the judgment being based solely on national actions, in complete disregard of official statements and learned apologetics. Given such an assignment, would the Man from Mars point his finger at the officially communistic state of the U.S.S.R.? It seems at least doubtful.

To suffer critically from an ideological disease may be the best way to acquire a permanent immunity to it. Certainly on the personal level, H. J. Muller recovered far sooner than did J. B. S. Haldane, whose cleverly evasive statements make us suspect that he is still the victim of a sort of intellectual rheumatic fever. A similar parallel may hold for certain nations. The disease organism called Lysenko, only a short while ago so powerful in the Soviet, has now been completely deprived of power in Russia. To a biologist it seems at least possible that other ideological pathogens may lead to similar sharp recovery processes in the country in which they are most strongly infective. This is the threat to any nation in which an ideological infection is seemingly more benign: the benign infection may be more prolonged and more insidious.

[It is most difficult to write a book about Russia that is wholly up to date; the book-making process is too slow. Before this account was set in type, reports of Lysenko's resurrection came out of the east, reports not clear but definite. Before publication date there may be another reversal. The reader will have to alter the story himself, to bring it up to date. Remissions and exacerbations (to use a medical phrase) make it difficult to determine the end of an undulant ideological fever.]

12

New Dimensions of Evolution

Behold a universe so immense that I am lost in it: I no longer know where I am. I am just nothing at all. Our World is terrifying in its insignificance!

—BERNARD DE FONTENELLE

CERTAIN types of error are so alluring that we can confidently expect them to be put forward in new dress at least once every generation. Lamarckism is such an error. We suspect the motivations of Lamarckians, and with good cause, heaven knows. Yet we would be less than honest if we left the impression that Lamarckism has no nobler source than ambition, jealousy, envy or stupidity. It has an intellectual source also. Symbolically stated, it is *that damned eye*—the human eye whose excellence Paley thought a refutation of atheism, and which Darwin freely conceded to constitute a severe strain on his theory of evolution. Is so simple a principle as natural selection equal to explaining so complex a structure as the image-perceiving eye? Can the step-by-step process of Darwinian evolution carry adaptation so far?

Competent opinion has wavered on this point. With no more than the historian's usual violence to the facts we may say (following Ledyard Stebbins) that Darwinism has passed through three periods: the Romantic Period (from 1860 to about 1900), the Agnostic Period (1900–1930), and the Period of the Modern Synthesis (1930 to the present). The first was the period during which Darwin's theory was so successful in drawing together the multitudinous facts of biology that it was in danger of becoming a panchreston—an explain-all. Naturalists, surveying the variety of plant and animal structures, performed prodigies of explaining them as evolutionary adaptations. There was, for example, an artist named Thayer, who, while doing some excellent pioneer work in pointing out the protective value of coloration, went so far as to maintain that flamboyant flamingos chastely blended into their surroundings—which he proved by painting these spectacularly colored birds against an equally spectacular sunset. (Where the birds stood during the remaining twelve hours of daylight the artist failed to indicate.) Coloration is generally adaptive; but, as Mark Twain said, "the truth can be exaggerated." Exaggerations like Thayer's finally turned many biologists against the Darwinian scheme. The reaction was particularly strong around 1900. Among the young skeptics of that time was an embryologist named T. H. Morgan, who published a very critical view of Darwinism under the title *Evolution and Adaptation*. This was 1903, and genetics was just having its second birth, an accouchement which Morgan presently assisted. The laboratory he headed, first at Columbia University and later at California Institute of Technology, became the most famous genetics laboratory in the world. Out of it came the majority of the most competent geneticists of our time. And out of a lifetime of study of genetics came, for the once-doubting biologist, a conviction that, with the new insights afforded by genetic knowledge, Darwinism was on a firmer foundation than ever. Morgan, the skeptic of 1903, had become a believer by 1925, when he published his *Evolution and Genetics*.

Orthogenesis and Other Monsters

During the years of doubt in evolution, most skeptical biologists became (like Morgan) simple agnostics. But biologists, like all groups of humans, include among their members some of that tribe of men whom Eric Hoffer has called the "true believers," the men who must believe one positive dogma or another, men for whom agnosticism is impossible. Some of these, in their attempts to "explain" evolution, created transparently primitive gods, like Henri Bergson's "élan vital," a non-material something that shoved the evolutionary cart along in a rut, ever onward and upward. Julian Huxley pithily pilloried this modern attempt at theogenesis: why not, he asked, explain the movement of a locomotive by postulating an "élan locomotif"? Gods, even when spelled *é-l-a-n*, are not part of scientific explanation. Biologists have largely ignored the creations of Bergson and his ilk.

More tempting to scientists was another word whose transcendental nature was better disguised: *orthogenesis*. This is one of those troublesome words that appear to enjoy a built-in ambiguity: it is alternately a mere descriptive term, and a metaphysical explanation. As a descriptive term, it refers to the supposed "straight-line evolution" in some groups. For example, there was a time when the existing fossils of the horses seemed to indicate a straight-line evolution from small to large, from dog-like to horse-like, from animals with simple grinding teeth to animals with the complicated cusps of the modern horse. It looked straight-line—like the links of a chain. But not for long. As more fossils were uncovered, the chain splayed out into the usual phylogenetic net, and it was all too apparent that evolution had not been in a straight line at all, but that (to consider size only) horses had now grown taller, now shorter, with the passage of time. Unfortunately, before the picture was completely clear, an exhibit of horses as an example of orthogenesis had been set up at the American Museum of Natural History, photographed, and much reproduced in elementary textbooks (where it is still being reprinted today). The frequency with which the complex facts of equine evolution have been ignored in favor of merely reprinting this celebrated chart has led one paleontologist to complain that "there is a tendency to put the chart before the horse." In general, it is clear that orthogenetic lines appear only when the data are fragmentary or when a biased sample is presented. As G. G. Simpson (1950) has remarked: "The extreme view that evolution is basically or over all an orthogenetic process is evidence that some scientists' minds tend to move in straight lines, not that evolution does."

The other aspect of orthogenesis—the word in its metaphysical connotations—can be quickly dismissed. It seems inevitable that anyone who habitually uses the word as a descriptive term should sooner or later come to regard it as a name for some underlying power that drives evolution in a way that is predetermined in some sense—in the mind of God, or of "Nature," perhaps. Such a power is, of course, just another *élan*, and needs no separate discussion.

There is yet one more unsuccessful alternate to Darwinism that deserves mention, an explanation that goes by the colorful name of the "hopeful monster hypothesis," a name actually proposed by its author, Richard Goldschmidt. This important geneticist believed, for reasons that are not at all clear to his colleagues, that: "Sub-species are actually neither incipient species nor models for the origin of species. They are more or less diversified blind alleys within the species. The decisive step in evolution, the first step toward macroevolution, the step from one species to another, requires another evolutionary method than that of sheer accumulation of micromutations." This other method is one by which a markedly different individual is produced at a single step—a "monster." Admittedly, most such monsters will be inviable, but now and then such a rare monster may find a new environment into which it fits well, as when a hereditarily achondroplastic dog like a dachshund finds itself admirably adapted to enter the burrow of a badger (*Dachs*). Thus new species—and perhaps even new genera—are created at a blow by "macromutations," according to Goldschmidt.

A thorough discussion of Goldschmidt's theory involves many technicalities and moot points. Suffice it to say that it is at present viewed askance by most geneticists for very general reasons: it is too easy an escape from the real difficulties of Darwinism. A poker player has a poor opinion of the neophyte who proposes to get good hands by making deuces, treys and one-eyed jacks wild. So also a geneticist thinks it a poor sort of game that avoids the difficulties of explaining evolution in terms of known, small mutations and their selection, by the postulation of larger, poorly specified, and quite possibly nonexistent "macromutations." And it is more than a trifling objection that Goldschmidt's scheme would seem to require *two* (male and female) monsters of the same type at the same time at the same place—monsters that, even their author admits, must be exceedingly rare even singly. Goldschmidt seems to have overlooked sex.

Diploidy: Waste on the Installment Plan

As a matter of fact, sex carries within itself an answer to the detractors of Darwinism. The Competitive Exclusion Principle states that if two different species are in complete competition with each other, one will always eventually displace the other *completely,* for any competitive difference, no matter how small, will inevitably produce this result in a finite population by virtue of the compound-interest effect. This principle must also apply to the genic level within a species. One allele should always completely displace the other, since it is inconceivable that any two alleles will ever have *exactly* the same selective value. If this is so, then we face again the Darwinian problem of evolving a complex many-genic structure through the step-by-step evolution in which each step—each new gene—must by itself be of positive selective value even in advance of assuming its role in the final structure. If the eye requires 100 genes for its elaboration (it can hardly require less) and if half an eye is no better than no eye at all, how can the necessary genes be accumulated, one after another?

The question as worded is much too difficult for a direct attack. We can, however, now describe one of the processes that permits the accumulation of presently-useless-but-possibly-ultimately-useful genes; this process is intimately connected with the mechanism of sex.

With respect to chromosome number, cells are either haploid or diploid— *i.e.,* they contain either one member of each kind of chromosome, or two. The life cycle of a sexually reproducing species includes both sorts of cells. In what we call the "higher" plants and animals (which include ourselves) the haploid phase is of very short duration—only the eggs and spermatozoa are haploid. As soon as they unite to form the zygote the diploid number is restored again. All of the somatic cells of the child and adult are diploid. Natural selection operates on the diploid cells.

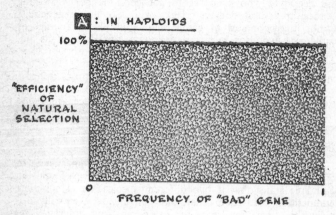

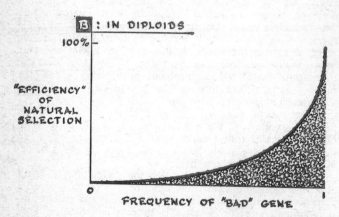

Fig. 16. Diploids are less efficient than haploids in eliminating "bad" genes. "Efficiency of Natural Selection" refers to the percent of individuals carrying the gene which show the gene and are thus subject to the force of natural selection.

It is not so in all organisms. There are many of the "lower" plants and animals—many algae, for example—in which the diploid phase is very transient, in which the zygote is the only diploid cell present in the life cycle, the first division of the zygote being a reduction division. In such an organism natural selection operates almost entirely on haploid cells.

Does it matter whether it is diploid or haploid cells that bear the brunt of natural selection? Indeed it does. A graphical comparison of the efficiency of selection in the two kinds of organisms should make the point clear. Let us define "efficiency" as the extent to which individuals carrying a defective gene are subjected to the selective process. In a haploid species, every individual that has the gene is exposed to the force of selection, and this is true no matter whether the gene is rare or common. The efficiency of selection in the haploid, we may say, is 100 percent (see Fig. 16). (We recognize that selection itself is a sort of chance affair—it does not necessarily eliminate a poor gene—but every haploid carrying a poor gene is subject to the same selective chance, regardless of the rarity of the gene.)

Now consider what a change is produced by a shift to diploidy. Remember, most "bad" genes are recessive; this means that they are apparent—and fully subject to the selective process—only when present in the individual in a homozygous condition. The Hardy-Weinberg Law states that if p is the frequency of the "good" gene, and q the frequency of the "bad" (where $p + q = 1$), then the frequency of the genotypes of diploids will tend toward the stable equilibrium,

$$p^2(AA) + 2pq(Aa) + q^2(aa).$$

This follows directly from probability principles. Our present concern is only with the last term, the q^2 fraction of the population that is homozygous for the recessive "bad" allele. As natural selection eliminates individuals homozygous for the gene, it decreases the value of q. As q becomes smaller, q_2 becomes *much* smaller (compare, for instance, $q = \frac{1}{2}, \frac{1}{4}, \frac{1}{10}$, with $q^2 = \frac{1}{4}, \frac{1}{16}, \frac{1}{100}$). Since natural selection can operate only on that fraction—q_2—that shows the gene, it follows that the "efficiency" of natural selection falls rapidly as the deleterious gene becomes rare (see Fig. 16B). "Bad" genes can, therefore, hide, so to speak, in a diploid species, whereas they cannot in a haploid. Or, to put it another way, the diploid state is less efficient in purifying itself of bad genes than is the haploid. This is true even when dominance is less than complete.

Now this is rather curious, for one of the few clear tendencies in biological evolution has been the increase in the

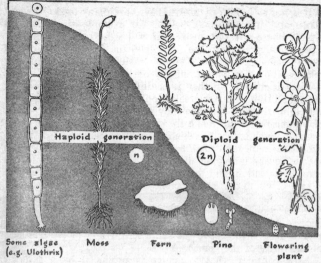

Fig. 17. Showing the general trend from a dominant haploid generation to a dominant diploid generation in the evolution of the plants. (From Hardin, *Biology: Its Human Implications,* 2nd ed., W. H. Freeman & Co., San Francisco; 1952. By permission.)

diploid portion of the life cycle at the expense of the haploid. This tendency is shown especially neatly by the plants (Fig. 17). In other words, in a sense, evolution has moved toward a state of *lesser* efficiency in eliminating waste—which is certainly not what we would have intuitively suspected. We cannot help being surprised.

The paradox can be explained. Imagine, if you will, two species that compete with each other. One species, during the significant part of its life cycle, is haploid, the other being diploid most of the time. Both are subject to the mutation process to the same degree, mutations of the same sort being produced. Since new mutations are usually bad, the mutation process causes a sort of loss or waste. We assume that in some sense, waste is competitively disadvantageous. We will suppose that, initially in both species, $q = 0$ for a given "bad" gene. Mutation now operates to increase the value of q in each species, the two mutation rates being the same. In the first generations, which species will suffer the greater losses? Obviously the haploid species. The other species possesses, as it were, a safety factor in having two doses of each type of gene (just as two kidneys and two lungs are safety factors). In the early generations, the diploid species will suffer less losses and will hence have a competitive advantage. However, ultimately, the diploid-shielded deleterious genes will increase in frequency until they occasion as much loss in the diploids as the corresponding genes do in the haploids—but this is ultimately, after many generations. Natural selection does not operate in terms of ultimates; it is the here and now that matter in selection. As Dobzhansky has aptly said, *Evolution is opportunistic.*

Opportunism has brought about the evolution of diploidy from haploidy; yet it is one of the marvels of this world that the opportunistically favored diploid condition has, through the strange workings of logical and mathematical principles, become the means whereby some of the apparent rigors of bare Darwinian selection have been escaped. For the better part of seventy years the strictures of Darwin's scheme seemed almost too severe to permit the development of the wonderful world of life that we know. Beginning in about 1930, the investigation of the mathematical consequences of diploid Mendelian heredity has shown us a wealth of mechanistic possibilities that we still have not exhausted. Our next task is to try to sketch in these new dimensions of evolution. The picture to be presented is largely the work of three artists: two English, R. A. Fisher and J. B. S. Haldane; and one American, Sewall Wright.

Statistics Versus Superlatives

The strength of colorful language is at the same time its weakness: it is ambiguous. What does the phrase, "the survival of the fittest" mean? From the way it is used it is apparent that it means different things to different people. To some, its meaning would seem to be adequately represented by the graph shown in *A* of Fig. 18, which implies that if one allele is superior to another then the superior allele should entirely replace the inferior in time. Yet the study of diploidy shows us that this is not true. As the gene frequency of the favored allele approaches closer and closer to 1, there is a larger and larger supply of genes available for mutation from favorable $\rightarrow$ unfavorable. Somewhere short of a gene frequency of 1, the mutation pressure exactly balances the selection pressure, and the gene frequency is at equilibrium, at a value of less than 1. That is, it is quite natural—indeed, it is the rule—that a diploid species always retains a small reservoir of even the most unfavorable genes (even such genes as that for hemophilia in humans). The correct way to indicate the result of natural selection operating in a

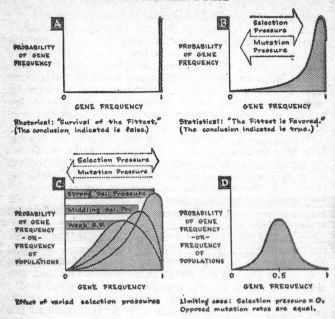

Fig. 18. For explanation, read in conjunction with text.

mutable species of diploid organisms is shown in Fig. 18. The peak ("mode") of this curve may be very close to 1, but it will never be at 1, so long as mutation continues (which is forever). Or, to put it more accurately, the most probable gene frequency of a population is some value less than 1; the probability of other frequencies falls off sharply on either side of this most probable value. "The fittest is favored" is a more accurate verbalization of the facts than is Herbert Spencer's "survival of the fittest," which somehow suggests that *only* the fittest survive. Even if man had no charitable impulses, each generation would include some individuals suffering from hereditary anemias, insanities, brachydactyly, hyperdactyly and hemophilia.

If selection is weaker, the mode of the curve will be farther from 1, and the "flatness" greater, as shown in *C* of Fig. 18. It is assumed that the mutation rate *favorable gene* → *unfavorable gene* is equal to the reverse rate, and that these rates are constant for all three cases of "strong," "weak" and "middling" selection. The limiting case, where selection =

0, is shown in *D* in Fig. 18: A Gaussian curve centered at gene frequency = 0.5.

In interpreting the last two curves an alternative meaning to the ordinate axis has been introduced. This new meaning will be particularly useful later, and so a word about it is in order here. Consider the following conceptual model: Think of a species as being broken up into many separate, isolated populations, each of which is large. (The reason for this last qualification will appear subsequently.) All the populations are identical with respect to their "other" genes, and each one includes both alleles of the gene we are interested in. Environmental conditions are identical. Suppose we allow a long time after "starting" these populations before observing them. What will be the gene frequency in the various populations? It will vary from population to population, but *the frequency of the populations* showing the various gene frequencies will be given by the curves already drawn in Fig. 18 *B–D*.

Chance Becomes Important

What is the dullest game in the world? The answer to this odd question is quite simple: *millionaires matching pennies.* Such a game would be unbearably boring to watch because it could not conceivably have an interesting outcome. Assuming honest pennies and no chicanery, the game would just go on and on, without significantly diminishing the wealth of either player. To be interesting, the stakes must be an appreciably great fraction of the total wealth of at least one of the participants; then one of the players may be ruined— and from this other interesting consequences may follow. Put the other way around: as the wealth of a player comprises a smaller and smaller number of stakes, the interest of the game heightens. The probability of ruin and novelty then increases. So it is also with evolution: small numbers—that is, small numbers in each breeding population—introduce significantly great probabilities that the unexpected (the "improbable") will happen, that variety will increase and novelty be generated.

The general effect of small numbers may be most easily seen by considering a specific, and rather contrived, example. For the moment we will ignore mutation. We will also (for simplicity) ignore sex and assume that we always have equal numbers of both sexes. Our model will consist of many separated breeding populations of exactly four individuals. Imagine, if you will, each group (rabbits, say?) living in a cave, on a tiny island that has food enough for only four animals of breeding age. Though many more young are born, only four in each generation survive to become breeders, replacing the generation just before, without interbreeding between generations. Let's assume that the rabbits are initially genetically identical, and that all are heterozygous (Aa) for albinism.

The *most probable* results are easy to predict, using the Hardy-Weinberg law:

Starting generation: 4 Aa

Second generation: 1 AA + 2 Aa + 1 aa

Each subsequent
    generation: 1 AA + 2 Aa + 1 aa

But wait! There's a serious error hidden here. Look again at the second generation. Admittedly, it will *most probably* be as given; but is there not also a chance that it may consist of, for example, 3 AA and 1 aa individuals? Or 1 Aa and 3 aa? or even 4AA or 4 aa? Yes, there certainly is the chance, and it is not negligible. In fact, paradoxical as it may sound, the probability that the most probable thing will happen is less than "50–50"—it is, in fact, only ⅜; the probability that some one (unspecified) less probable event will happen is ⅝. (No *particular* less probable event has a probability as great as ⅜, of course.)

Suppose the second generation happens to consist of 2 AA and 2 Aa individuals: what will the third generation most probably be? Assuming the sexes are equally distributed among the genotypes, we calculate the third generation from the formula:

$$(¾ A + ¼ a)^2$$

which gives us:

$$⁹⁄₁₆ AA + ⁶⁄₁₆ Aa + ¹⁄₁₆ aa$$

as the most probable distribution in a large population— which is not at all what we had predicted before. In fact, given the restriction to a surviving generation of *four* breeders, the "most probable" distribution cannot even be realized, but only an approximation to it.

From this example we see a remarkable thing about the Hardy-Weinberg law: what it predicts is not an equilibrium at all, in the sense of cybernetic equilibria. There is no self-correcting tendency in a Hardy-Weinberg distribution—no tendency for the third generation to correct the "error" of the second, for example. The third merely tends to be like the second, whatever it was, "error" and all; the fourth like the third, whatever it may have been; and so on. The Hardy-Weinberg law asserts the most conservative and shortsighted of inertial principles: "let's make the next one like the one before." As a result, the gene frequency "drifts" constantly.

With large numbers, the drift is insignificant: it's like our millionaires matching pennies. With small numbers, drift is significant, and many have irreversible consequences. Two men with only 4 pennies each *may* play forever—but it is not likely. Far more probable is it that, sooner or later, one man (either one) will have all the pennies, the other man being "ruined." At that point the game stops, and other consequences—part of the larger game of life—may ensue. So it is with the breeding situation. With a population restricted to only 4 breeders, it is "inevitable" (in a probable sense) that sooner or later all the genes will be either *A* or *a* (either one). When that has happened, the "game" is through: we say "gene fixation has occurred." The consequences from that point on are part of a larger game in which the population is being weighed in the scales of its environment.

The principle of gene fixation has been developed using a model with only 4 breeders: but the same principle applies also to populations of 8 or 10 or 50 breeders—though with each increase, the drifting effect is diminished, and gene fixation in a specified number of generations becomes less probable. The Hardy-Weinberg "equilibrium" obtains only with an infinite population. How "near" does a real population have to be in order to be—in the time scale of terrestrial evolution—in the Hardy-Weinberg condition? Sewall Wright, who is largely responsible for this phase of evolution theory, commonly gives 100 breeding pairs—200 individuals—as the practical upper bound of the region in which significant genetic drift ("the Sewall Wright effect") occurs.

When the Wright effect was first proposed, there was widespread doubt as to whether it was important in evolution. It postulates, and requires for its working, small populations: but do these occur in nature? Everyone knows that ants and aphids and oysters occur in the millions of millions; even elephants exist in the thousands. Do small-number theory have any application to such species? Stimulated by theory, naturalists took a second look at organisms in nature and discovered a number of situations that could lead to the Wright effect.

First. The environment may be discontinuous, thus segmenting the species into many small breeding populations that are rather well isolated from each other. A classic study is Gulick's of the snails of Hawaii. The structure of the island—a volcanic peak with radiating valleys separated by high ridges—makes for isolation of the snails in the many valleys, which is accompanied by an extreme variation in the (apparently) non-adaptive coloration of the many races. The observation fits in well with Wrightian theory.

Second. Limited mobility may introduce the small-numbers effect even into a large population living in a continuous environment. For example: field studies show that snails have "home territories" of very limited ranges. In such populations, the "friction" in the flow of genes throughout a continuous range may be great enough to produce the small-numbers effect. The Hawaiian snails studied by Gulick vary even within a valley. Even species that are as mobile as birds may be subject to isolation effects resulting from their habit of returning to the same nesting territory, year after year.

Third. Social organization may segment a species in the absence of environment barriers in the ordinary sense. Many species of apes and monkeys live and breed in small bands of only a very few dozen adults, with little exchange of genes between groups that are in howling distance of each other. Among men, the caste system of India is a similar segmenting factor.

Fourth. The small-numbers effect may be present periodically in a species that undergoes extreme fluctuations in numbers, seasonally, for example. In such cases, the *effective* number of the breeding population is much nearer the lower limit than the upper. Dobzhansky and his students, who have been very active in gathering and analyzing field data on *Drosophila* collected in southwestern United States, have found evidence that, quite commonly, the effective breeding population lies in a Wrightian range, because of the severe reduction in numbers every winter, and in spite of the almost astronomical numbers of flies during the summer.

It may be that changes in gene frequencies arise in a population whose numbers are fluctuating, for reasons somewhat different from that emphasized by Wright. The English workers, Fisher and Ford (1950), seem to think so, basing their argument in part on a fifty-year study of the butterfly *Melitaea,* published by Ford and Ford (1930). Good records show that this butterfly, which underwent considerable fluctuations in numbers during the period, did *not* show its greatest variation during the time when its numbers were smallest, but rather during the period when its numbers were increasing most rapidly. The phenomena can be explained in the following way: Relative constancy in the species is maintained by selection pressure. An explosive increase in numbers betokens a (temporary) diminution in selection pressure. This permits greater survival of genes that would ordinarily be kept at very low levels. The large number of the variants observed in explosively growing populations is difficult to reconcile with the Hardy-Weinberg Law. Their great number is probably accounted for by the fact that the great weakening in the strength of the principal over-all selective factors, ordinarily operative, permits much weaker, and probably very local, selective factors to be of significance, thus producing a great abundance of local variations, not so much in response to a small-numbers effect as in response to local variations in the "definition" of Darwinian fitness. This explanation may or may not be entirely correct, but the facts appear to be genuine. They remind one of a not-dissimilar flowering in the variety of human institutions, customs and arts under conditions of temporary prosperity. Perhaps one might call this effect the "prosperity relaxation effect." In biology, as in human culture, the occasional relaxation of the strictures of competition is conducive at least to variety, and very likely to progress.

Evolutionary Degradation

The relation between theory and observation is a reciprocal one, with each serving as the origin of the other; the question, *Which comes first?* is more difficult here than it is in the case of the chicken and the egg. (The egg came first, as every geneticist knows.) Wright's small-numbers theory led to the discovery of small populations in nature, but the theory itself was the outgrowth of mulling over observations made in the laboratory and in the breeding pens of animal husbandmen.

It has long been known that the fastest way to secure a "pure strain" is by closely inbreeding a stock, generation after generation. It has also long been known that the practical breeder who continuously inbreeds his stock for many generations courts ruin. Frequently, in spite of the fact that he is constantly selecting for the "best" characteristics available, his inbred stock becomes progressively worse. The strain may become so susceptible to disease, and so generally weakly, that it dies out altogether, unless he reverses his procedure and crosses his organisms with unrelated stock. Note the puzzle: according to the simple Darwinian cybernetic scheme it should be impossible for a strain to become progressively worse. It should be impossible for natural selection to act diabolically, so to speak. How, then, can one make sense of this tendency of inbreeding? As always, of course, the intellectual short cut of mysticism was taken by many, who spoke of the in-

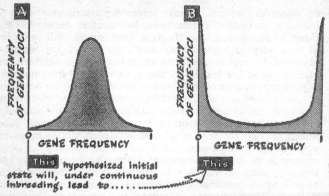

THE TWO SITUATIONS SHOWN ABOVE ARE ONLY PART OF A LARGER 3-DIMENSIONAL GRAPH THAT INCLUDES TIME AS ONE OF ITS DIMENSIONS

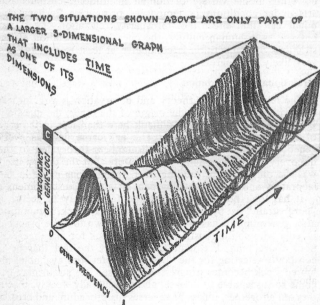

Fig. 19. How inbreeding reduces heterozygosity, with the passage of time.

herent "degenerative" or "enervating" tendencies of inbreeding. Opposed to this was, of course, the inherent "stimulating" effect of "new blood" brought in by outcrossing. All this was, of course, just a verbal smoke screen for ignorance.

In 1915, Sewall Wright, who had studied under W. E. Castle at Harvard, joined the U.S. Department in a program of breeding guinea pigs. The object was to obtain exceptionally pure strains of animals for experimental purposes (variability in test-animals is always a nuisance) and to study the consequences of inbreeding. It was in this study of a practical problem that Wright's important contributions to the theory of evolution originated. His accomplishments led to his being called to the University of Chicago in 1925, where he continued his investigations in an atmosphere more favorable to pure science.

The theory of inbreeding can be best illustrated by a graph in which we will give a new interpretation to the ordinate axis (valid also for the earlier graphs). The new interpretation is not inherently difficult, but it is a bit tricky, and needs to be approached circumspectly.

Suppose we begin with a stock that is heterozygous for many gene loci,

$$AaBbCcDdEeFf \ldots$$

and inbreed this stock as intensively as possible (brother-sister matings in mammals), saving only a small number of each generation for breeding the next. What will happen? With respect to any one gene locus, say A, there will always be a chance that *all* the individuals we save—even if we make no conscious selection—will be homozygous for the same allele at that locus (AA or aa). If the size of our breeding stock is such that this chance is $3/8$, then it will be true that of all the loci for which the parents were heterozygous, 3 out of 8 of these loci will be homozygous for a given allele among the offspring. (The actual fraction will, of course, vary inversely as the size of the breeding population.) We can, then, speak of the *frequency of gene loci* that possess a given gene frequency. This will be our new interpretation of the ordinate axis (Fig. 19). Beginning with a highly heterozygous stock in which the gene frequency for many alleles is about 0.5, as shown in A, inbreeding will result in a steady "migration" of gene loci toward one extreme of homozygosity or the other, until most of the gene loci are pure, as shown in B. That is, the heterozygous condition Aa will, in time, probably give way to either AA or aa; Bb will probably be replaced by BB or bb; Cc by cc . . . and so on. Soon very few of the gene loci will show any variety whatever in our inbred population. Instead of the initial type:

$$AaBbCcDdEeFf \ldots$$

we will now have (if we keep only one population), say

$$AABBccddeeFF \ldots$$

or perhaps

$$aaBBccDDeeff \ldots$$

or . . . and so on. We do not, in advance, know which particular type of homozygote we will have in a particular pen (population), but we know we will have a population that will, with a high degree of probability, be homozygous for most of its gene loci.

With only one breeding population, only one pure stock will be obtained. But if we start ten separate inbred strains from the same original heterozygous stock we will get ten pure stocks, and it is extremely unlikely that any two of them will be pure in the same way. Inbreeding, then, immensely increases the variability *between* strains while it decreases the variability *within* a strain. This will be true even if the breeder makes no conscious selection whatsoever. If

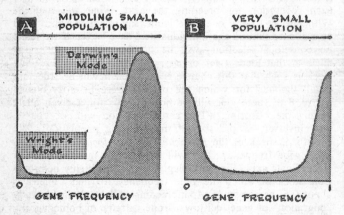

Fig. 20. Showing how size of population influences the relative importance of Darwin's mode and Wright's mode. (Ordinates to be interpreted in any of the ways given on previous graphs.)

he does select, the effects of inbreeding are magnified. By inbreeding and selection, there have been produced, for example, the great differences between breeds of dogs, combined with comparatively little variability within each strain.

Chance Versus Selection

Evolutionary degradation is possible because, with small numbers, the direction of change in gene frequency will sometimes be counter to that which natural selection tends to bring about. For a certain population size there may be *two* "most probable" gene frequencies (Fig. 20A)—one produced by Darwin's factor of natural selection plus a small addition contributed by Wrightian drift, and the other near the fixation point for the less favorable allele, produced entirely by the random drift associated with small numbers. We may refer to these two maxima as "Darwin's mode" and "Wright's mode." As the size of a breeding population increases, Darwin's mode increases and Wright's mode decreases to insignificance. But with very small populations the effect of Darwinian selection may be negligible, the two maxima (Fig. 20B) being both attributable almost exclusively to the Wright effect.

There is, then, in a small population always an appreciable probability that evolution may go counter to natural selection, that the population may naturally become less fit. This may be one of the factors operating in the terminal stages of the extinction of species. Several times man has brought wild species near extinction and then reversed his role and tried to preserve what he has so nearly destroyed. Sometimes the reversal has been effective, sometimes not. The American buffalo (bison), after being reduced to a few score of animals, now number in the thousands. The heath hen of New England, however, in spite of valiant efforts, finally perished, the last bird, a cock, being seen in the early 1930's. Its end was no doubt aided by a succession of unfavorable accidents (fire, storm, etc.) and the depredations of ever-present house cats, but it is not impossible that unadaptive genic drift may have done its bit, too.

Cousin Marriages

One of the commonest questions of the beginning student of genetics is: "Are cousin marriages bad?" To which the geneticist must give an equivocal answer: *They may be either good or bad.* Cousins have more genes in common than do two individuals chosen at random. Rare recessive genes have a better chance of appearing in the homozygous condition among the children of married cousins than they do among the children of unrelated parents. If the rare recessive gene that is thus brought to the homozygous condition is a desirable one, we say the effect of the marriage is good; if undesirable, then bad. No more general answer can be given to the individual who faces this personal problem.

From the point of view of the population as a whole, we can give a more general answer. Cousin marriage is a form of inbreeding, as are also brother-sister, half-brother-sister and parent-child matings. Inbreeding introduces the Wright effect; it tends to "purify" the stock—that is, make it more

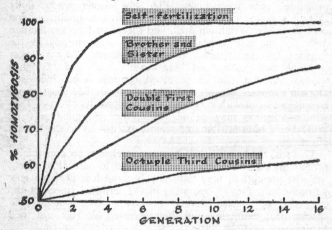

Fig. 21. The rate at which different degrees of inbreeding produce homozygosis (purity). (After S. Wright from Srb and Owen, *General Genetics,* W. H. Freeman & Co., San Francisco, 1952. By permission.)

homozygous—the rapidity of purification being proportional to the degree of inbreeding (*see* Fig. 21). Is inbreeding in the best interests of the community? The only certain effect will be to decrease the variety within the community. If inbreeding is combined with rigorous selection, the process might be defended on the ground that the community thus becomes what it wishes to be. (Can we assume that it wishes well?) If rigorous selection is not used, the community will certainly become relatively pure for some genes that are rather undesirable. In any case, variety within the community will be diminished. Is this good or bad? To arrive at an answer, we need to enlarge the scope of inquiry considerably. We need first to ask once more what we mean by "fittest"; and second, to lay bare the consequences of the immense number of genes available for evolution.

The Relativity of the "Fittest"

We have spoken repeatedly of the selective value of a gene allele, and always with the implicit assumption that the allele has a value *per se*, a value in a vacuum, so to speak. It is now time to abandon that position for a more realistic one.

As our example, let us take one that has immediate meaning to us, even though the genetic basis of it has not yet been elucidated. Let us consider skunks. These lovely animals are notable for two characteristics: their odor and their fearlessness. Suppose we were asked, "What is the selective value of their odor?" or—separately—"What is the selective value of their fearlessness?" How would we answer? Plainly we could not give a simple answer to either question, as framed. Fearlessness is an advantage if you can afford it, for you can use the twenty-four hours of the day more economically and need not restrict your foraging to inconvenient hours or secluded places, as a field mouse must. On the other hand, the ability to discharge odorous mercaptans into the air is a wonderful weapon—but it would be of only slight advantage to Burns's sleekit, cowrin, tim'rous beastie.

Sans peur et sans odeur would be a fine, poetic motto for the escutcheon of skunks—but only in heaven. And smelly skunks with retiring ways would certainly prosper much less than our present kind. (At least this was true in the days before the appearance of that great and non-discriminating enemy, the automobile: but we will ignore this new complication.)

Plainly, the selective value of a trait or a gene depends not only on the external environment (*the* environment, as we ordinarily think of it), but also the *internal* environment, on the other genes. Selective value, in a constant external environment, is a characteristic of an entire system of genes, not of any one gene considered separately. To represent this fact, let us assume, just for purpose of illustration, that the entire odor-mechanism of a skunk—structures, instincts and all—is due to a single gene; and similarly for the complex of psychological traits we call "fearlessness." (The principles we develop will be even more true if the genetic situation is more complex—which it undoubtedly is.) We will, then, represent the distribution of the two hypothetical gene frequencies along the two axes of a plane, and at the same time add another dimension to represent the selective worth ("W"). The result is a three-dimensional surface, as shown in Fig. 22. A population that has a high frequency (near 1,1) for both the odor and fearlessness genes has a high adaptive value, as has also one with a low frequency of both (near

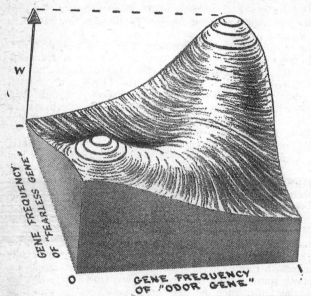

W

GENE FREQUENCY
OF "FEARLESS GENE"

0   GENE FREQUENCY
            OF "ODOR GENE"   1

Fig. 22. Showing that the "fitness" of a gene is a relative matter—
relative to the other genes present. See text for discussion.

0,0). Which of the two "adaptive peaks" is better, we do not
know, but we have arbitrarily pretended that (1,1) is better.
On the other hand, to be odorless and fearless (0,1) is bad,
and the adaptive value must be near zero. To be odoriferous
and fearful, though no peak condition, is probably not nearly
as bad (1,0).

With this model of Wright's in mind, we are ready to re-
state the principles of evolution in language that is metaphorical but accurate. First we must try to gain a faint appreciation
of the immense complexity of the situation—of the almost
unimaginable variety possible in the living world. With two
genes, as we have seen, the inclusion of the statistic W (selective worth) leads to a surface in three dimensions. To chart
the same information with three genes we would need four
dimensions; with four genes, five; in general, for n genes,
$n + 1$ dimensions. How many genes are there in an organism?
We have no exact estimate, but a great deal of evidence that
10,000 genes is unlikely to be an overestimate; it may be a
gross underestimate. To represent the selective worth of all
possible gene combinations in an organism of 10,000 genes

we would need, then, a surface in 10,001 dimensions. We can hardly claim to be able to visualize this in any direct sense. Yet we can claim to have some sort of a picture of it,

Fig. 23. The genetic landscape, as pictured by Wright. Each peak represents a favorable configuration of genes. Some peaks are higher (better adapted) than others. The number of dimensions, here shown as three, is actually of the order of 10,000.

in our mind's eye. It is something like Fig. 23 "only more so." In a realm of 10,001 dimensions there are an uncounted number of "adaptive peaks," gene combinations that are harmonious with their environment. Here and there a peak is "occupied" by a particular species, or by one race of a species. Many of the peaks are undoubtedly not now occupied, and perhaps never have been. One cannot but wonder how many of these there are, how *full* the world is, how completely it realizes its potentialities.

How many adaptive peaks are there? We cannot answer this, because to do so we would need to know *all* of genetics. We must ask another question. How many might there conceivably be, as an outside limit? To try to estimate this, let us assume that at every gene locus only two variations (alleles) are possible and that dominance is always complete. Then with two gene loci, say *A, a* and *B, b*, there would be these different stable combinations:

$$AABB \qquad aaBB$$
$$AAbb \qquad aabb$$

with three gene loci, we could have:

$$AABBCC \qquad AAbbCC \qquad aaBBCC \qquad aabbCC$$
$$AABBcc \qquad AAbbcc \qquad aaBBcc \qquad aabbcc$$

The pattern is clear:

No. of gene loci	No. of different isogenic stocks
2	4
3	8
4	16
•	•
•	•
•	•
n	2^n
10,000	$2^{10,000}$

With 10,000 genes there are $2^{10,000}$ different isogenic stocks possible. How large a number is this? We can see more easily if we first convert it to a power of ten. Since 2^{10} is slightly more than 10^3, we can say that 10^{3000} is an *underestimate* of the number of different isogenic stocks possible.

How big a number is 10^{3000}? Well, it is 1 followed by three thousand zeros. Written out thus: 1,000,000,000 . . . it would occupy almost two pages of a book like this. . . . But how *big* is it? We need something to compare it with. According to a commonly quoted figure from theoretical physics, the number of electrons in the *entire* universe is only about 10^{87}. Somehow this looks like a ridiculously small figure, but that's just because the exponential way of writing numbers has the psychological effect of minimizing them. When we try to compare

$$10^{87} \qquad \text{with} \qquad 10^{3000}$$

we gasp at the extreme disparity of the two. Even if every one of our electrons were a universe the size of ours with as many subelectron particles (10^{87}) in it as there are electrons in our universe, there would be only 10^{174} of these hypothetical subelectrons—a number still far removed from 10^{3000}.

The number 10^{3000} is, remember, not a number of things, but a number of combinations of things. It is the conceivable number of different combinations of genes in isogenic organisms that have 10,000 gene loci. Such a number still must be a great *under*estimate of the possible variety of the world, for we have neglected several variety-increasing factors, among which are:

1. Variation in the number of gene loci.
2. Existence of multiple alleles (more than two alleles at a locus, as in the A-B-O blood group system).
3. Variations in the external environment (we assumed only one) which will increase the W dimension from one to many.

It would be pointless to try to develop the theory further to take account of these real and important factors. To do so would only be to make an already inconceivably large number inconceivably larger. The number 10^{3000} is quite large enough, gross underestimate though it undoubtedly is of the conceivable variety of the living world. We will make do with it.

Unimaginably Immense Universes

It is clear, of course, that the great majority of the gene combinations possible are "bad"—for we have the evidence from our study of mutations. When we say that most new mutations are bad, we mean that they are bad in the particular combinations they turn up in. In some other combinations they might be good. For instance, a mutation producing deafness in a mouse is certainly bad; and a mutation producing audiogenic seizures is also bad. But the combination of the two would probably be better for the mouse than either one alone. Such a mouse, though deaf, would at least not be in danger of losing his life at the first clatter of a dishpan.

The great majority of the conceivable gene combinations are bad—but how great is this majority? Is one combination in a million good? Or one in a million million? We have neither experience nor theory to guide us here, but if we assumed even so small a fraction (as it seems to us) as one in a million million million million million (1 in 10^{30}) to be the fraction of all combinations that is good, this tells us that there would be *10^{2970} gene combinations that would represent adaptive peaks*—a number that is still immensely, inconceivably large.

The particular fraction assumed can hardly be defended; and yet we feel it is not unreasonably large. In the complete absence of adequate theory, we cannot help but feel in our bones that the conceivable number of species of organisms is immensely greater than the actual number, which is certainly not more than 10^7 (ten million). Even if we assume, say, 100 different races (genetic combinations) for every existing species, the number of working combinations of genes would rise only to 10^9—a number still far short of 10^{2970}.

For what it is worth, suppose we add geological time to our calculations. Suppose we assume that the number of contemporaneously existing species and races has been 10^9 at all times during the last 10^9 years (ignoring, for simplicity of arithmetic, the billion or so years before then, when life was also present, but undoubtedly with far fewer species and races). Suppose, further, that we assume that once every 10,0000 years (10^4) every existing harmonious combination is replaced by a new and novel one. How many adaptive peaks would have been used up in all of geological time, under these assumptions? Only 10^{14}. Still far, *far* from 10^{2970}.

Suppose we try to use really ridiculous figures and assume that *at the end of every second* during the last billion years the entire existing flora and fauna have been liquidated and replaced by a set of completely new species and races, never before in existence—would we then have exhausted nature's possibilities? Alas, no. In spite of this most valiant attempt to be extreme, we have scarcely nicked the surface of the possible. In a billion years there are only about 1.6×10^{16} seconds. Let's be generous and allow 6 billion years (our motive is less one of generosity, than it is one of laziness—the arithmetic is easier). Six billion years gives us 10^{17} seconds. If 10^9 different adaptive peaks are used up every second for 10^{17} seconds, only 10^{26} out of Nature's practically inexhaustible supply of 10^{2970} harmonious combinations would be used. . . .

It is with new wonder that we recall Voltaire's Dr. Pangloss saying, "This is the best of all possible worlds." To this travesty of Leibnitz's philosophy we can only answer, *Possibly* —but when so small a fraction of all the conceivable types of living beings can have been generated by the processes of evolution acting over all of geologic time, it is hard to believe that this world of ours could include—now or ever—the best of all conceivable organisms.

We harken back to the time when the first great popularizer of science, Bernard de Fontenelle (in the seventeenth cen-

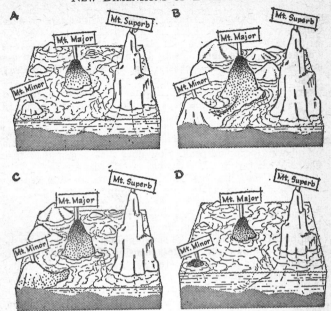

Fig. 24. How speciation may occur with a lessening of the selective pressure, here represented as a dangerous body of water.

tury), exhibited the wonders of the new universe of Copernicus and Newton as seen through the wondering eyes and voluble exclamations of a noble lady who, when she at last grasped the immensity of the known universe—which was, even so, much smaller then than it is now—exclaimed: "Voilà l'univers si grand que je m'y perds, je ne sais plus où je suis; je ne suis plus rien.—La terre est si effroyablement petite!" In our time, genetics has revealed a new world, a world of microscopic genes that, in their combinatorial variety, open up to our eyes a universe of possibilities that is truly astronomic in dimensions. *Here, we say, is a universe so immense in its inexhaustible variety that the imagination loses itself in the exploring of it. We do not know where we are with respect to its possibilities. What we know is scarcely more than nothing of what is to be known. It is almost terrifying to contemplate how insignificant a fraction of the universe's possibilities will ever be known to us.*

The Question of Progress Again

The chessboard on which the game of evolution is played,

then, is this: a genetic surface in at least ten thousand dimensions, having here and there an "adaptive peak" on which a species may find existence and refuge. Such peaks are rare—but they are more numerous by far than the electrons in the universe. And of all the peaks available, only a small minority —far fewer than one electron out of a universe of electrons— is ever occupied. There are less than ten million species at the present time, with perhaps a billion peaks now occupied by the various races. The path of evolution must be one in which one peak after another is occupied for a time by actual population of organisms, the immigration taking place from a neighboring occupied peak. How does such a migration take place? What favors it? And what are the dangers?

We can visualize the problem in terms of our genetic-topographic model again (Fig. 24). Suppose, to begin with, that of the adaptive peaks shown in A, only the one labeled Mount Major (following a suggestion of W. C. Allee) is occupied by a species. Mutations that are non-adaptive occur continually, but they are selected against, consequently the population shows the greatest density at the apex of the adaptive peak, the density (relative number of individuals) being progressively less as the genotype departs more and more from the most favored type. Extreme variation will be lethal, which fact we have indicated metaphorically by water sluicing around in the non-adaptive valleys. Normally, a large population will be up above this lethal water line.

As matters stand to begin with, life cannot pass from Mount Major to any of the other peaks shown. If, however, natural selection should decrease in intensity, as indicated by the lowered water level in B, then the population can safely vary more, that is, spread out more widely from the peak, and it may be able to spread across the valley between Mount Major and Mount Minor. Reaching the foothills of Mount Minor, it will, by natural selection, rapidly spread upward (C). If natural selection subsequently becomes more stringent, the rising water level will eliminate the individuals in the unadaptive valley, leaving two separate populations—two races, or two species (depending on the degree of difference)— where there was one before.

Several points should be made before going on. First, evolution is, as we have said before, opportunistic: it carries species where the road is open. When the way was clear from Mount Major to Mount Minor, evolution moved in that "direction." An Olympian god might well be able to discern at a distance the vastly superior Mount Superb, but the evolving species, without vision or foresight, and able to respond only to the pressures of the moment, cannot reach Mount Superb if the unadaptive valley between is too deep.

Secondly, our model gives us new insight into the question: *Is evolution progress?* The evolution just described, from Mount Major to Mount Minor, is one in which the new peak is actually lower on the scale of adaptive worth than the old, and yet it occurs. It might have been higher, of course. The new peak that is occupied is neither necessarily higher nor lower than the old one. Just different. Whether or not the evolution occurs is determined not by the height of the new peak, but by the depth of the intervening valley.

If evolution is not necessarily "upward," may it not be generally "outward"? T. H. Huxley, remember, compared evolution to a filling of a barrel first with apples, then with marbles, then with sand. Is this not a necessary aspect of evolution—to exploit the environment ever more thoroughly (as Lotka thought), to occupy ever more of the adaptive peaks? No, not even this simplicity is saved for us. Two types of processes act counter to this postulated tendency.

First of all, from time to time there must be considerable over-all changes in selective intensity. It is as though the water level in our model should rise higher and higher, covering adaptive peak after adaptive peak, extinguishing race after race and species after species until only a very few of the species, occupying only the highest of adaptive peaks, are left. A subsequent recession of the selective waters will leave an impoverished genetic landscape with only a fraction of the percentage occupancy that obtained before the rising of the waters. To visualize the kind of change postulated, call to mind the poverty of species in the Arctic tundras as compared with the superabundance of species in a tropical rain forest, where seldom are two adjacent trees members of the same species. Some such impoverishment in the number of species must have occurred—at least in limited regions of the world —at each ice age. There may have been other widespread changes in the past that have catastrophically reduced the number of species. In our age, Man promises to be the great catastrophe.

Another way to visualize an effect that reduces the degree of fullness of the world is to think of qualitative change in the environment. The adaptiveness of the peaks is nothing absolute: it is determined by the nature of "the environment," which enters into our picture only implicitly. The environment is another dimension, or more exactly, another domain of dimensions, an invisible flux permeating the genetic-topographic domain. As the environment changes, the support for one adaptive peak disappears, so to speak, leaving in its place a deep valley in which a formerly prosperous species perishes. Elsewhere a peak may push up out of a valley, perhaps to be occupied almost immediately by a colony from a neighboring peak, perhaps to be uninhabited for a million years—or perhaps never to be occupied. By such environmental changes the degree of fullness of the world fluctuates continually, never realizing, except to the smallest extent, the complete potential of what Haldane has called "that inexhaustible queerness which is the main characteristic of the universe." With fluctuations taking place in ten thousand dimensions in genetic space and several in environmental space, it is all but inconceivable that the same species should ever be twice evolved, or that—if there be other worlds of life—that there should be any two forms of life that are alike on two different planets. Whether better or worse, our world is unique in time and space.

Escape from Conservatism: Small Numbers

The mechanism that permits evolution to take place is a cybernetic system that tends to keep each species near its adaptive peak. The basic Darwinian mechanism is a conservative one. To speak anthropomorphically, the species is timid about straying far from the home peak, avoiding almost entirely even short excursions away from the tried and true. But in evolution, as in human life, "nothing ventured, nothing gained." As it happens, nature also knows a way of taking greater chances.

A small population differs significantly from a large population in that changes in gene frequency will often take place in a direction counter to selective forces; the smaller the breeding population, the oftener will this happen. Is this good or bad? *It depends*. On what it depends, we can see by contrasting the possibilities of two different species, one in the large-population state, the other in the small.

In Fig. 25, adaptive peak Mount Tory is occupied by a species that occurs as a single large interbreeding population. Mount Risky, on the other hand is inhabited by a species that happens to be broken up into many small breeding populations almost or entirely isolated from one another. Between these two peaks lies Mount Opportunity, a favorable configuration of genes, at present unoccupied. The adaptive valleys on either side, though low, are above the lethal limit. Will either of the two species nearby ever send out migrants to take over Mount Opportunity?

Certainly the species on Mount Tory will not. It is a large population, beautifully and closely adapted to its environment (for it is most responsive to the slightest hint by "natural

Fig. 25. A large population, which is very sensitive to selection pressure, is narrowly confined to an adaptive peak (Mount Tory). A species broken up into many separate small breeding populations is much less responsive to selection pressures; its populations will wander widely from their adaptive peak (Mount Risky)—some to perish, some, perhaps, to find the way to new adaptive peaks like Mount Opportunity. As before, the water represents the threatening natural selection.

selection"), and it sits way above the lethal limit of variation; so far above, in fact, it has no chance of discovering the causeway leading to an even better adaptive peak. The species on Mount Risky, on the other hand, is subdivided into many small populations. *On the average,* they cluster around the peak as a mean point, but this is just a statistical matter. Individually they wander all over the place, as suggested by the arrows. The wandering is largely at random, like Brownian movement. Occasionally a population may wander so far down the W scale as to go beyond the lethal limits, and perish. But it is also possible that sometime another population may go far enough along the causeway to reach the foothills of Mount Opportunity. Once there, the way is open to the top. Thus may small populations do what is impossible for a large one—open up new territory that can be reached only by traversing low-lying genetic valleys.

Is it good or bad for a species to be broken up into small populations? The answer certainly depends on the point of view. For the individual member of a species, things are, on the average, better in the large, conservative population. For subdivided populations there is greater variability from generation to generation, which insures that there will be greater losses for most of the colonies, but opens the possibility of much greater gain for a few of them. By what system of accounting is one to strike a balance of these debits and credits? And how long a time is one to include in the accounting? In the long run, the small-population species has an advantage in that it is more likely to leave descendant species than is a large-population species. The advantage of the subdivided species is especially notable during a time of rapid environmental change. At such time, some of the adaptive peaks may become lethal valleys too fast for a "well-adapted" species—that is, a species well adapted to the status quo—to migrate from the old maximum to a new one. A subdivided species whose descendant species have managed to occupy many peaks has a greater chance of being represented in a later age.

Is that an advantage? Is there any sense in which we can say that it is "better" for the dog-size *Eohippus* of the Eocene to be represented by the horse of our own time than to have no descendants at all? It's a curious question. The best we can do is to say, as Sewall Wright has said, that the most favorable conditions for continued existence and evolution are those that include at least occasional periods of segmentation of the species into fairly completely isolated breeding populations. Groups that never undergo such segmentation will, we expect, sooner or later be completely extinguished. Such may be the explanation of the extinction of some of the conspicuously successful, widespread species in the past. They may have suffered from putting all their genetic eggs in one basket.

Competition and Extinction

The phenomenon of species extinction is as fascinating to the evolutionist as is the decline and death of nations to a historian. For neither is there any universal explanation. Sometimes species extinction seems to be brought about solely from without, by a sudden change in the environment; for example, if there were any species confined to the island of Krakatoa when that East Indian volcanic island blew up in 1883, we would hardly wonder at their extinction. At other times, the extinction seems to proceed more from internal evolutionary tendencies of the organism, and we can hardly help speaking of the extinction of the species as being "its own fault"—though such an expression has no rational defense.

Consider, for example, some of the animals in which *sexual dimorphism* takes the form of extreme disparity of size or armoring of the two sexes, as it does in deer and walruses. It has long been suspected that the extinction of such forms as the "Irish elk," with its mammoth superstructure of antlers, was at least partly brought about by its most characteristic feature, which had evolved to the point where it was more a burden than an advantage. (For instance, the necessity of producing a new set of such antlers yearly must be a tremendous metabolic strain on the males.) But how on earth could a species evolve toward extinction? How could successive evolutionary steps that yielded a competitive advantage add up to extinction?

The clue to the logical puzzle has been pointed out by Julian Huxley: it lies in the sometimes opposing effect of *inter*species competition and *intra*species competition. Consider, for example, walruses. The male is not only much more heavily armored than the female, but he also is more than twice as big. The size of walruses must be determined by the usual sort of cybernetic system that defines the "most fit size." With respect to the defining of fitness by the environment external to the species, it seems hardly likely that there is any reason for *two* different fittest sizes, one for males, one for females. Observation shows that the explanation lies in the intraspecies competition. The males are polygamous and fight viciously themselves for mates. Each successful male has a harem of a dozen or so of the smaller, docile females; unsuccessful males are exiled to bachelors' quarters. Such a competitive system selects for an extreme in size among males that is probably of actual disadvantage in other selective terms, and may well result eventually in the extinction of the species at a distant time when the external selective conditions become unusually rigorous. This is most likely to happen in a polygamous species. This fact is, as Huxley points out, a sound biological objection to polygamy.

Escape from Specialization: Fetalization

"To have the defects of one's virtues . . ." This phrase makes sense among species as it does among human personalities. The tendency of evolutionary processes in general is toward greater specialization. The honeybee has special leg structures for scraping the pollen off its body. The hummingbird has a long bill and tongue specialized for nectar-sipping. There is a cactus that can be pollinated by only one species of moth, and the moth, in turn, lays its eggs only on this kind of cactus. There is a species of barnacle that attaches itself only to barnacles attached to whales. Each of these specializations probably gives its possessor an advantage over other, less-specialized organisms, but in so doing it places the species in, or near, an evolutionary cul-de-sac. For it is one of the few rules of evolution that extreme specialization results in eventual extinction. Environmental changes are inevitable, and the specialist-species is too strongly committed to one way of life to be able rapidly enough to "back up" genetically and take off in another "direction." All the evidence of comparative morphology and paleontology, fragmentary though it is, indicates that each great new group of organisms arises from very unspecialized species of the group "below" it, not from the conspicuously specialized ones. The reptiles gave rise to the birds, but it was not from such specialized marvels as the great dinosaurs that the class *Aves* was derived; rather it was from small and otherwise quite un-notable kinds of reptiles.

As human beings we view this pattern of evolution to extinction through specialization with less than detachment. We cannot but wonder: *Is this man's fate?* Is man highly specialized? The answer seems fortunately to be *No*. Not his are those morphological specializations that restrict a species to a single kind of food or to a single climate. Of superlatives, he boasts few: he is not the largest or the smallest, the swiftest or the slowest, the most rapidly breeding or the least, the strongest or the weakest. In most things, he seems to be but middling. *But not in intelligence.* Here, he is clearly the greatest of all living things. Is this a specialization, and hence a factor leading to extinction? It may be plausibly argued that it is not: however we define intelligence, it involves an idea of the adaptive, the unspecialized. It is not like an instinct, finely adapted to an immediate solution of but one problem. It is more a sort of skeleton key, capable of opening a wide variety of doors. But with it man may now have opened one door too many and thus have led the way to his own extinction. We don't know. But if he does not kill himself, it will be because his godlike intelligence enables him to find yet one more door.

How has man succeeded in remaining so unspecialized? No simple answer is adequate, but there is one feature of the total picture that is seldom appreciated, though it was first pointed out by Bolk as long ago as 1926. Bolk called our attention to the significance of the number of young produced at a birth. Now the difference between a gestation involving 2 offspring and one involving 20 is probably not very significant. But the difference between 1, and more than 1, is profound. In those mammals that carry a litter, an appreciable proportion, perhaps as much as a quarter, of the offspring die in embryo. *Intra*specific competition among gestation-mates is the order of the day, and the premium is on rapid development. The same type of process continues after birth among litter-mates competing for nipples, and later for food brought into the den, with again the same result: the pay-off is for rapid maturation.

If there is one feature for which man is remarkable among the mammals, it is in his extraordinarily slow maturation. The time required to reach sexual maturity—say fifteen years—is about a fifth of his total life span, and is exceeded only by the rhinoceros (twenty years). (A whale, *Balaenoptera borealis,* requires only two years to reach breeding condition.) Other aspects of maturity require even more time: the cranial sutures do not completely fuse until about age thirty. If one compares the face of man with the developing face of other mammals, one is struck by the fact that the protruding snout, which develops at various degrees of lateness in other animals, never develops in man. His face remains permanently flat, like the face of a fetus. Man has, says Bolk, been fetalized. His condition is the result of a great slowing down of various growth processes, a slowing that has been made possible by virtue of the fact that man does not compete with his own kind during the period of gestation and nursing.

The partial moratorium on competition is extended even beyond the nursing period by the institution of the family. If primate young were reared wholly in nurseries, the young of similar age being kept together, competition would be keen; but, in fact, the family is the unit in which much of early development takes place, and in such an environment the relative lack of competition with age-mates permits development to continue at a slow, and if you wish, inefficient pace. As an indication of the wastefulness of the human developmental process we may cite Rubner's finding that the amount of food—expressed in terms of final body weight—required to reach the mature state is about 7 times as great in human beings as it is in other mammals. It is doubtful if an animal in which competition played a large role during childhood could afford such extravagance.

More important, surely, than this caloric inefficiency is the delay in mental maturity of the young, or to put it more positively, the prolongation of the teachable period. The mammals, more than any other group, are characterized by the habit of *playing*, and man is, of all organisms, the most playful. It is not easy to define "play" precisely, but whatever it is, it is something that is in some sense non-competitive, non-rational, non-economic. It is also productive of novelty in viewpoints, opening a path to new ways of doing things that would often never be discovered if only direct, completely rational, wholly efficient approaches were employed. Play, for many men, is by no means confined to childhood; it extends into the adult state, only changing its form. Freud has said, "The child has toys; the mature man has art and science." Out of the play called science—which is possible only to a society rich enough to suspend partially the laws of competition—out of the economically non-competitive intellectual play called science there comes, in fact, a competitive weapon of the most powerful sort, technology. Competition has its own dialectic.

←•→ *13* ←•→

In Praise of Waste

On they go—an invincible army yet not a victorious one. The aristocrats, the elect, the chosen, the Best People—all the words that describe them are false, and all attempts to organize them fail. Again and again Authority, seeing their value, has tried to net them and to utilize them as the Egyptian Priesthood or the Christian Church or the Chinese Civil Service or the Group Movement, or some other worthy stunt. But they slip through the net and are gone; when the door is shut, they are no longer in the room; their temple, as one of them remarked, is the Holiness of the Heart's Affection, and their kingdom, though they never possess it, is the wide-open world.

—E. M. FORSTER

MODERN science is the product of two great revolutions in thought, one that we call the Newtonian revolution, the other the Darwinian. It is often implied that the principal distinction between these two is that one took place in physics, the other in biology. In reality, neither was so confined and the difference between them is more profound. Without intending to belittle the Newtonian revolution we may, with some justice, say it was mainly a semantic revolution. Before Newton, the motions of the world were rigidly determined: some thought the planets were kept in their courses by personal angels who controlled them, as it were, at the end of a leash. After Newton, the motions were still rigidly determined—but now by impersonal forces. God had given way to Gravity—but still the world moved the same.

The Darwinian revolution involved a far more profound reassessment of the sense of the world, resulting in a view that no merely verbal substitution could make consonant with the old. It was for this reason that the reaction to the change was many times more emotional than had been the reaction to the earlier revolution stemming from physics. Taste, if you please, this sample from an anonymous analysis in the *Athenaeum* for 1868:

259

In the theory with which we have to deal, Absolute Ignorance is the artificer; so that we may enunciate as the fundamental principle of the whole system, that, IN ORDER TO MAKE A PERFECT AND BEAUTIFUL MACHINE, IT IS NOT REQUISITE TO KNOW HOW TO MAKE IT. This proposition will be found, on careful examination, to express, in a condensed form, the essential purport of the Theory, and to express in a few words all Mr. Darwin's meaning: who, by a strange inversion of reasoning, seems to think Absolute Ignorance fully qualified to take the place of Absolute Wisdom in all the achievements of creative skill.

The typographic emphasis brings to mind the Russian writer, Chekhov, who, setting out to ridicule the simplicity of a loving woman, ended in creating a paean of praise in his short story "The Darling." So also must this English critic have intended to damn Darwinism beyond hope, though he ended by epitomizing its essence admirably. *In order to make a perfect and beautiful machine, it is not requisite to know how to make it.* Quite so.

It is surely improbable that a perfect and beautiful machine could be made without foreknowledge of what was wanted: but only improbable, not impossible. It does not matter that it is *highly* improbable, for the Darwinian system of natural selection is equal to the task. Natural selection, as R. A. Fisher has pointed out, is a mechanism for generating improbabilities. Such a mechanism was utterly undreamt of by the Newtonians.

To Darwinians, Design emerges from blind Waste. "To be an Error and to be cast out is a part of God's Design," said William Blake. How old is this thought? Who can trace the earliest embryological stages of so tenuous an entity as an idea? Perhaps it is centuries old, but certainly its form was not unambiguously clear until Robert Malthus wrote his *Essay on Population* in 1798. This much misunderstood work, yearly buried by liberal critics and yearly resurrected by its own vigor has (entangled in its many errors) a correct view of stability achieved through waste—the Malthusian cybernetic scheme of population. From the superabundant vitality of nature comes the ever-present threat of geometric increase, but this is opposed by the limitations set by the environment. The result is a cybernetic equilibrium achieved through waste, an equilibrium that may, it is true, be subject to temporal shifts, but an equilibrium nonetheless. Forethought, planning and charity are either of secondary importance, or are self-defeating in such a system. It is a "tough-minded" view of life, a view that has been singularly identified with English thinkers; particularly, it is interesting to note, with sons of

Cambridge: Malthus, Darwin, Galton, Fisher, Keynes, Charles Galton Darwin and J. B. S. Haldane (who was not always a Communist). All of these men were either trained at Cambridge, or taught there at one time. Ideas have a sort of heredity of their own.

In one context or another, with more or less qualification, these men have asserted that the world is capable of governing itself—wastefully perhaps, but adequately. This is a tough view. It has been opposed from 1798 down to the present day by another stream of thought and feeling, the tenderer view that it is our humane duty to maintain a minute control over the system of nature, trying always to eliminate waste and suffering completely. The two streams of thought have, in fact, waxed in strength together. During most of man's history, the greater part of mankind—at least in the Western world—has had a pretty tough attitude toward life. The *idea of cruelty*—*i.e.*, cruelty as something to be abhorred rather than enjoyed—scarcely existed. The gentle Jesus was a real exception among men. Beginning apparently in the late eighteenth century, a significant quantitative change in the heart of mankind began to take place: Christians started to become *christian*. Perhaps I am my brother's keeper, men said, as they became concerned about the cotter's Saturday night; the wee . . . sleekit . . . tim'rous beastie; the girl on the Bridge of Sighs; Black Beauty; the neighbor's dog; the lace-maker; the woman in the mine—naked, on all fours—drawing the coal cart; the chimney sweep's cancerous little devil; Oliver Twist; Uncle Tom and Little Eva; and—significant name!— Captain Bligh's *Mr. Christian*.

Why the new concern with cruelty? Perhaps in part because, with the Industrial Revolution, things changed for the worse, rapidly, in Blake's dark, satanic mills. Physiological psychology tells us that it is not the absolute state of a sense organ that we perceive, but the rate of change. (The scalding hot bath of the Japanese is bearable so long as you hold *very* still.) The principle applies to cultural evils as well. Cruelty, if traditional and constant, may not be perceived as such; but let it suddenly double, however low the base from which it begins, and it will be abhorred.

The increasing concern with cruelty and suffering may also have been due in part to a change in perspective. In the middle ages it was common for the population of a city to be lowered as much as 10 percent in a single year as a result of disease or famine; even a lowering of 25 percent was not unknown. In a world so filled with suffering not caused by humans it would, to some, seem rather out of perspective to complain of a little human fun (like the Spanish Inquisition, say). As the suffering and death from seemingly divinely caused diseases decreased—as it did even before Pasteur and bacteriology—man's view of his own cruelties changed, perhaps because they loomed larger proportionately. Cruel fate was becoming reformed; cruel man now looked crueler. Tender-minded poets and novelists were determined that he, too, should reform, and quickly.

Into this world of tender intentions burst Malthus, asserting that suffering was inevitable, simply because population had the capability of increasing more rapidly than the means of subsistence. A reasonable balance between population and subsistence—a decent scale of living for some—could be maintained only if others suffered from insufficient means of subsistence. Nor would it be a true solution for the *haves* to divide their means with the *have-nots*—this would merely encourage the production of more have-nots, and hence greater misery for all. In a famous passage Malthus said:

> A man who is born into a world already possessed, if he cannot get subsistence from his parents on whom he has a just demand, and if the society do not want his labour, has no claim of *right* to the smallest portion of food, and, in fact, has no business to be where he is. At nature's mighty feast there is no vacant cover for him. She tells him to be gone, and will quickly execute her own orders, if he do not work upon the compassion of some of her guests. If these guests get up and make room for him, other intruders immediately appear demanding the same favour. The report of a provision for all that come, fills the hall with numerous claimants. The order and harmony of the feast is disturbed, the plenty that before reigned is changed into scarcity; and the happiness of the guests is destroyed by the spectacle of misery and dependence in every part of the hall, and by the clamorous importunity of those, who are justly enraged at not finding the provision which they had been taught to expect. The guests learn too late their error, in counter-acting those strict orders to all intruders, issued by the great mistress of the feast, who, wishing that all guests should have plenty, and knowing she could not provide for unlimited numbers, humanely refused to admit fresh comers when her table was already full.

This sentiment provoked a storm of protest from the *literati*, who were now making the cause of the poor and the unfortunate *their* cause. The wealthy Percy Shelley saw a great social threat in "sophisms like those of Mr. Malthus, calculated to lull the oppressors of mankind into a security of everlasting triumph." His friend Henry Hazlitt asserted that "Mr. Malthus's gospel is preached only to the poor."

This is not the place to examine Malthus's thesis—or rather, his theses, for there were several. We need only point out that the early decades of the nineteenth century saw an establishment of sharp lines of battle between—shall we say?—*humanitarians* and *analysts*. (It is difficult to name the factions without arousing prejudice.) It must not be supposed that men like Malthus were inhumane; in his personal relations with family and friends, Malthus was the kindest and most considerate of men. But in his public statements he insisted on the primacy of analysis in the attack on social problems, whereas his opponents insisted on the humanitarian treatment of all existing people—particularly the poor and unfortunate—in the hope, or belief, that future generations would present no problem. The here and now is much more real than the there and tomorrow. The humanitarians won the minds of common men (who are, in the nature of things, the majority). The analysts continued their activities, but rather quietly. They knew that at the slightest public utterance an avalanche of criticism was awaiting them.

This recognition must certainly have been one of the factors contributing to Darwin's twenty-year-long hesitation to publish. He undoubtedly saw that his "struggle for existence"—remember the phrase was coined by Malthus—would be viewed as a rationalization for the oppression of the poor. (Spencer's phrase, "the survival of the fittest," suggested this possibility even more clearly.) The *Origin of Species*, when it finally appeared, significantly contained absolutely no mention of the possible implications of the theory for the political and social behavior of human beings. Darwin kept his kind eyes averted from the human problem and deprecated the inferences of others from his theory. In one of his letters to Lyell he wryly remarked, "I have received, in a Manchester newspaper, rather a good quib, showing that I have proved 'might is right,' and therefore that Napoleon is right and every cheating tradesman is also right." He was personally as little in sympathy with what came later to be known as "Social Darwinism" as were his bitterest enemies.

Impotence Principles

In the minds of most laymen, and indeed of many scientists, science is primarily an activity in which one discovers how to do today what was yesterday thought impossible; for many, science is a faith that nothing is impossible. But to the more profound students of the philosophy of science such a faith is impiety. The history of science may quite properly be variously interpreted; for one thing it may be correctly interpreted as the search for the definition of the impossibilities of this world. Edmund Whittaker, a mathematical physicist, has called these the *impotence principles*. It is difficult to word such principles in an unexceptionable way, and the number of them known is, so far, small; but their number is increasing, and the wording of them is growing in precision.

A few examples may help our understanding. In mathematics, there is an impotence principle that may be stated: "It is impossible to trisect an angle with straightedge and compass." This is true. Or rather, there is something true which this statement is aimed at. Actually it *is* possible to trisect an angle with these instruments if one will be satisfied with an approximate answer—which is all we ever need in daily affairs. In the light of this fact, we may revise the impotence principle thus: "It is impossible to trisect an angle *exactly* with straightedge and compass. . . ." Is it true now? Well, not quite. By resorting to an infinity of operations with these tools, exact trisection is possible. Of course, an infinity of operations is, in a practical sense, impossible. But this theoretical possibility may make us propose another revision: "It is impossible exactly to trisect an angle with straightedge and compass, *in a finite number of steps*."

Is the impotence principle now correctly stated? Are there other loopholes in the wording? Perhaps; perhaps not. But whether we discover them or not, we believe that we are dealing with a genuine principle of impotence. We may not soon—perhaps not ever—state it perfectly, but we believe it is *there*. Only if some things are impossible can other things be. The task of science is to discover, and put into words, the impotence principles. In mathematics these include the nontrisectability of angles, and the rule that a circle cannot be squared. In physics, the first and second laws of thermodynamics are impotence principles. These laws not only rule out the possibility of perpetual-motion machines; they also rule *in* all the other wonderful machines we have invented. Impotence principles are not merely restrictive; in the larger framework of science, they are also permissive.

The recognition and acceptance of impotence principles do not come easily. On a thoroughly rational level, we can always doubt whether a particular impotence principle is truly such, or accurately stated. We have been wrong in the past in believing things are impossible. Lord Rutherford, to the day of his death in 1937, thought it would never be possible to harness nuclear power; Simon Newcomb, on the eve of Kitty Hawk, thought human flight impossible. We have been wrong before. We can be wrong again.

Less defensible is opposition to impotence principles because of a psychological need of an unbounded world. This is the only remaining source of opposition to the well-established impotence principles. Those who have had any contact with angle-trisectors, circle-squarers, or the inventors of perpetual-motion machines will attest to their being a very queer bunch of people, indeed. It is not their proposals that merit study, but their personalities. What defect in their character is it that makes them unwilling to accept the idea that perhaps they cannot have everything they want? Whatever it is, it is akin to the immaturity of the spoiled child and the compulsive gambler.

Impotence Principles of Evolution

It is an evidence of the maturing of biology that it, too, is accumulating impotence principles—not as precisely stated or as certain as those of the physical sciences, perhaps, but just as important in their implications. Let us review the impotence principles that have to do with evolution.

I. *Weismann's Principle* of the separation of soma and germ plasm is certainly a principle of impotence. It might be called the anti-Lamarckian principle. One suspects that a convincing theoretical justification of the necessary character of this principle could be given, though this has not yet been done. In the meantime, Weismann's principle rests on a large mass of negative evidence. There is no repeatable positive evidence for Lamarckism, in experiments properly carried out. Conceivably, such evidence might turn up tomorrow. To the professional biologist this seems most improbable, and his attitude toward the Lamarckian is much like that of professional mathematicians toward the circle-squarers, before the time of Lindemann. To paraphrase Poincaré—Which is the more probable: that this new publicity seeker has proved that Lamarck was right after all, or that the world is the richer by one more fool?

II. *The Competitive Exclusion Principle.* No two organisms that compete in every activity can coexist indefinitely in the same environment. To coexist in time, organisms that are potentially completely competitive must be geographically isolated from each other. Otherwise, the one that is the less efficient yields to the more efficient, no matter how slight the difference. When two competing organisms coexist in the same geographical region, close examination always shows that they are not *complete* competitors, that one of them draws on a resource of the environment that is not available to the other. The corollary of the principle is that where there is no geographical isolation of genetically and reproductively isolated populations, there must be as many ecological niches as there are populations. The necessary condition for geographical coexistence is ecological specialization.

III. *Waste is inevitable.* Waste, in the Darwinian cybernetic scheme, produces not only progress, but also the conservation of what is. There is no heredity without its tax of mutation; most mutations are bad; their production and elimination are a kind of waste. The sentimentalist who seeks to eliminate the waste in a species by preserving all of the mutants and breeding equally of all genetic types ultimately brings about the extinction of the entire species. It is a throwing of good money after bad. It is the saving of pawns and losing the game.

IV. *In a state of nature, each lethal mutation causes one "genetic death," on the average.* This fact is called the Haldane-Muller principle. Different systems of mating, with different degrees of inbreeding, cause different degrees of loss among immediate offspring. If there are many recessive lethals in common between two closely related partners, the loss among their offspring will be greater than the average in the population. By outbreeding they could avoid this personal loss, but only by saddling it onto later generations. Mathematical analysis shows that the loss is precisely the same, whatever the mating procedure. Sexual reproduction is a kind of stirring of the genes. Ultimately, the lethal mutation must be paid for by death. It is just a question of what "ultimately" means. The removal of a gene from the population is spoken of as "genetic death."

V. *In a state of nature, all bad mutations are, in their cumulative, ultimate effects, equally bad.* Science, which begins as common sense, in its fullest development produces concepts that seem most surprising to "common sense." The impotence principle just given is a fine example of this truth about science. To say that a gene that is only mildly harmful to the individual is just as harmful to the race as is one that is completely lethal seems to be flying in the face of reason. But such is the case. This is another aspect of the Haldane-Muller principle; it is demonstrable by a simple mathematical analysis, which may be found in Crow (1957). The sense of the demonstration can be given in words.

When we say, "Gene A is not as bad as gene B," what do we mean? How do we measure "badness" in nature? The only acceptable way, in an evolutionary sense, is by its effect on success in leaving progeny. The "worse" the gene is, the greater the diminution in progeny it causes in early generations, and consequently the sooner the gene is completely eliminated. A gene that causes only slight damage in each generation does so for many generations. These two factors—damage in one generation, and number of generations sustaining damage—bear a reciprocal relation to each other. As a result, the total damage of a gene, summed over all generations, is a fixed quantity, the same for all deleterious genes. In saying this, we assume a population of static size. For a population that is constantly growing in size, the situation is slightly altered: in this case, the less harmful genes exact a greater numerical toll than the more harmful, because a larger proportion of the loss is postponed to the later generations when the population is larger. So, if we have our eye cocked on the human situation of the past three centuries, during which the population of *Homo sapiens* has been increasing, we should be not less, but more concerned about the ultimate cost of the mildly defective genes. In a static population, all defective genes cost the same; in an expanding population, lethal genes are the cheapest tax of all to pay.

Can Genetic Waste Be Eliminated?

Some of the preceding impotence principles included the unexplained phrase "in a state of nature." The meaning and the reason for the qualification should be fairly clear: the principles apply to all organisms except man, organisms that do not consciously control their breeding. Man, *if* he consciously controls his breeding, may be said, in some sense, to be living not in a state of nature, in which case the problem of the losses exacted by mutation need to be examined all over again. Can man alter these losses?

Certainly he can increase them. In fact, he is increasing them now deliberately (though not intentionally) by increasing the general radiation level through medical X rays, atomic bombs and atomic-energy installations. How much he is increasing the mutational losses in man through his present actions we do not yet know: nor do we know how much he will increase the general radiation level in the future. We play with atoms because we believe there are benefits to be gained from our play. We know there are losses. Ethics is not so well-developed a science that it can tell us how to balance possible profits and certain losses. At the present time, unavoidable mutations cause the production of about 2,000,000 defective babies per year throughout the world. Suppose we increase radiation to such a level that it brings about an ultimate increase in the number of defective babies produced each year by 200,000. Is this a trivial addition or not? Is it small in comparison to the gains brought by atomic energy? How can we say?

Can man decrease natural losses? Yes, eugenists say. Let us see what is signifies to say *Yes*—what means may be used, and what their cost is.

First means: "loading the scales." Suppose we take albinism as an example. Undoubtedly, there are natural disadvantages to being an albino. Eyesight, for example, is adversely affected. In a state of nature, each new mutation would ultimately be eliminated, with a constant loss. Each genetic death would, in a particular social order, entail a certain emotional cost, in human suffering. A eugenicist might propose to minimize the emotional cost by invoking immediate genetic death among albinos—not necessarily personal death, be it noted, but non-reproduction, the evolutionary equivalent of death. If failure to reproduce involves no emotional cost, then non-reproduction of a disadvantageous type (like albinos) will certainly decrease the magnitude of the loss to society. If non-reproduction is itself emotionally painful, then no answer can be given until we learn how to reckon up accounts in emotionality—how, for instance, to weigh the grief of child-lessness against the guilt feelings caused by the recognition that one has deliberately brought handicapped children into the world. It is not for the biologist to give an answer. How-ever, he insists on reminding moralists of these facts: (1) There is no such thing as a "reproductive instinct"—only an urge for certain sorts of sensual stimulation. (2) The act of fertilization is only a small part of the experience of parent-hood; adoptive parents often feel that they are truly parents. (3) Different societies, with different values, will equate the opposing interests differently.

There is one important limitation to eugenic action that needs to be stated. In a diploid organism, elimination of a disadvantageous recessive gene takes place more slowly the rarer the gene is. This fact follows from the Hardy-Weinberg law. (*See* Fig. 16 once more.) If selection is exerted only against those that show it, it follows that selection (whether natural or artificial) has very little influence on a gene that is already rare. This is no argument against the elimination of rare, deleterious genes—Huntington's chorea and hemophilia are still undesirable conditions—but it is a caution against optimism. We can't expect to do *much* good by preventing rare homozygotes from breeding. (We can only do harm by allowing them to breed, however.)

Second means. By "making book" on breeding. One may not be able to identify the heterozygotes of an unwanted gene, but one may be able to state the probability of their existence. For instance, the sister of a hemophilic man has a fifty-fifty chance of being a carrier of the gene. If she has the gene, a child of hers has one chance in four of being hemophilic. Therefore, without knowing her genotype, she knows that if she is to have a child the chance that it will be hemophilic is 1 in 8. For so serious a condition as hemophilia this would be regarded by most civilized and sensitive women as too great a risk. If those who have a significantly high probability of being the carriers of bad recessives refrain from having children, the gene frequency will fall.

Third means. By the positive identification of heterozygotes. There is some indication that the blood-clotting ability of women heterozygous for hemophilia is poorer than it is in homozygous normals. If this is so, then heterozygotes can be identified positively, instead of merely probably. From an emotional point of view, this would be a definite advance. It may be irrational for women to become mothers when they have a probability of 0.5 of being carriers, but many do. We all are guilty of wishful thinking; and there is something healthy about having a bit of the gambler's spirit. ("The ship that *I* am on won't go down," said D. H. Lawrence contemptuously, during a terrible voyage to Australia.) *It is not I who have bad genes, says Everyman the Gambler.* Positive identification of heterozygosity would cut down on the gambling.

Fourth means. By positive eugenics. Gene frequencies can be changed in a favorable direction as well by encouraging the breeding of favorable types. Since negative eugenics involves what some regard as infringement of personal liberties, one might suppose that positive eugenic measures would be viewed with greater favor, but such a supposition does not reckon with human nature. *No one is my superior; but I will accept you as an inferior*—this is the basic presupposition of the competitive social animal. Men accept, to a greater or lesser extent, segregation and sterilization of mental defectives, but not the designation of a select group as "State Breeders." The measure that honors a few degrades the egos of many. From Plato's *Republic* to Muller's *Out of the Night,* the dream of positive eugenics has been utopian, in a derogatory sense.

And yet, we may someday come to it. Though probably by a roundabout route. In fact, there is already in existence a social practice that is, in fact, a form of positive eugenics, though the motivation for it is quite different. This is the practice of artificial insemination by a donor other than the husband. It is used to remedy the defect of a childless marriage. That it has the effect of a positive eugenic measure seems highly probable from the following facts. Semen donors are chosen very carefully on the basis of their superior physical and mental health, and freedom from known genetic defects. In the nature of things, donors probably are genetically superior to most husbands, for it is seldom that a nubile girl will choose her husband as carefully as a mature physi-

cian will choose a semen donor. On the average, donor insemination upgrades the human stock. (Since most donors
are, for convenience's sake, medical internes, this is a new
reason for maintaining high standards of admission to medical
school.) How many babies are produced every year by this
method is not a matter of record, but competent specialists
estimate the number at 1,000 to 10,000 per year in the United
States. As the practice becomes more widely known, and as
the shock of novelty wears off, we suspect that resort to it
will become more common. With 10 percent of all marriages
being involuntarily unfertile, half of them presumably because
of male sterility, and with the supply of adoptable orphans
becoming increasingly outstripped by the demand, there is a
large field for donor insemination.

Competition in the Evolution of Man

Many biologists—I confess I am one—find few things so
dreary as a discussion of the "missing links" in man's
evolution. Whether this or that jawbone found in a distant
gravel bed of uncertain age is part of an evolutionary series
that leads directly to modern man, or is instead a relic of a
dead end, is so exasperatingly undecidable a question that I
cannot maintain an interest in it.

Yet there is a way of looking at man's evolution that is not
without interest. Try as we will to be objective and modest,
we cannot but conclude that man is a very remarkable animal,
perhaps the most remarkable of them all. In what way is he
remarkable, and how did he get this way?

There is no objective way of picking out man's most remarkable or characteristic features, but probably most of
us would agree that any such list should include his eyes, his
hands and his speech. He owes the development of at least
the first two of a life in the trees, which his more monkey-
like ancestors led. Such an animal, swinging from limb to
limb, needs not only delicately grasping organs, like the
hands, but also good eyesight. Its vision need not be as
keen as that of a hawk, for the problems of arboreal life
are more local, but the three-dimensionality gained by having
both eyes directed toward the same scene is of vital importance. This orientation of the eyes and the eventual diminution in the importance of the sense of smell ultimately led to
the relatively flat, snoutless face of the anthropoids. Had our
ancestors never taken to the trees, our idea of facial beauty
would undoubtedly have been much different: something more
like a collie's head, perhaps.

And *speech*. Here, as we know, is the most remarkably
human trait of all, but how can we descry its evolution,

since it leaves no fossils? We can only guess at it. The word "speech" actually stands for a complex of ideas. We can only gloss over some of them. Undoubtedly vocalization was in the beginning only for the conveyance of emotion, as it is for most animals now. *Look out! Food! Sex!* (What an inadequate word!) *I'm mad* . . . Then somewhere along the line, sounds must have become identified with objects—perhaps food objects first. Thus, perhaps, were nouns developed. And then somehow, two modes of statement were developed: a reportive and an expective (to follow hints of Whorf's). The distinction was between what is (or was) and what will be (*I hope.*). These led eventually to what we recognize as tenses, the reportive mode to the present and past tenses, the expective to future and conditional. Elaboration followed elaboration until we find, in some languages, more than a dozen tenses. Man's ability to conceive of the non-existent (in the future tense, for example) found a different outlet among the nouns in the development of verbal substantives for the non-substantial: *existence, good, justice, energy, power, entropy, spin, curl.*

The ability to create "concepts" is truly wonderful—but has it done more harm or more good? In its pathological aspects, it has resulted in such dreadful productions as Plato's dialogue *Euthydemus.* (Perhaps Popper was right, in *The Open Society and Its Enemies,* in identifying Plato as one of the arch-enemies of society.) On the other hand, the fruitfulness of the major concepts of physics and chemistry makes one rather proud of man. And concepts themselves occur in various grades of generality, forming a hierarchal complex that has not yet been explicitly described. Language is a wondrously subtle and complicated tool; by far the greater part of it is to be found only in mathematics. That which most men call "language" is only a small part of man's concept-handling machinery, scarcely the ABC's of it.

Speech has developed far beyond any *merely* emotive needs, yet it undoubtedly had its origin in emotion, and very likely in emotions evolved by social situations. The stock from which man sprang was undoubtedly a social one—more so than that of most animals. It has often been remarked that the excessive sociality of the monkeys and apes (as it might seem to other animals) is probably a consequence of their excessive sexuality (again, "excessive" from a biased point of view). Most of the vertebrates are only intermittently sexual; the restriction is connected with the hazards of having off-spring out of season. The primates, probably because they underwent a considerable part of their evolution in the relatively seasonless tropics, became all-year breeders. The selective advantages of seasonal frigidity and seasonal impotence disappeared. With the continuous interest in the opposite sex, there developed a need for more elaborate and satisfactory forms of social discourse than are required by the merely momentarily amorous. With sociality came conflict, and as sociality became the norm, conflict became an ever-present force in life. A species can survive such an erosive force only if it evolves modes of conflict that permit competition to be worked out by means that stop far short of the lethal point. Threat replaces attack, a snarl replaces a slash. Ultimately (in part at least) words replace weapons. The ability to communicate well, to subdue an enemy with words that evoke the support of the bystanders, becomes of paramount importance. In the social arena, tact becomes of greater value than overt aggressiveness.

Sociality is no one thing: it is many things, many units, with which the individual identifies to varying degrees. Within the greater unit of tribe, clan or nation, the much smaller unit of the family has been of paramount importance in lessening the degree of competition. Because the members of a family are unequal in fact they can live together amicably; specialization permits coexistence. The parents, different sexes, *are* different. They can accept a child because it is inferior. The antagonism that develops when an offspring grows up and competes as an equal with a parent is obvious in other animals, and is often only thinly disguised among humans. The importance to a fetus of being an only fetus has already been pointed out by Bolk: non-competition permits delayed maturity. In the months and years after birth, the same principle applies. An only child, lacking competition with litter-mates, can take its time in maturing. Slower maturation permits greater indulgence in wasteful play, lesser responsibility, greater juvenility, more interest in such non-practical affairs as the sciences and the arts. Good and bad are two faces of the same coin. Were humans to be born regularly in litters, one would predict they would be more competitive, more aggressive, more practical and faster maturing; also less interested in the daydreaming that is the necessary soil of the arts and sciences. (Technology, however—the application of the science already known—is possible in a completely competitive society.)

David Riesman's distinction of inner-directed and other-directed men is of interest in this connection. The child who is brought up by himself is ideally situated to develop whatever inner-directness is inherent in his genes, for he has no equals, no direct competitors. Isolation favors the development of a strong self-image. But if he has a twin, or brothers nearly his age, or if families band together to raise their young in nurseries, then the child is subjected to the pressure of "others" and will become as other-directed as his genes permit. This is the biology that explains the tendency that Riesman points out—that increasing population promotes other-directedness. First the environment influences personality. Secondly (but more important in the long run), the environment selects for those genetic types that are capable of developing the kind of directness it promotes. So the species changes: but it is still called man.

The other-directedness (ultimately the tradition-directedness) that comes with dense population is but a manifestation of unavoidably increased intraspecific competition. Among the impotence principles of socio-biology is surely this: *competition is inescapable*. That species which has succeeded in eliminating all other species as competitors, ends by becoming its own competitor. The world, in spite of comic-strip science, is a limited one. Man, freed of the population-controlling factors of predators and disease organisms, must —willy-nilly, like it or not—control his own numbers by competition with his own kind. By taking thought he can elect the kind of competition he employs; but he cannot escape all kinds. This is not to imply that the election is a trival matter. Surely there are few who would not prefer the endemic celibacy of the Irish to the ritual blood sacrifices of the Aztecs, who, at the dedication of the temple of Huitzilo-potchli in 1486 slaughtered at least twenty thousand victims (by the most conservative accounts), tearing the hearts out of the living bodies. There surely can be no serious question as to which behavior is preferable, but we should note that, though both practices have a religious "reason," both are, in the eyes of a biologist, competitive techniques associated with the threat of overpopulation, however unconscious of that threat the practitioners may be. The question is not whether competitive techniques shall be employed, but what techniques, and by whom.

The game must go on: that is Nature's command. But it is up to man to determine the ground rules and the teams. The determination of the rules is principally the responsibility of the specialist in ethics. The delineation of the teams—well, that is a task for which many disciplines are needed. It may be that no synthesis of all the relevant considerations is yet possible. But such a synthesis is one that we must work toward. The biologist, with the wisdom gained from a century's preoccupation with evolution, has some things to say about the choosing of the teams.

One World—Or Many?

Few dreams are as pervasive in our time as the dream of "One World," a brotherhood of man, a world in which we are all members of the same team, a world in which competition is at an end. It is an ancient dream, rooted in the fantasy of "The Kingdom of Heaven" of pre-Christian days. It is a noble dream, one that has agglomerated to itself much that is gentlest and finest of man's aspirations. It is a growing dream: in the last century it has increasingly shaped men's political actions in the world at large. The "best" elements of our society believe in it—those who are most liberal, most tolerant, most loving in their attitudes toward other men. Those who strongly repudiate the dream include many with whom one hesitates to associate—men who may be ignorant, narrow-minded, sadistic, or intolerant. Yet a biologist, however much he may dislike the complexion of this group, can hardly throw in his lot with the opposing camp, those who think that One World is both possible and the best of all possible worlds.

In the first place, in a profound sense, One World is a mirage. To eliminate all international competition by abolishing nations would be but to intensify the competition between other groups within the single society—the competition for wealth and honor between labor unions and white-collar workers, for example, or between skilled and unskilled workers, or between farmers and city dwellers. International competition is replaced by class competition. Can one get rid of classes? Possibly. Karl Marx thought so. This man, militant atheist though he was, gave a new lease to the religious idea of the Kingdom of Heaven in his dream of the Classless Society. One nation in our time has tried to achieve this Kingdom of Heaven on earth, with what results we have seen: in proportion as class competition has decreased, so has the competition between individuals increased in intensity and vindictiveness. The complete elimination of classes would mean the installation of a dog-eat-dog society. In recent years, there has been a reverse tendency in the Soviet heaven, a formation of new classes (bureaucrat versus subject, party member versus citizen, intellectual versus clod), and consequently an increase in social stability. Competition there must be, even in One World. The choice is in the number of teams—which may vary from a minimum of two to a number equal to the population of the entire world—and in the rules of the game. (Is the penalty of defeat to be death, sterilization, celibacy, or what?)

One World in the sense of a competition-free world is

impossible. Is it possible in any other sense? Certainly it is possible in a political sense; in fact, the superlative military weapons we have devised seem to indicate that One World is inevitable, in some sense. But is it desirable? Here the biologist, flying in the face of recent tradition and apparent logic, must answer *No*. Such a minority position certainly needs to be justified.

Any position rests on assumptions, which are themselves "taken for granted," i.e., not proven. An important premise of what follows is the assumption that the continued survival of mankind is desirable. This can certainly not be proven from any point of view that is demonstrably "objective," but most men will be willing to accept it. Accepting it, we see immediately, in terms of the picture of evolution developed in the last chapter, that the wisdom of man's dream of One World is highly questionable, to put the matter mildly. Any species that becomes one big melting pot of genes puts (to change the metaphor) all its eggs in one basket. There are countless adaptive peaks available; the one-population species can occupy only one. If circumstances change rapidly, it may be unable to adapt, and so will perish. Conspicuous success in evolution, as in human affairs, is all too likely to be the prelude to extinction. That the dinosaurs should have become extinct at the end of the Mesozoic Era is no cause for wonder; what needs explaining is how such highly successful forms lasted as long as they did.

It is not that the relatively unsuccessful have a better chance of survival *because* of their deficiencies. Rather, their advantage comes when their lack of success results in the species being broken up into many separate breeding populations, among which there is very little interchange of genes. Under these conditions, there is a great increase in variety within the species, each isolated population necessarily differentiating into a different race. (*How* different will depend on many factors, including the extent of environmental differences.) With a greater variety of harmonious genotypes in existence the species is better adapted to face a varying and unpredictable future. Not all of its breeding populations may survive a change; but the chance that at least some will is greater than it would be for a single, large population. And those races that survive a change can then repopulate regions left vacant by those that have succumbed.

Such is the picture presented to us by a spelling out of the consequences of biological inheritance. But man is subject also to a kind of inheritance that we may call cultural. Will this not alter the picture? We don't know. The Mendel of cultural inheritance has not yet appeared. But there are strong intuitive reasons for believing that the mechanism of cultural inheritance will, if anything, merely increase the contrast in the picture. The loss of adaptability of a species is the result of the inevitable tendency of a breeding population to become genetically uniform. Surely we, in our time, have seen enough of social power to realize that the pressure toward uniformity is even greater in the cultural realm than it is in the biological. As Phyllis McGinley, in *In Praise of Diversity*, complained:

> One shrill, monotonous, level note
>   The human orchestra's reduced to.
> Man casts his ballot, turns his coat,
>   Gets born, gets buried as he used to,
> Makes war, makes love—but with a kind
> Of masked and universal mind.

Genuine tolerance of human variety has been strongest in frontier situations, where men competed with Nature rather than with other men. With the closing of frontiers and the increase in pressure of population, tolerance of real diversity becomes more difficult and the movement toward uniformity much accelerated. The conclusions of the Wrightian picture of evolution are undoubtedly strengthened and exaggerated when we include cultural inheritance in a social animal. Diversity within the species demands isolation of populations—many worlds, not one.

How Regulate Competition?

To the biologist it is clear that the best chances for man's long-time survival depend on the fragmentation of the species into well-separated populations. But it would be foolhardy to say what form the separation should take. It might be a matter of nations, as we know them; or some sort of caste system, that would permit genetic isolation with geographic unity; or—far more likely—some new kind of communities that are neither nation nor caste nor anything that has yet been conceived of.

We can hardly talk in term of units that have not yet been invented, so we must talk in terms of units that now exist, to develop the consequences of inter-group competition further. Some error in prediction will certainly result; we can hardly estimate its magnitude; we can only try to remember that it exists.

If one were to conceive of the present world reorganized as if by magic into a system of worlds that would give man the best chance of survival, it might be into many nation-like communities. The biological differences between communities would be not differences of single genes, but of whole constellations of genes. The cultural differences would be also in terms of constellations of culture traits. Just as the fitness of a gene does not inhere in the gene itself but rather in a whole complex of genes, so is the fitness ("wisdom" or "morality") of culture traits a property of the complex, rather than of the individual elements.

If there are separate communities, there will surely be competition between them. But of what sort? Plainly, there must be ground rules to prevent the use of any competitive device that could permit one community to eliminate all others, thus instituting One World. This means, of course, the successful outlawing of atomic bombs and, indeed, of all international warfare as we now know it. But it means something else as well: the elimination of one of the most potent means of warfare known, though one not often recognized as such.

Suppose that in this universe of many communities, one of them, say a remote tribe of very primitive aborigines—let's call them the Polyovacians—announce that they have it as a matter of divine revelation from their god (whose name is Ova) that it is a sacred duty of all men to indulge in sexual intercourse whenever the divine spirit moves them and that intercourse must never be in the slightest way altered by foresight, device, or restraint; and that their god Ova has revealed to them that all life is sacred and must not be extinguished, no matter what the circumstances. What will happen if the Polyovacians develop such a set of religious beliefs, and the rest of the world does not? If the rest of the world believes in sexual restraint, plainly the Polyovacians will outbreed all others and will ultimately replace all other peoples just as surely as if they had used atom bombs. The elimination of warfare by military means is tolerable only in a world that has outlawed reproductive warfare. The competitive use of human gonads in a pacifistic world is every bit as vicious and productive of suffering as is the militaristic use of atomic bombs.

Plainly there must be some sense in which our world must become One World. There must be a few moral principles that are accepted by all, if all are to survive. But these moral principles should be only such as will assure the continuing existence of the smaller units. Beyond that, it is very questionable whether man has the wisdom to go. It seems very doubtful that any body of united nations can draw up a universal bill of human rights that will not do more harm than good if put into effect. There are millions of different constellations of genes that *work*, that produce organisms that are fit for some sort of life. May there not also be very many constellations of moral principles that will work, too, in one sort of life or another? The good constellations in either case are only a tiny fraction of all that are possible, but this fraction is surely a large number. It may be hard to resist trying to punish a society whose moral practices are repugnant to us, but only a policy of live-and-let-live will permit the development of the variety of communities that is needed to insure man's continued existence.

Our kind of community has as a foundation stone the doctrine of freedom of speech. We have learned by bitter experience that this must not be interpreted to mean that "men have freedom to speak only the truth," for who is to determine the truth? Freedom of speech, to mean what it says, must mean freedom to lie; otherwise the phrase is a mockery. Is it not dangerous to permit the broadcasting of falsehoods? Indeed it is. But we must have Milton's firm faith that

> . . . though all the winds of doctrine were let loose to play upon the earth, so Truth be in the field, we do injuriously by licencing and prohibiting to misdoubt her strength. Let her and Falsehood grapple; who ever knew Truth put to the worse in a free and open encounter?

In the realm of inter-community affairs an analogous moral principle must be espoused—freedom to err. Within a single community there cannot be freedom of action for individual members. It will not do, for example, for a community that disapproves of murder, to wink at murder by individuals who want to be free. But, as between communities, there must be freedom for each community to determine its own moral principles. Other communities must be free not only to live morally (by our standards) but also to live immorally (again by our standards). Put bluntly, every community must be free to go to hell in its own way, so long as its action does not endanger the continued existence of other communities. A community must, for instance, enjoy the freedom to breed itself into a state of starvation, if it so wishes, without a finger being lifted elsewhere to interfere with its stupidity. To interfere, to save it from the consequences of its own immorality is but to postpone and aggravate the problem, and to spread the moral infection. By not interfering, however, we make it more probable that a community will see its error in time, will see that a moral principle of unlimited reproduction is incompatible with the principle of unlimited use of medicine in the prevention of crowd diseases. If we have any responsibility at all with respect to other communities, it is only because we ourselves failed in the past to see the cultural incompatibility of the above-mentioned principles and freely gave of our medicine without at the same time seeing to it that the gift was coupled with the principle of birth limitation.

Is This Utopia?

Library shelves groan with utopias, blueprints of ideal communities, of varying degrees of realism and phantasy, motivated by varying degrees of pathological psychology. Is this just another utopia that has been sketched in the preceding section? At first glance it might appear so; yet will I argue *No*. At worst, what has been sketched here is a utopia-generating system.

Utopias, however much they vary, agree in two characteristics. The societies they sketch have a high degree of rigidity and finality; and they seek to eliminate all waste, which is variously conceived in terms of economic waste, human suffering, or moral turpitude. The student of biological evolution cannot accept a utopia that embodies either of these features. Evolution is an unending process, in which waste plays an indispensable role. Until proof to the contrary is forthcoming, the evolutionist must assume that man is a part of nature. The biologist sees no end-state for man and his society, which must continue evolving until the day of extinction. No one has conceived any substitute for the mechanism of evolution (whether biological or social) that does not necessarily involve variation and selection—that is to say, waste. Man, the slender reed that thinks, can alter the force and direction of natural forces somewhat, but only within limits. The wisdom of so doing is at least questionable. Who is so wise as to descry the lineaments of man a thousand millennia from now, using these now as guides for consciously warping the course of human evolution toward these goals? And as for waste, the more we try to eliminate it, the more we are impressed with its protean changeability and elusiveness. The time-study man who saves a thousand man-hours by altering work procedures may be astonished to find himself faced with a sitdown strike that costs a million man-hours; reducing the waste of walking to work by inventing horseless carriages may ultimately double the time wasted in transportation by making possible the modern city and its congestion. And so it goes. We have no scientific theory of waste yet, but all men of experience and realism recognize its ubiquity and its inevitability. We can often exchange one kind of waste for another; and we can sometimes—though not as often as we like—decrease it somewhat in amount. But always we must live with it. If we are wise, we even make waste work for us a bit.

In Praise of Waste

When did man first perceive that waste may be fruitful? We do not know: the history of waste is yet to be written. But it may plausibly be argued that conscious charity owes its origin at least in part to a subconscious realization of the value of waste. Most interesting of early prescriptions for charity is the Jewish "Law of the Corner," which is given thus in Leviticus (19: 9–10): "And when ye reap the harvest of your land, thou shalt not wholly reap the corners of thy field, neither shalt thou gather the gleanings of thy harvest. And thou shalt not glean thy vineyard, neither shalt thou gather every grape of thy vineyard; thou shalt leave them for the poor and stranger." Such a directive sprang, no doubt, in part from a tender heart; but it may also have indicated an embryonic recognition of the danger of an unmodified competitive exclusion principle in human affairs—a recognition that if competition were pure and unbridled, the more efficient man (the landowner) would starve out the man who was less so (the poor and the stranger), coupled with a surmise that perhaps this eventuality might not always be best or right. In Deuteronomy 24: 19 there is a further injunction: "When thou cuttest down thine harvest in thy field, and hast forgot a sheaf in the field, thou shalt not go again to fetch it: it shall be for the stranger, for the fatherless, and for the widow . . ." Thus there came into being that curious entity of Jewish practice known as "that-which-is-left-through-forgetfulness," which belongs to the poor. The devout were urged always to see to it that something was left through forgetfulness. It is certainly difficult to remember to forget. It is no wonder that the principle of the deliberate tithe—one tenth of one's income given to charity—later replaced so operationally difficult a procedure as deliberate forgetfulness.

The first glimmerings of the importance of waste are quite old, but waste did not really come into its own until the last of the eighteenth century, with the work of economists, particularly of Adam Smith (and later Ricardo). Before them, many economists dreamed of a world made perfect and waste-free through law—through regulations governing the prices of commodities, for example. It was Smith's insight that showed that the world works very well with waste. In effect, Smith said that the world is best and most equitably governed when waste governs it. It does not matter if some men place too high and others too low a price on a commodity. The former goes bankrupt from too little business, the latter from too much; their wiser competitor survives. Through waste, we learn what is the "right" price. Such a cybernetic system is infinitely flexible. Every day, even perhaps every hour it can adjust to the slightest change in circumstances. Adaptation is made possible by waste. That which man's poor intellect may be incapable of creating directly can be produced indirectly through the waste-actuated Smith-Ricardian cybernetic system.

It was Darwin's genius to show that the same system would explain the fact of biological adaptation. Design in nature required no supernatural intelligence to explain it; a cybernetic system based on waste rather than intelligence does so just as well. There is a perpetual production of mutations that are random with respect to need, which means that most of them are bad. They are an unavoidable form of waste. But no matter. Should external circumstances alter the meaning of "fitness," the species is instantly prepared to alter to meet the new demands, through mutations that a moment before were bad, but are now good. A supernatural Designer might, one suspects, occasionally doze and neglect to redesign some of his million different children to meet changing circumstances. But not the impersonal Darwinian system of mutation and natural selection. The needs of the emergency are met through the adaptability conferred on the organism by ever-present waste. No organism is infinitely adaptable of course: the new environment cannot suddenly be too different from the old, else the species simply becomes extinct. (Here we see a difference between gods and Nature. Gods, addicted to miracles, probably do better in the great emergencies, great demands being more worth the while of a divine intelligence. Nature, more humble, works only by littles.)

Evolution has involved not merely the evolution of species but the evolution of systems of evolution. An example of one such evolution at this higher level of meaning is found in the displacement of haploidy by diploidy. The waste in both systems is precisely the same, but in diploidy it is paid for on the installment plan. The diploid species accumulates debts to nature, debts that are paid for, for the most part, by a posterity remote from the generation in which they were incurred. "Am I rich?" a Texas oil magnate asked, repeating the query of a reporter. "I guess you might say I am; I have a million dollars in debts." So it is with organisms. Diploid species are immensely richer in debts than haploid. Out of this genetic richness, multitudinous new combinations of genes are evolved, and (by a magic known only in nature?) an occasional combination of genetic "debts" turns into a new asset, an asset which a more honest, more efficient haploid would, in all probability, never uncover. Diploidy gains its first advantage because of its relative irresponsibility; ultimately it is superior because it is more creative. The association of creativity with a modicum of irresponsibility is not confined to nature.

That the magnificent progress of historical evolution is impossible to the cybernetic process conceived in the most narrowly Darwinian terms has been an intuition of countless minds. Efforts to conceive of other processes have not been wholly happy. Lamarckism, entelechy, *élan vital*, orthogenesis and the hopeful monster are only a few of the terms associated with the less fortunate efforts. More successful have been Wright's, and Fisher and Ford's proposals that Nature may suspend, as it were, the ordinary laws of accounting—now and then and for a while—during which moratorium improbable new combinations may be thrown together to be tested later. Wright works the miracle by the errors of small numbers; Fisher and Ford by the extravagance of unaccustomed prosperity. Both involve an increased measure of irresponsibility; both increase waste; both are creative. This description might be regarded as a paean to inefficiency, but we must not forget that inefficiency is creative only when it is limited. Natural selection is the firm's auditor. If one threw him out forever, the result would surely be ugly chaos. But by postponing his visits now and then while the treasurer places a few three-horse parlays on long shots, an occasional fortune may be made: a new adaptive constellation of genes. Most of the time, of course, the result is closer to bankruptcy—but, no matter, for Nature is infinitely wealthy. Thus nature shows she knows the meaning of Keynes's famous advice: "The poor man should never gamble; the rich man should do nothing else."

The Cost of Therapy

Again we ask our question: *Is man a part of nature?* At times we have answered *Yes,* at times *No.* Perhaps in our time the latter answer is the one more often given. We are terribly clever people, we moderns: we bend Nature to our will in countless ways. We move mountains, and make caves, fly at speeds no other organism can achieve and tap the power of the atom. We are terribly clever. The essentially religious feeling of subserviency to a power greater than ourselves comes hard to us clever people. But by our intelligence we are now beginning to make out the limits to our cleverness, the impotence principles that say what can and cannot be. In an operational sense, we are experiencing a return to a religious orientation toward the world.

That this orientation was lost for a while was perhaps—at

least from a certain point of view—good for man. Man refused to accept the world as it is, and out of this *impiety* came technological science. No world of thoroughly pious men could have achieved what we have achieved. In spite of all that may be said—and much truly said—about the perils of eating of the tree of knowledge, we do not honestly regret that we did so, whatever the final outcome. It has been a wonderful adventure, this science of ours, and we would not have even suspected its magnificence had we not impiously refused to accept the world as it appeared to be. By so doing we have plunged beneath the appearance, ultimately (we believe) to discover the real. Impiety, coupled with honesty, will lead us finally to a new and defensible piety.

The scientific temper has been one of rejection of the appearances of the world, and among the appearances most vehemently rejected has been the wastefulness of life, wastefulness of many sorts—of fuel, of natural beauty, of human spirit, of time. The rejection has been productive of much good. We now make two blades of grass grow where but one grew before; we make one lump of coal do the work of four; we save the countryside from devastation by industrial fumes by collecting and making a profit out of the contaminants; we save the lives of jaundiced babies; we restore madmen (some of them) to useful life; we prevent the erosion of the spirit of the poor by taking care of the young. By these and countless other means we have immensely reduced some of the wastes to the world—though, be it noted, not entirely without introducing new wastes of our own invention. But as we have really come to grips with the question of waste, we have discovered its power, the extent to which it is unconquerable. The Second Law of Thermodynamics tells us not only that a perpetual-motion machine is impossible, but it also defines the limits of efficiency, *i.e.,* the extent of irreducible waste, for our machines. Engineers long ago gave up even thinking of circumventing this impotence principle. To try seriously to do so is a sign not of commendable ambition, but of emotional immaturity.

In biology, the wastefulness of mutation is a great impotence principle. Laymen sometimes ask: May we not someday learn how to control the mutation process, so that we can produce only those mutations that we want? Good ones. Thus permitting idiots to give birth to Einsteins. After all, when science has done so many other wonderful things, may it not learn to tailor-make mutations?

It is a plausible surmise. But no geneticist known to me holds out the slightest hope for such a discovery. The reasons are hard to put into words, but they are felt to be very strong reasons. Perhaps the simplest way to put the difficulty is in terms of scale, as has been done for the Second Law of Thermodynamics by Leo Szilard. James Clerk Maxwell, as a fantasy, created a demon who could sit at the door between two equal temperatured rooms and, by allowing only fast-moving molecules to go through in one direction, and only slow-moving ones in the opposite way, could, without the expenditure of energy, eventually bring into being rooms of different temperature. This is, as we know, contrary to experience. Szilard has shown that the impossibility (or rather, the exceedingly high improbability) is connected with the scale of the molecules relative to the demon; involved is a matter of information and its cost. Now genetic theory is by no means so far advanced as to permit a similar analysis, but intuitively it appears that scale is again involved, that the cost of directively controlling mutations will far exceed the value received. Mutations, we are sure, are just naturally wasteful; refusing to accept the waste is a sign of emotional immaturity.

This is not to say, of course, that the waste cannot be reduced. It can. But to see in what sense we mean "can" we must look at "it" again, *i.e.*, at waste, trying to define it more closely.

The Haldane-Muller principle says that every bad mutation causes one genetic death. Genetic death is a subdivisible quantity: it may occur by degrees and over many generations. A lethal gene kills at one fell stroke—this is death as we ordinarily conceive it. But a gene that has a selective worth of 0.9 diminishes the reproductivity of every individual in which it shows by 10 percent. If we multiply the fraction of the population that suffers this loss by the amount of loss each individual suffers, we come out with the number 1, no matter what the selective worth. This then is an impotence principle: each bad gene, no matter how bad, causes exactly one genetic death. But it does not follow from this that there is nothing that can be done to diminish the loss to human beings. To say nothing can be done is to assert that death is the only form of human waste, a thesis that surely few would hold. The sub-lethal gene does not merely diminish the reproductivity of its possessor, it usually also diminishes his vigor, his health, his *joie de vivre*. We would be little concerned if genetic death were the only consequence of Huntington's chorea, Mongolism, phenylketonuria, pyloric stenosis, or fibrocystic disease of the pancreas. But these conditions cause other losses that we state in terms of human suffering. These losses can be reduced.

Until very recent times, the only method of attacking the

problem of suffering was by medicine. Medicine is surely one of the glories of mankind, but we are now perceiving its limitations. For a disease in which it is accurate to say that the hereditary component is negligible—say, for smallpox —medicine has been an unalloyed blessing. But where the hereditary component is great—for instance in phenylketonuria—we have our doubts. Let's see what these are by examining phenylketonuria more closely.

Phenylketonuria is a chemical disease. One of the twenty or so amino acids present in proteinaceous food is called phenylalanine. Most people can change this into tyrosine which is used in synthesizing various constituents of the body. But a person who has a double dose of the phenylketonuria gene cannot do this: the phenylalanine is changed instead to the ketone, phenylpyruvic acid which appears in his urine, hence the name. If this were all, there would be no need to worry. But for some reason that is not yet understood, the deranged metabolism affects the brain, causing the phenylketonuria child to develop into an idiot or, at best, into a moron. The hair is unusually light in color also, perhaps because there isn't as much tyrosine available for melanin formation.

Since the results seem to stem from the abnormally high concentrations of phenylalanine in his system, some workers have recently devised a tailor-made diet of specially selected substances that do not include the offending amino acid. The diet is expensive. But, it is maintained, if the phenylketonuric child is early identified and kept on such a diet, it will develop with an I.Q. several points higher than it would otherwise. Is this not progress? *No,* says Dr. J. E. Cawte of Australia, who writes:

> The new clan of treated phenylketonurics cannot be assumed to be a happy one, or one with a high proportion of well adjusted individuals. Conceding for the moment that the phenylketonuric, if he sticks to his diet, will retain much of his intelligence, it is safe to predict that he will be miserable. One of his life's basic processes for satisfaction, his food, has been seriously tampered with and replaced by a conflict. Eggs, milk, cheese, meat, fish, poultry, most fruit, even ordinary bread, are taboo for his table. He will consume a diet which will be cunningly prepared and flavored, but we can hardly say that he 'eats food'. . . .
>
> More than this, the legitimate diet permitted him conceals risk. He must plot a careful course between the Scylla of too little phenylalanine and the Charybdis of too much. Too little will lead to tissue breakdown, generalized amino-aciduria, and return of the old biochemical abnormalities. Too much will intoxicate his neurones and start his progression down the

slippery slope of mental dullness. The margin for error in a given case may not be great.

So the act of eating, instead of being pleasurable, is beset with difficulty and anxiety of a degree which the diabetic, or even the obsessional neurotic, never encounters. Furthermore the phenylketonuric child will learn guilt as the response to natural appetite, while he is too young to appreciate that it is not his craving that is dangerous, so much as the medical progress which has landed him in his predicament.

How will the poor phenylketonuric handle these problems? Because he is not likely to be of exceptional intelligence or adaptability, it is not going to be easy for him to find satisfaction compensating for all this. The less stable ones will not need to turn to alcohol for oblivion to the burden imposed by medical science. All they have to do is substitute milk or some such beverage for the wine with which disappointed Omar Khayyam, in that profane poem, proposed to fill another and another cup to drown the memory of this impertinence. They can cloud their consciousness on bacon and eggs.

Komm' Susser Tod

"All of us," said George Eliot, "get our thoughts entangled in metaphors, and act fatally on the strength of them." Colorfulness is one of the hazards of communication. The apt metaphor cuts two ways and in the end may do more harm than good. Muller's phrase "genetic death" is a dangerous one. Our traditional reaction to the word "death" is so automatic, so unthinking, that we suppose quite unconsciously that "genetic death" is wholly undesirable. This is far from the truth. Genetic death is not always to be shunned; it is often to be welcomed.

We do not say that the cause of the genetic death is to be desired; the cause is a "bad" mutation, and we mean *bad*. The cause is not desired, but we must accept it. Having received the mutation, the question is: How are we to pay for it? What does it cost?

It has two costs. The primary one we have already seen: genetic death. Every bad mutation has the same cost, in this sense: precisely one genetic death, one extinction. (*"After the first death there is no other. . . ."*) Genetic death may be variously subdivided. With a dominant lethal mutation it occurs in one stroke. With a recessive sublethal mutation it is spread over a number of generations, depending on its seriousness and on the mating system. All its partial deaths add up to 1. In a state of nature, the total cost, in terms of reproduction, is constant.

But there is another cost that is not constant: this we may call the suffering-cost, for want of a better name. This is not constant. A lethal gene acting before birth costs the least.

About 10 percent of all human pregnancies end in spontaneous abortion. Of these an appreciable fraction, apparently more than half, is attributable to lethal genes. The suffering involved is certainly not great, perhaps none for the embryo and seldom much for the mother or disappointed relatives. Even gentler in their action are the still more lethal genes that cause the death of the embryo in the first week or two of its existence. Such an embryo is conceived, started on its way, and then killed by its genes without a twinge of pain or regret in the mother, who idly wonders how it happened that menstruation came a few days late. With really lethal genes, death comes softly.

It is the sublethals that exact the highest price in suffering. Consider hemophilia. Who can add up its total cost in terms of fear and the foreboding of a death brought on by some minor and unforeseeable accident? The cost to the hemophiliac himself is not all: he has parents, perhaps later a wife. All these share in the suffering-cost.

In a state of nature each bad gene causes one genetic death. Man can delay or avert this if he wishes—but only at the expense of increasing the suffering-cost. Hemophiliacs are now kept alive by frequent, sometimes daily, blood transfusions. We can, if we wish, encourage them to have children. Suppose we saw to it that hemophiliacs had, on the average, precisely as many children as normal people, what would be the result? Genetic death would thus be completely eliminated, but the cost in suffering would be established as a perpetual and continuing cost, a sort of overhead if you wish. However small the cost might be per generation, it would increase without limit as time went on. Every bad mutation is a sort of fine levied against mankind. We can either pay the fine promptly or we can delay or avoid payment altogether—by paying in another way.

We are in the position of the traffic violator who can either pay a fifty-dollar fine *once* in court, or can pay one dollar hush money every week to a dishonest officer to keep from having the violation reported. In the long run, even the cheapest blackmail charge mounts up to more than the most expensive fine. In the long run, unobstructed genetic death is the cheapest way to pay for the unavoidable misfortune of mutation.

The Predicament of Man

Is man a part of nature? Insistently this question returns to us as we lay bare layer after layer of truth. The progress of our knowledge of man has in large part been achieved by successively deeper insights into the senses in which man is seen to be part of nature. Yet at the same time, we see with increasing clarity senses in which man may properly be said to be *not* part of nature, to be something standing outside of nature, something unique in nature, a being wonderfully unique in his capabilities, and wonderfully, painfully unique in his predicament.

What man's predicament is entirely escaped the early eugenicists. The utopia of classical eugenics is nowhere clearly and completely outlined, but it was something like this. It was a world in which breeding is controlled by the state. (Not marriages, necessarily, for this can be separated from breeding, especially by using artificial insemination.) The markedly "unfit" are prevented from breeding. What does one mean by "unfit"? Principally those defective in intelligence (since the plans are drawn up by a very intelligent person). But such "negative eugenics" is not enough. As was said in 1952 by Charles Darwin's grandson, Charles Galton Darwin:

> This restraint of the breeding of the feeble-minded is important, and it must never be neglected, but it cannot be regarded as a really effective way of improving the human race. If by analogy one wished to improve the breed of racehorses, one might accomplish a little by always slaughtering the horse that finished last in every race, but it would be a much slower process than the actual one of sending the winner to the stud farm.

So utopia must include positive eugenics as well. We must, by artificial insemination or other means, make it possible for the "fittest" to have more than the average number of children. But how do we decide who the fittest are? Here's the rub. Fittest is a relational term: an organism's fitness refers to its fitness for a particular environment. The environments of men are many and various. Bernard Barber (1953) points out that one describes some 17,000 different jobs in modern society. This is admittedly an incomplete list, though on the other hand not all these jobs are different in terms of their demands on genetic endowment. But there must be thousands of genetically different environments into which humans can fit. If we conceive of a utopia in the simplest form possible, as consisting of a director and his people, we can easily postulate that the director could selectively breed his subjects so as to increase the fitness of each occupational group for its particular occupation. He could, in fact, breed improved successors for all the occupations save one: *his own*. As C. G. Darwin puts it:

> If the director had foreseen his death, he would have tried to produce a successor to himself. Since his profound belief in

heredity had been so fully confirmed by the remarkable changes he had made in his subjects, he would naturally expect that it would be one of his own sons that would be best fitted to succeed him, but his difficulty would be just the same if he were trying to find a successor elsewhere. The matter is on quite a different footing from all his other decisions. For the others he could say: 'I have improved all our breeds, by seeing which son improved on the qualities of his father. That is why I select you.' For his own successor the utmost he could say would be 'I am selecting you in the hope that you may be a better director than I have been. But I have no idea how you will set about it, since *if I had known what I was failing in, I should have set it right myself.*'

In the last phrase, to which italics have been added, the author has pointed out a weakness of the eugenic utopias that seems to have escaped the attention of most of the eugenicists from Francis Galton's day to the present. It is of more than a little interest to note that the author is not only the grandson of Charles Darwin, but also is a distant cousin of Galton's. Thus, in our own time, significant contributions to evolutionary thinking continue to be made by a member of a family that, with Erasmus Darwin, began thinking about the matter more than a century and a half ago. The Darwins have become one of their own best arguments for hereditary and evolutionary principles in man, even to the extent of pointing out how exceptional man is.

How is man to control his own evolution? How can he possibly have the wisdom to do so? How can the animal-that-makes-himself conceive the best possible image to mold himself into? We see no answer to this problem. The worst of it is, we have forced ourselves into a position in which we *have* to give an answer. In the days before Pasteur man's population was maintained approximately constant from generation to generation by a cybernetic system in which the principle feedback element at the upper limit was disease. The crowd-diseases—smallpox, cholera, typhoid, plague, etc.—are, by the ecologist, labeled "density-dependent factors," whose effectiveness in reducing population is a power function of the density of the population. No growth of population could get out of hand as long as the crowd-diseases were unconquered, which means that man did not have to sit in judgment on man, to decide who should have a cover at Nature's feast and who should not. With the development of bacteriological medicine, all this has been changed. Now, the feedback control is man himself. The reality of this truth is temporarily obscured by the increasing of the size of the feast, through technological advances, but the increase is only a passing phase which must soon come to an end. (Even now, for the majority of the people of the world, there has been no increase per person.) Having eliminated all other enemies, man is his own worst enemy. Having disposed of all his predators, man preys on himself.

"Man preys on himself . . ."—the language is too colorful. Many eugenicists, from Plato onward, have postulated severe controls: infanticide, involuntary sterilization, and putting males out to stud. No such direct and controversial measures need be used to achieve genetic effects. Controls, to be effective, need operate with no more than statistical precision. No judgment need be passed on individuals; it is enough if a law affects the reproductivity of one definable class more than another. If it does, it will have genetic effects, and may be called a eugenic law, whether it is consciously such or not, whether its eugenic effects are good or bad. Taxation is a measure that is notoriously impossible to free from eugenic side effects. Consider the income tax in the United States. By creating a deduction for each child that is a constant figure regardless of parental income, the poor are encouraged to have children, while the rich are discouraged from doing so, since the cost of bringing up a child is unavoidably proportionate to one's income rather than a fixed cost. *If* the poorer taxpayer is genetically superior to one who is richer, the eugenic effect of this law is good. If the deduction for dependents were a proportionate one (rather than a constant), its eugenic effect would be different. What is desirable is not here in question. The point is, it is difficult, if not impossible, to draft a law, any law, that is without eugenic effects.

"Man is condemned at every moment to invent man." So said Jean Paul Sartre, in another context. By his every law and action, in this finite, crowded world, the man of today invents the man of tomorrow by affecting the reproduction of competing genes differently. Does man do well in this inventing? If so, it is only by chance, for he pays little attention to the eugenic consequences of his laws. As the world becomes more crowded, he may pay more attention, and here enters another danger—the danger arising from his limited wisdom. In principle, no definitive answer can be given to C. G. Darwin's objection; the only hope is to "spread the bets" enough to hit on the right answer somewhere, sometime.

In *Heads and Tales,* the sculptor Malvina Hoffman tells a charming story of a Mohammedan who made for her an exquisite tiled fountain, perfectly paved—except for one tile which was conspicuously missing. When Miss Hoffman asked why he had deliberately introduced this imperfection he replied, "Only Allah can create the perfect."

However curious this sentiment may seem to us, we recognize it as a piety. Something of this piety must enter into our making of man. If we deliberately make man in the best image we can conceive, insisting that every tile be in place, the result will surely be unhappy, because our wisdom is not perfect. As we increasingly take tighter hold on our own destiny we must see to it that a considerable measure of disorder is retained—out of humility. Waste and disorder, properly controlled, are fruitful of good, as we have seen at many levels. The Law of the Corner, tithing, diploidy and fragmentation of a species into many separate breeding populations—all these, in their various ways, mitigate the full severity of the logical working out of the Competitive Exclusion Principle. They increase the variety of life by saving part of the relatively "unfit"—as defined by today's world—for possible use in the different world of tomorrow. Those who, in the name of whatever principle, seek to put an end to all waste threaten a very foundation stone of evolution and progress. However different they may be in ideology, Capitalist and Socialist all too often, in the name of efficiency, join hands in throttling life.

Science as Waste

Just as biological evolution has been made immensely more luxuriant and productive through mechanisms that prevent complete efficiency in the working out of the competitive processes, so also has social evolution progressed most rapidly under circumstances that insured a considerable measure of waste. Countries that have been fully populated for long periods of time—*e.g.*, classical China—have produced a negligible amount of science. The reason is not difficult to find. Science—pure science—is, in its inception, pure waste. An item of information in pure science "pays off" in a practical way only after it has long been in existence and has been combined with other items of pure science. We are reminded of the new mutation, which is almost always bad, but which—if protected by diploidy—may eventually be able to combine with other and similarly "wasteful" genes to produce a new and superior constellation of genes. Diploidy is the great protector of novel genes; prosperity is the great protector of novel thought. A people whose nose is constantly to the grindstone of poverty cannot look up to see the world as it is; all that exists is the nose and the grindstone. A people living under completely Malthusian conditions cannot discover even so much as the Malthusian principle. Science is not produced by eternally busy, miserable people. The flowering of science in the Western world in the last four centuries paralleled the increase in prosperity. Cause? Effect?

Both. However the new science got started (prosperity was only a necessary condition, not a sufficient), once started, it produced more prosperity as an effect which fed back into the system as a cause. Science and technology make a system with positive feedback. No such system can go on forever in a finite world. How it will stop, and when, we cannot but wonder.

And who is it that makes science? Who, indeed, makes poetry or music or art, or any of the creations that stretch the minds and spirits of men? The normal psychiatry of occupations is just beginning to be explored. We know little for sure about this problem. But already there is enough biographical detail to suggest the form of the answer.

Darwin's life is symbolic. His *Autobiography* clearly and unconsciously reveals two elements that are needed to produce any creative genius: irresponsibility and alienation. Is this surprising? We do not ordinarily count these as desirable things; surely they are not so when present in the extreme. But in small measure they are essential to the development of the creative spirit. When Darwin, in about his seventeenth year, learned that his father would leave him enough property so that he need never work, he gave up all pretense of preparing himself for a professional job. The roster of scientists of the eighteenth and nineteenth centuries is replete with the names of men of wealth: Darwin, Galton, Lyell, Cavendish and Boyle, to name only a few. Wealth relieves one of the responsibility of making a living; one then *may* become a scientist. (Why wealthy men of our time do not do so we will see later.)

He who is to see what other men have not seen must, in a real sense, become alienated from the crowd. The manner in which this alienation occurs is subject to an infinity of permutations.

>   *Most wretched men*
> *Are cradled into poetry by wrong:*
> *They learn in suffering what they teach in song,*

said Shelley. How great the wrong must be is problematical. For many a scientist of the nineteenth century the process of alienation began when he embarked on an extended journey: so it was for Darwin, Hooker, Huxley, Galton and von Humboldt. A man of the twentieth century might suppose that these voyagers had many companions, but not so. In a world in which class distinctions were so much a part of a man's unconscious, no man's world was very populous. Darwin on the *Beagle*, surrounded by lowly sailors, was virtually alone.

His only real equal, his cabin-mate, Captain Fitz-Roy, was himself so weird a psychiatric specimen that young Charles had to withdraw into himself to preserve his sanity. Thus began his alienation.

Alienation breeds alienation. Through the lens of his loneliness Darwin saw the world as it was, not as people thought it. In the Galápagos he apprehended the fact of evolution. Then began his real ordeal. The feeling that he was about to commit murder (as he expressed it to Hooker later) now became part of his daily burden. Illnesses of the voyage that may have been initially "organic" continued at the psychic level. Fearing the disapproval of his fellows, he withdrew from their fellowship, which he so dearly loved, and holed up in Down for the rest of his life, thus creating the conditions for thinking even more alienating thoughts. There is positive feedback in this system, too.

But there is a limit to the alienation a man can endure and still retain his sanity. In some way every great creator must find a companion. For some, it is the felt presence of a past master, who may, from long study, seem like an actual contemporary, like a household spirit. For other thinkers, support comes with the vision of an understanding posterity. ("My time will come," said Mendel, who had spoken in vain to the scientists of his own age.) Still others, most fortunate of all, find a living confidant. For Darwin, it was Hooker— Hooker, the sad young botanist; Hooker, who was near enough to Darwin's age to be an equal, but just young enough to be forever the admiring disciple. To Hooker, Darwin poured out his heart in hundreds upon hundreds of letters. In the strict sense, this was the great love affair of Darwin's life. It made his alienation from the mass of society bearable and productive.

Nurturing the Spirit of Science

The problem of fostering science is one of the great unsolved problems of our day. T. H. Huxley once remarked that the new truths of science begin as heresy, advance to orthodoxy, and end up as superstition. It is not science in its last two phases that we are interested in promoting: such kinds of science can take care of themselves all too well. It is young science, new science, science that is heretical that is our problem. How do we encourage this?

It is not enough merely to vocalize in favor of heresy. Surely we in our day know all too well the harvest that comes from this kind of cultivation.

Heretics choose for heresy
Whatever's the prevailing fashion.

So Phyllis McGinley has lampooned the efforts of those who
have as their *goal,* heresy. And she's right. It is not possible to
found an effective Society for the Cultivation of Heresy.
Heretics are lonely seers. They cannot be institutionalized.

We cannot deliberately produce heretics. But we can make
the conditions favorable for their spontaneous generation. We
can see to it that a substantial minority have available to them
that indispensable ingredient of heretical and creative thought,
irresponsibility. In the past, men of wealth have had this
gift. Now they seem not to have. *Fortune* magazine, after
making a survey of the sociological origins of science, came to
the conclusion that "the broadest generalization that may be
made is that scientists tend to come from the lower-income
levels." Many students of law and medicine have their school-
ing entirely paid for by the family; among graduate students
in science, such support is rare—their families seldom have
money.

The wealthy of our age are probably the most responsible
Croesuses the world has ever known. Inherited wealth is almost universally acknowledged by its recipients to carry with
it a heavy load of obligation—obligation to one's forebears to
preserve and increase the wealth, to one's successors to
pass it on, and to society as a whole *to do good.* The
wealthy eccentric is a nearly extinct dodo. The man of wealth
is now an other-directed man. He may become a lawyer or a
doctor. But not a scientist. He is too much a part of the
world to achieve the alienation required to be creative. (What
millionaire today would have the nerve to do what Darwin did—retire to a "non-productive" life in the country *to
think?*)

The discipline of science has little to recommend it as a way
of life to those well supplied with this world's goods and
breathing an atmosphere of fellowship and togetherness. Its
appeal, like that of professional sports and the performing
arts, is to the relatively impoverished. For the ambitious
youngster of the lower classes these three routes offer the best
avenues to social promotion. These occupations, perhaps
more than any other, offer rich rewards to inner-directed men,
rewards based almost entirely on individual merit; family
and connections count for little. In terms of basic biological
endowment the rich, one would suspect, are at least as well
fitted to become independent thinkers as the poor; but their
environment is unfavorable to independence.

If we lived in a non-competitive One World the non-cre-

ativity of what is undoubtedly a genetically superior class
would not matter; but this is not One World, and does not
promise to be. The world is highly competitive and shows
signs of becoming more so. The creative spirit that character-
izes, but is not confined to, science is of great competitive
value. How can we establish the conditions needed for this
creativity?

There was a time when hereditary wealth, coupled with a
tolerance of eccentricity, created the necessary conditions. In
the more recent past, freedom from workaday cares and
responsibilities has been more often furnished by an academic
position. Scientists occupying university posts produced so
much pioneering research precisely because they weren't paid
to do it. For, as the Nobel laureate, J. J. Thomson, remarked:

> . . . if you pay a man a salary for doing research, he and you
> will want to have something to point to at the end of the year
> to show that the money has not been wasted. In promising
> work of the highest class, however, results do not come in this
> regular fashion, in fact years may pass without any tangible
> results being obtained, and the position of the paid worker
> would be very embarrassing and he would naturally take to
> work on a lower, or at any rate a different plane where he could
> be sure of getting year by year tangible results which would
> justify his salary. The position is this: You want this kind of
> research, but, if you pay a man to do it, it will drive him to
> research of a different kind. The only thing to do is to pay
> him for doing something else and give him enough leisure to
> do research for the love of it.

As it became generally realized that an important fraction
of the world's research in pure science was done by academic
men, administrators defined research as part of the job, and
made productivity in research a criterion for advancement.
The consequences of this meddling have been about what
one would expect. There is now a tendency to choose
projects that are pretty sure to give quick results, and to avoid
questions on tabooed subjects. This is why so little work is
done in human heredity, so little inquiry made into human
differences. As research has become more expensive, the academic man has had to develop a talent for beginning. He
gets subsidy from foundations by telling committees what he
hopes to accomplish with their money if he gets it. The successful beggar often gives more attention to the committee
than he does to the scientific problem. The result: other-
directedness is introduced into a realm where it has no business being, the realm of inner-directed science. Orthodoxy is
encouraged. This may not be too bad for what we *call* "sci-

ence," for its fields are almost all freed now of conflict with tradition, and its methods systematized to the point where innumerable and immensely important discoveries can be made by men who are not in the first rank of the heretics. But there is need for the spirit of science to move into the fields not now called science, into fields where tradition still holds court. We can hardly expect a committee to acquiesce in the dethronement of tradition. Only an individual can do that, an individual who is not responsible to the mob. Now that the truly independent man of wealth has disappeared, now that the independence of the academic man is fast disappearing, where are we to find the conditions of partial alienation and irresponsibility needed for the highest creativity?

If we solve this problem, we can expect progress to be made in fields more important to man's welfare than is science as presently conceived. Social inheritance will be based on new foundations, and ways will be found to secure the blessings of non-material inheritance without nullifying the implications of genetic recombination. Light will be thrown on the problem of the value of life.

Authors of the greatest persuasiveness seem to be convinced that tomorrow is the world of the other-directed man. Perhaps they are right. No one sees how this eventuality may be easily avoided in a Pasteurian world. However, no fate may ever be said to be an inevitable one for man, for merely saying so may alter the truth. (Here is a mode of truth, undreamed of and unallowed for in what we now call science. Here is a problem that requires its own Bolyai and Lobachevsky.) Even other-directed men may be rational, and if rational, may be convinced of the necessity of cherishing those not of their own kind. The inner-directed man, he who is answerable only to his own conscience, is always a thorny tablemate, doubly so when Nature's board is crowded. To ask that all men be inner-directed would be quixotic in the extreme; but it is not unreasonable to ask that other-directed men add the care and nurture of a small corps of inner-directed men to their tithing duties. It is not planning that is needed here, certainly not organization. It is, rather, a systematic allowance for waste, for hetrodoxy, for the unforeseeable. It is perhaps not even understanding that is demanded— that would be asking too much of other-directed man—but something in the nature of faith. Faith in the future, and faith in the fruitfulness of waste, properly allowed for.

Those who have painted pictures of an organized heaven have, implicitly or otherwise, appealed to the esthetic sense in man to try to gain assent to their plans. We know now that a completely planned heaven is either impossible or unbearable. We know that it is not true that design can come only out of planning. Out of luxuriant waste, winnowed by selection, come designs more beautiful and in greater variety than ever man could plan. This is the lesson of Nature that Darwin has spelled out for us. Man, now that he makes himself, cannot do better than to emulate Nature's example in allowing for waste and encouraging novelty. There is grandeur in this view of life as a complex of cybernetic systems that produce adaptedness without foresight, design without planning, and progress without dictation. From the simplest means, man, now master of his own fate, may evolve societies of a variety and novelty—yes, and even of a beauty—that no man living can now foresee.

References

THIS book has been written primarily for the general reader, rather than for the scholar. However, even the general reader may now and then wish to check on the origins of an idea, or the evidence. The Bibliography includes, I believe, all the relevant documentation. As a matter of fact, it includes a bit more, and for this I must apologize. I have not intended (in William Harvey's words) "to make a parade of the strength of my memory, the extent of my reading, or the amount of my pains." Originally the Bibliography was *just* sufficient, no more. But as revision succeeded revision, more and more details were thrown out; my bibliographic apparatus, however, was not equal to the task of eliminating all the once-relevant references without running the danger of throwing out some that were still needed. I have, therefore, retained them all.

References to the Bibliography that are clear from the text alone are usually not further discussed. In the citations below, the number following the topic refers to the numbered citation in the Bibliography. Numbers in parentheses refer to volume number (if in **bold face**) or to page number (if not).

Chapter 1

For Charles Darwin's life: 12, 50, 156; Erasmus Darwin: 76, 150 (**1**: 261). Thanks to William Kennedy for Coleridge: 34 (**2**: 648); thanks to Douwe Stuurman for Goethe. Copleston, 132 (879); da Vinci, 126 (313). The geology battle, 206.

Chapter 2

Unnoticed predecessors of Darwin, 175. Darwin generally: 50, 51, 118; his health, 97, 98: his wealth, 108. Robert Darwin on confiding in wives, 104 (61). Reactions to Chambers, 22, 135, 172. On Hooker, 101.

Chapter 3

On Darwin's exposition, 50 (**1**: 80), 100 (**2**: 190). Ricardo, 164 (52, 53, 61). Darwin on metaphor 48 (76). Paley vs. Darwin, 61a. On panchrestons in general, 88, 89.

Chapter 4

On the Idea of Progress, 24, 36, 192. Haldane, 86. Darwin, on the eye, 50 (**2:** 67); on the competitive exclusion principle, 48 (114). Lyell on shell-collectors, 129 (**2:** 24). The anonymous zoologist on taxonomy is Stresemann, 79 (156). Vanderplank, 149 (545). *Anableps,* 148 (296). On the introduction of animals from one region to another, see 200. Von Haller, 8 (45). Conversations with John Cushing have been particularly helpful in developing this chapter.

Chapter 5

For the Huxley-Wilberforce affair, see 20, 50, 66, 100, 101. For the subsequent warfare, see 14, 67, 206. For Galileo, see 169. For Darwin's ordeal, see 50. Planck's quotation, 153 (34). On Jenkin, see 136, 188, 189. Owen's quotation, 80 (211).

Chapter 6

For Mendel, 103. For a more thorough, though still brief, treatment of genetics, see 87; for more extensive treatments, see 182, 186.

Chapter 7

For Bateson, 13; Michelson, 91; Spemann, 179. Treatments of human genetics: 146, 162, 186. On Tertullian and the idea of "natural," 124. On legality of insemination, 209a. Thanks to Jack Snidecor for Greenwood, 81.

Chapter 8

On human differences, see especially 210, 211, 212, 213. See also 4, 146, 162, 186. For Freud, see 106 (**1:** 320). For the social worker's resistance to genetics, see 95 (122). For the account of the 1907 transfusion, see 33 (170).

Chapter 9

For a not-too-old summary of the effects of radiation, see 171. To keep posted in this rapidly changing field, regularly examine the *Bulletin of the Atomic Scientists.*

Chapter 10

On Galton, see 19, 69-74, 151. B. Webb, 19 (78). The Bernoullis, 15 (131). Confucius, 137 (14). Bateson, 13 (388, 305). J. J. Thomson, 160 (2). Depew, 94 (31). Muller, 144.

Chapter 11

For the Lysenko affair, see 18, 19 (268), 99, 114, and above all, 214. For Kammerer, see 75.

Chapter 12

No place is there an adequate synthesis of the work of Fisher, Haldane and Wright. For some of the early work of the first two, see 62, 86. For Wright, we must be content with 3 and 55. For the history of hybrid corn, see 33. The remark on putting the chart before the horse is found in 105 (495); on what subspecies actually are in 79 (183). For Haldane's comments on "that inexhaustible queerness," see 86 (169).

Chapter 13

Malthus, 128 (531). Shelley on Malthus, 173; Hazlitt on same, 96 (101). On "Social Darwinism," see 94; Darwin on same, 50 (2: 56). D. H. Lawrence, 116 (60). C. G. Darwin, 49 (122, 120). For Shelley's wretched men, 174. J. J. Thomson, 160 (199). For eugenic utopias, see 19, 145. On the evolution of genetic systems, a topic which I have inadequately treated, much to my regret, see Darlington's classic, 43. This book has come to an end all too soon (in the *author's* opinion).

Bibliography

1. AGAR, W. E., F. H. DRUMMOND & O. W. TIEGS. 1948. Third report on a test of McDougall's Lamarckian experiment on the training of rats. *J. Exp. Biol.*, **25**: 103–122.
2. ALLEE, W. C. 1926. Distribution of animals in a tropical rain-forest with relation to environmental factors. *Ecology*, **7**: 445–468.
3. —— 1938. *The Social Life of Animals.* 293 pp. N.Y.: Norton.
4. ALLISON, A. C. & K. G. McWHIRTER. 1956. Two unifactorial characters for which man is polymorphic. *Nature*, **178**: 748–749.
5. ANDERSON, R. C. & S. C. REED. 1954. The likelihood of recurrence of congenital malformations. *Journal-Lancet* (Minneapolis) **74**: 175–176.
6. ANONYMOUS. 1868. [Book review.] *Athenaeum*, No. 2102, 8 Feb. 1868, p. 217.
7. ANONYMOUS. *The Birth of Genetics.* [Trans. of Mendel's letters to Naegeli, and of Correns', de Vries' and Tschermak's papers of 1900]. 47 pp. Brooklyn, N.Y.: Brooklyn Bot. Garden. 1950.
8. ARBER, AGNES. 1954. *The Mind and the Eye.* ix + 146 pp. Cambridge: University Press.
9. ARBUTHNOT, JOHN. 1710. An argument for divine providence, taken from the constant regularity observ'd in the births of both sexes. *Philos. Trans., Roy. Philos. Soc.*, **27**: 186–190. (1710–1712).
10. ASHLEY-MONTAGU
    See MONTAGU
11. BARBER, BERNARD. 1953. *Science and the Social Order.* 288 pp. London: Allen & Unwin.
12. BARLOW, NORA. 1946. *Charles Darwin and the Voyage of the Beagle.* 279 pp. N.Y.: Philosophical Library.
13. BATESON, BEATRICE. 1928. *William Bateson, F.R.S.* ix + 473 pp. Cambridge: University Press.
14. BEECHER, HENRY WARD. 1885. *Evolution and Religion.* 440 pp. N.Y.: Fords, Howard & Hulbert.
15. BELL, E. T. 1937. *Men of Mathematics.* xv + 592 pp. N.Y.: Simon & Schuster.
16. BELL, JULIA. 1934. Huntington's chorea. *Treas. Hum. Inher.*, **4**: 1–67.
17. BENEDICT, RUTH. 1934. *Patterns of Culture*, xvii + 272 pp. N.Y.: Penguin Books. 1947. The New American Library (MD89). 1946.
18. BERNAL, J. D. 1949. The biological controversy in the Soviet

Union and its implications. *Modern Quarterly,* **4:** 203–217.

19. BLACKER, C. P. 1952. *Eugenics: Galton and After.* 349 pp. London: Duckworth.

20. BLINDERMAN, CHARLES S. 1957. Thomas Henry Huxley. *Sci. Monthly,* **84:** 171–182.

21. BOLK, LOUIS. 1926. *Das Problem der Menschenwerden.* Jena. (Taken, however, from Haldane, 1932)

22. BOSANQUET, SAMUEL R. 1845. *Vestiges of the Natural History of Creation. Its Argument Examined and Exposed.* 56 pp. London: John Hatchard & Son.

23. BRIDGMAN, P. W. 1957. Some of the broader implications of science. *Physics Today,* **10** (10): 17–24.

24. BURY, J. B. 1920. *The Idea of Progress.* xv + 377 pp. London: Macmillan.

25. BUTLER, SAMUEL. 1872. *Erewhon.* The New American Library (CD41). 1961.

26. CANNON, WALTER B. 1932. *The Wisdom of the Body.* xv + 312 pp. New York: Norton.

27. ——— 1940. The role of chance in discovery. *Sci. Monthly,* **50:** 204–209.

28. CASTER, W. O. 1957. Strontium-90 hazard: relationship between maximum permissible concentration and population mean. *Science,* **125:** 1291–1292.

29. CASTLE, W. E. & JOHN C. PHILLIPS. 1909. A successful ovarian transplantation in the guinea pig, and its bearing on problems of genetics. *Science,* **30:** 312. [Reprinted in Gabriel and Fogel, 1955].

30. CAWTE, J. E. 1956. A note on the future of phenylketonuria. *Jour. Mental Sci.,* **102:** 805–811.

31. [CHAMBERS, ROBERT] 1844 (published anonymously). *Vestiges of the Natural History of Creation.* 4th Amer. ed. from the 3rd London ed. vi + 353 + 142 pp. N.Y.: Wiley & Putnam. 1846.

32. CLAUSEN, JENS. 1951. *Stages in the Evolution of Plant Species.* viii + 206 pp. Ithaca, N.Y.: Cornell Univ. Press.

33. COHEN, I. BERNARD. 1948. *Science, Servant of Man.* xiv + 362 pp. Boston: Little, Brown.

34. COLERIDGE, ERNEST HARTLEY, ed. 1895. *Letters of Samuel Taylor Coleridge.* 2 vol. Boston: Houghton Mifflin.

35. CONANT, JAMES B. 1947. *On Understanding Science.* xv + 145 pp. New Haven, Conn.: Yale Univ. Press. The New American Library (MD68). 1951.

36. CONDORCET, ANTOINE-NICHOLAS DE. 1795. *Sketch for a Historical Picture of the Progress of the Human Mind.* xvi + 202 pp. New York: The Noonday Press, 1955.

37. COOLEY, C. H. 1897. Genius, fame and the comparison of races. *Ann. Amer. Acad. Polit. Soc. Sci.,* **9:** 1–42.

38. CORRENS, CARL. 1900. Gregor Mendels Regel über das Verhalten der Nachkommenschaft der Rassenbastarde. *Ber. deutsch. Bot. Ges.,* **18:** 158–168.

39. CROMBIE, A. C. 1947. Interspecific competition. *J. Anim. Ecol.,* **16:** 44–73.

40. CROW, JAMES F. 1957. Possible consequences of an increased mutation rate. *Eugenics Quarterly*, **4**: 67–80.

41. CURTIS, CHARLES P., JR., and FERRIS GREENSLET, eds. 1945. *The Practical Cogitator*. x + 577 pp. Boston: Houghton Mifflin.

42. CUSHING, JOHN E., JR. 1941. Non-genetic mating preference as a factor in evolution. *Condor*, **43**: 233–236.

43. DARLINGTON, C. D. 1939. *The Evolution of Genetic Systems*. x + 151 pp. Cambridge: Univ. Press. 1946.

44. DARLINGTON, C. D. & K. MATHER. 1950. *Genes, Plants and People*. xxi + 187 pp. Philadelphia: Blakiston.

45. DARWIN, CHARLES. *The Foundations of the Origin of Species*. Two Essays written in 1842 and 1844. Edited by Francis Darwin. xxix + 263. pp. Cambridge: University Press, 1909.

46. ——— 1859. *On the Origin of Species by Means of Natural Selection*, or *The Preservation of Favoured Races in the Struggle for Life*. Reprint of 1st ed. xx + 426 pp. N.Y.: Philosophical Library, 1951.

47. ——— 1868. *The Variation of Animals and Plants under Domestication*. 2 vols. London: Murray.

48. ——— 1872. *The Origin of Species*. 6th ed. reprinted. xxxv + 557 pp. N.Y.: Macmillan, 1927.

49. DARWIN, CHARLES GALTON. 1952. *The Next Million Years*. 210 pp. London: Hart-Davis.

50. DARWIN, FRANCIS, ed. 1887. *The Life and Letters of Charles Darwin*. 2 vol. N.Y.: D. Appleton. 1898.

51. DARWIN, FRANCIS and A. C. SEWARD. 1903. *More Letters of Charles Darwin*. 2 vol. London: John Murray.

52. DAVENPORT, CHARLES BENEDICT. 1903. The animal ecology of the Cold Spring Sand Spit, with remarks on the theory of adaptation. *Univ. Chic. Decennial Publ., 1st Ser.*, **10**: 157–176.

53. DOBZHANSKY, THEODOSIUS. 1927. Studies on manifold effect of certain genes in Drosophila melanogaster. *Zeit. ind. Abstam. u. Vererb.* **43**: 330–388.

54. ——— 1941. *Genetics and the Origin of Species*. 2nd ed. xviii + 446 pp. N.Y.: Columbia Univ. Press.

55. ——— 1951. *Genetics and the Origin of Species*. 3rd ed. x + 364 pp. N.Y.: Columbia Univ. Press.

56. ——— 1956. *The Biological Basis of Human Freedom*. vi + 139 pp. N.Y.: Columbia Univ. Press.

57. DOBZHANSKY, T. and M. F. ASHLEY MONTAGU. 1947. Natural selection and the mental capacities of mankind. *Science*, **106**: 587–590.

58. DRAPER, JOHN WILLIAM. 1874. *History of the Conflict Between Religion and Science*. 8th ed. xxii + 373 pp. N.Y.: Appleton. 1876.

59. DUCLAUX, ÉMILE. 1920. *Pasteur, the History of a Mind*. xxxii + 363 pp. Philadelphia: Saunders.

60. EAST, EDWARD M. and DONALD F. JONES. 1919. *Inbreeding and Outbreeding: Their Genetic and Sociological Significance*. 285 pp. Philadelphia: Lippincott.

61. ELIOT, GEORGE. 1872. *Middlemarch*. (Many editions.)

61a. ELLEGARD, ALVAR. 1956. The Darwinian theory and the argument from design. *Lychnos* (1956), 173–192.

62. FISHER, R. A. 1930. *The Genetical Theory of Natural Selection*. 272 pp. Oxford: Oxford University Press.

63. FISHER, R. A. and E. B. FORD. 1950. The "Sewall Wright effect." *Heredity,* **4:** 117–119.

64. FONTENELLE, BERNARD LE BOVIER DE. 1686. *Conversations with a Lady on the Plurality of Worlds.* (Transl. by Mr. Glanvill.) 4th ed. x + 211 pp. London: M. Wellington. 1719.

65. FORD, H. D. and E. B. FORD. 1930. Fluctuation in numbers and its influence on variation in Melitaea. *Trans. Ent. Soc. London,* **78:** 345–351.

66. FOSKETT, D. J. 1953. Wilberforce and Huxley on evolution. *Nature,* **172:** 920.

67. FURNISS, NORMAN F. 1954. *The Fundamentalist Controversy, 1918-1931.* viii + 199 pp. New Haven, Conn.: Yale Univ. Press.

68. GABRIEL, MORDECAI L. and SEYMOUR FOGEL. 1955. *Great Experiments in Biology,* xiii + 317 pp. Englewood Cliffs, N.J.: Prentice-Hall.

69. GALTON, FRANCIS. 1865. Hereditary talent and character. *Macmillan's Magazine,* **12:** 157–166, 318–327.

70. ——— 1869. *Hereditary Genius: an Inquiry into its Laws and Consequences.* vi + 390 pp. N.Y.: Appleton, 1870.

71. ——— 1883. *Inquiries into Human Faculty and its Development.* xix + 261 pp. London: Eugenics Society, 1951.

72. ——— 1889. *Natural Inheritance.* ix + 259 pp. London and N.Y.: Macmillan.

73. ——— 1905. Eugenics as a factor in religion. *Sociological Papers,* **2:** 52–53.

74. ——— 1908. *Memories of My Life.* 2nd ed. viii + 339 pp. London: Methuen.

75. GARDNER, MARTIN. 1952. *In the Name of Science.* x + 320 pp. N.Y.: G. P. Putnam.

76. GARFINKLE, NORTON. 1955. Science and religion in England, 1790–1800: the critical response to the work of Erasmus Darwin. *Jour. Hist. Ideas,* **16:** 376–388.

77. GAUSE, G. F. 1934. *The Struggle for Existence.* ix + 163 pp. Baltimore: Williams & Wilkins Co.

78. GLASS, BENTLEY. 1954. (Discussion) *Amer. Jour. Hum. Genetics,* **6:** 187–188.

79. GOLDSCHMIDT, R. 1940. *The Material Basis of Evolution.* xi + 436 pp. New Haven, Conn.: Yale Univ. Press.

80. GRAY, ALEXANDER. 1946. *The Socialist Tradition.* xx + 523 pp. N.Y.: Longmans, Green.

81. GREENWOOD, ERNEST. 1957. Attributes of a profession. *Social Work* (July) 45–55.

82. GRUNEBERG, HANS. 1943. *The Genetics of the Mouse.* xii + 412 pp. Cambridge: University Press.

83. —— 1947. *Animal Genetics and Medicine.* xii + 296 pp. N.Y.: Paul B. Hoeber.

84. GULICK, J. T. 1905. Evolution, racial and habitudinal. *Carnegie Inst. Washington Publ.*, **25:** 1–269.

85. HALDANE, J. B. S. 1924. A mathematical theory of natural and artificial selection. *Trans. Camb. Philos. Soc.* **23:** 19–41.

86. —— 1932. *The Causes of Evolution.* vii + 235 pp. N.Y.: Harper & Bros. n.d.

87. HARDIN, GARRETT. 1952. *Biology: Its Human Implications.* 2nd ed. xii + 720 pp. San Francisco: W. H. Freeman & Co.

88. —— 1956. Meaninglessness of the word Protoplasm. *Scientific Monthly,* **82:** 112–120.

89. —— 1957. The threat of clarity. *Amer. Jour. of Psychiatry,* **114:** 392–396.

90. HERSHEY, A. D. 1946. Spontaneous mutations in bacterial viruses. *Cold Spr. Harbor Symp. Quant. Biol.,* **11:** 67–77.

91. H. F. N. 1932. [A. A. Michelson] *Obit. Not. Fellows of Roy. Soc.,* **1:** 18–25.

92. HOFFER, ERIC. 1951. *The True Believer.* xiii + 176 pp. N.Y.: Harper. The New American Library (MD228). 1958.

93. HOFFMAN, MALVINA. 1937. *Heads and Tales.* xx + 416 pp. N.Y.: Scribner's.

94. HOFSTADTER, RICHARD. 1945. *Social Darwinism in American Thought. 1860–1915.* viii + 191 pp. Philadelphia: Univ. Penn. Press.

95. HOLMES, S. J. 1933. *The Eugenic Predicament.* xi + 232 pp. N.Y.: Harcourt, Brace.

96. HOWE, P. P. 1923, *The Life of William Hazlitt.* 2nd ed. ix + 484 pp. N.Y.: George H. Doran.

97. HUBBLE DOUGLAS. 1943. Charles Darwin and psychotherapy. *Lancet,* **244:** 129–133.

98. —— 1953. The life of the shawl. *Lancet:* 1351–1354.

99. HUXLEY, JULIAN. 1949. *Heredity East and West.* x + 246 pp. N.Y.: Schumann.

100. HUXLEY, LEONARD. 1900. *Life and Letters of Thomas Henry Huxley.* 2 vols. London: Macmillan.

101. —— 1918. *Life and Letters of Sir Joseph Dalton Hooker.* 2 vols. London: John Murray.

102. HYLAND, STANLEY. 1955. *Curiosities from Parliament.* xii + 211 pp. London: Allan Wingate.

103. ILTIS, HUGO. 1932. *Life of Mendel.* 336 pp. N.Y.: Norton.

104. IRVINE, WILLIAM. 1955. *Apes, Angels, and Victorians.* 399 pp. New York: McGraw-Hill.

105. JEPSON, GLENN L. 1949. Selection, "orthogenesis," and the fossil record. *Proc. Amer. Philos. Soc.,* **93:** 479–500.

106. JONES, ERNEST. 1953–1957. *The Life and Works of Sigmund Freud.* 3 vols. N.Y.: Basic Books.

107. KALLMAN, FRANZ J. 1956. Psychiatric aspects of genetic counselling. *Amer. Jour. Hum. Gen.,* **8:** 97–101.

108. KEITH, ARTHUR. 1955. *Darwin Revalued.* ix + 294 pp. London: Watts & Co.

109. KEYNES, JOHN MAYNARD. 1926. *The End of Laissez-Faire.* 54 pp. London: Leonard & Virginia Woolf.

110. KINSEY, A. C., W. B. POMEROY, and C. E. MARTIN. 1948. *Sexual Behavior in the Human Male.* xv + 804 pp. Philadelphia: Saunders.

111. LACK, DAVID. 1954. *The Natural Regulation of Animal Numbers.* viii + 343 pp. Oxford: Clarendon Press.

112. LAMARCK, J. B. DE. 1809. *Zoological Philosophy.* Tr. by H. Elliott. xcii + 410 pp. London: Macmillan. 1914.

113. LAMOTTE, M. 1951. Recherches sur la structure génétique de populations naturelles de Cepaea nemoralis. *Ann. Biol.,* **27:** 39–49.

114. LANGDON-DAVIES, JOHN. 1949. *Russia Puts the Clock Back.* 160 pp. London: Gollancz.

115. LANGE F. A. 1877. *The History of Materialism.* 3rd ed. 3 v. in 1. Trans. by E. C. Thomas. N.Y.: Harcourt Brace. 1925.

116. LAWRENCE, FRIEDA. 1934. *Not I, but the Wind . . .* xi + 297 pp. N.Y.: Viking.

117. LI, CHING CHUN. 1955. *Population Genetics.* xi + 366 pp. Chicago: Univ. of Chicago Press.

118. LITCHFIELD, HENRIETTA, ed. 1915. *Emma Darwin: A Century of Family Letters.* 2 vol. London: John Murray.

119. LOTKA, A. J. 1922. Contributions to the energetics of evolution. *Proc. Nat. Acad. Sci.,* **8:** 147–151.

120. ———— 1925. *Elements of Physical Biology.* xix + 460 pp. Baltimore: Williams & Wilkins.

121. ———— 1932. The growth of mixed populations: two species competing for a common food supply. *Jour. Washington Acad. Sci.,* **22:** 461–469.

122. LORENZ, KONRAD Z. 1952. *King Solomon's Ring.* 202 pp. London: Methuen.

123. LOVEJOY, ARTHUR O. 1936. *The Great Chain of Being.* ix + 328 pp. Cambridge, Mass.: Harvard Univ. Press.

124. ———— 1955. " 'Nature' as Norm in Tertullian." In *Essays in the History of Ideas.* xv + 359 pp. N.Y.: Braziller.

125. McCANN, ALFRED WATTERSON. 1922. *God—or Gorilla.* xiii + 368 pp. N.Y.: Devin-Adair.

126. MacCURDY, EDWARD. 1939. *The Notebooks of Leonardo da Vinci.* 1247 pp. N.Y.: Braziller, 1954.

127. McGINLEY, PHYLLIS. 1954. *The Love Letters of Phyllis McGinley.* ix + 116 pp. N.Y.: Viking (Compass Books). 1956.

128. MALTHUS, T. R. 1803. *An Essay on the Principle of Population.* 2nd ed. viii + 610 pp. London: J. Johnson.

129. MARCHANT, JAMES. 1916. *Alfred Russel Wallace: Letters and Reminiscences.* 2 vols. London: Cassel & Co.

130. MATHER, KENNETH. 1949. *Biometrical Genetics.* ix + 158 pp. N.Y.: Dover.

131. MAYR, Ernst. 1942. *Systematics and the Origin of Species.* xiv + 334 pp. N.Y.: Columbia Univ. Press.

132. MENCKEN, H. L. 1942. *A New Dictionary of Quotations.* xiii +1809 pp. N.Y.: Knopf.

133. MENDEL, GREGOR. 1866. Versuche über Pfanzen-Hybriden. *Verhandl. naturf. Vereines. Brünn,* **4:** 3–47.
134. ——— 1866. *Experiments in Plant-Hybridisation.* 41 pp. Cambridge, Mass.: Harvard Univ. Press. 1938.
135. MILLHAUSER, MILTON. 1951. *Robert Chambers, Evolution and the Early Victorian Mind.* 451 pp. Ph.D. Thesis, Columbia University.
136. MIVART, ST. GEORGE. 1871. *On the Genesis of Species.* 314 pp. N.Y.: Appleton.
137. MONTAGU, M. F. ASHLEY. 1951. *Statement on Race.* xi + 172 pp. N.Y.: Schuman.
138. MORGAN, THOMAS HUNT. 1903. *Evolution and Adaptation.* xiii + 470 pp. N.Y.: Macmillan.
139. ——— 1925. *Evolution and Genetics.* ix + 211 pp. Princeton: Princeton Univ. Press.
140. MORTON, NEWTON E., JAMES F. CROW, and H. J. MULLER. 1956. An estimate of the mutational damage in man from data on consanguineous marriages. *Proc. Nat. Acad. Sci.,* **42:** 855–863.
141. MULLER, H. J. 1927. Artificial transmutation of the gene. *Science,* **66:** 84–87.
142. ——— 1928. The production of mutations by X-rays. *Proc. Nat. Acad. Sci.,* **14:** 714–726.
143. ——— 1932. Some genetic aspects of sex. *Amer. Nat.,* **66:** 118–138.
144. ——— 1933. The dominance of economics over eugenics. *Sci. Monthly,* **37:** 40–47.
145. ——— 1935. *Out of the Night.* x + 127 pp. N.Y.: Vanguard.
146. NEEL, JAMES V. and WILLIAM J. SCHULL. 1954. *Human Heredity.* vii + 361 pp. Chicago: Univ. of Chicago Press.
147. NEWMAN, JAMES R., ed. 1956. *The World of Mathematics.* 4 vols. N.Y.: Simon & Schuster.
148. NORMAN, J. R. 1931. *A History of Fishes.* 463 pp. N.Y.: Frederick A. Stokes.
149. PATTERSON, J. T. and W. S. STONE. 1952. *Evolution in the Genus Drosophila.* 610 pp. N.Y.: Macmillan.
150. PAUL, C. KEGAN. 1876. *William Godwin: His Friends and Contemporaries.* 2 vols. Boston: Roberts Brothers.
151. PEARSON, KARL. 1924. *The Life, Letters and Labours of Francis Galton.* 3 vols. Cambridge: University Press.
152. PENROSE, L. S. 1939. Maternal age, order of birth and developmental abnormalities. *Jour. Mental Sci.,* **85:** 1141–1150.
153. PLANCK, MAX. 1949. *Scientific Autobiography, and Other Papers.* 192 pp. N.Y.: Philosophical Library.
154. PLATO. *The Dialogues of Plato.* Transl. by B. Jowett. 3rd ed. 2 vols. N.Y.: Random House, 1937.
155. POPPER, K. R. 1945. *The Open Society and Its Enemies.* 2 vols. London: Routledge & Kegan Paul.
156. POULTON, EDWARD BAGNALL. 1909. *Charles Darwin and The Origin of Species.* xv + 302 pp. London: Longmans, Green.
157. PRESCOTT, WILLIAM H. 1898. *Mexico, and the Life of the*

Conqueror Fernando Cortes. 2 vols. N.Y.: Peter Fenelon Collier.

158. PUNNETT, R. C. 1950. Early days of genetics. *Heredity,* **4:** 1–10.

159. RANDALL, JOHN HERMANN. 1926. *The Making of the Modern Mind.* x + 653 pp. Boston: Houghton Mifflin.

160. RAYLEIGH LORD. 1942. *The Life of Sir J. J. Thomson.* x. + 299 pp. Cambridge: University Press.

161. READE, WINWOOD. 1875. *The Outcast.* London.

162. REED, SHELDON C. 1955. *Counseling in Medical Genetics.* viii + 268 pp. Philadelphia: Saunders.

163. RENAN, ERNEST. 1891. *The Future of Science.* xxiv + 491 pp. London: Chapman and Hall.

164. RICARDO, DAVID. 1817. *The Principles of Political Economy and Taxation* xvi + 300 pp. London: J. M. Dent (Everyman's Library). 1911.

165. RIDDLE, OSCAR. 1949. Biographical memoir of Charles Benedict Davenport, 1866–1944. *Biogr. Mem., Nat. Acad. Sci. (U.S.),* **25:** 75–110

166. RIESMAN, DAVID. 1950. *The Lonely Crowd.* xvii + 386 pp. New Haven, Conn.: Yale Univ. Press.

167. RUSSELL, BERTRAND. 1920. *The Practice and Theory of Bolshevism.* 2nd ed. 131 pp. London: Allen & Unwin, 1949.

168. RUSSELL, W. L. 1957. Shortening of life of the offspring of male mice. *Proc. Nat. Acad. Sci.* **43:** 324–329.

169. de SANTILLANA, GIORGIO. 1955. *The Crime of Galileo.* xiv + 339 pp. Chicago: Univ. of Chicago Press.

170. SCHATKIN, SIDNEY B. 1954. The legal aspect of artificial insemination. *Fertility and Sterility,* **5:** 40–43.

171. SCHUBERT, JACK and RALPH E. LAPP. 1957. *Radiation: What It is and How It Affects You.* 314 pp. N.Y.: Viking Press.

172. [SEDGWICK, ADAM] (published anonymously). 1845. Natural history of creation. *Edinburgh Review,* **82:** 1–85.

173. SHELLEY, PERCY B. 1818. *Revolt in Islam.* (Many editions.)

174. ——— 1824. *Julian and Maddalo.* (Many editions.)

175. SHRYOCK, RICHARD HARRISON. 1944. "The Strange Case of Wells' Theory of Natural Selection," in *Studies and Essays in the History of Science and Learning, Offered in Homage to George Sarton,* M. F. Ashley Montagu, ed. xiv + 594 pp. N.Y.: Henry Schumann.

176. SIMPSON, GEORGE GAYLORD. 1950. *The Meaning of Evolution.* xv + 364 pp. New Haven: Yale Univ. Press.

177. SMITH, ADAM. 1776. *The Wealth of Nations.* (Many editions.)

178. SONNEBORN, T. M. 1931. McDougall's Lamarckian experiment. *Amer. Naturalist,* **65:** 541–550.

179. SPEMANN, HANS. 1938. *Embryonic Development and Induction.* 401 pp. New Haven: Yale Univ. Press.

180. SPENCER, WARREN. 1947. Mutations in wild populations in *Drosophila. Adv. in Gen.,* **1:** 359–402.

181. SPIETH, HERMAN T. 1951. Mating behavior and sexual isola-

tion in the *Drosophila virilis* species group. *Behavior*, 3: 105–145.

182. SRB, ADRIAN M. and RAY D. OWEN. 1952. *General Genetics*. x + 561 pp. San Francisco: W. H. Freeman & Co.

183. STADLER, L. J. 1928. Mutations in barley induced by X-rays and radium. *Science*, 68: 186–187.

184. STEBBINS, G. LEDYARD, JR. 1950. *Variation and Evolution in Plants*. xix + 643 pp. N.Y.: Columbia Univ. Press.

185. STERN, CURT. 1943. The Hardy-Weinberg law. *Science*, 97: 137–138.

186. ———— 1949. *Principles of Human Genetics*. xi + 617 pp. San. Francisco: W. H. Freeman & Co.

187. STEVENSON, ROBERT LOUIS. 1878. "The Suicide Club." (In: *The New Arabian Nights*). (Many editions.)

188. ———— 1887. *Memoir of Fleeming Jenkin*. viii + 302 pp. N.Y.: Scribner's. 1902.

189. ———— "Talk and Talkers." (In *Memories and Portraits*). (Many editions.)

190. STURTEVANT, A. H. 1915. Experiments on sex recognition and the problem of sexual selection in *Drosophila*. *Jour. Anim. Behav.*, 5: 351–366.

191. TAYLOR, G. RATTRAY. 1953. *Sex in History*. 336 pp. London: Thames & Hudson.

192. TEGGART, FREDERICK J., (ed.) 1949. *The Idea of Progress*. xi + 457 pp. Berkley, Calif.: Univ. of California Press.

193. THAYER, GERALD H. 1909. *Concealing-Coloration in the Animal Kingdom*. xix + 260 pp. N.Y.: Macmillan.

194. TJIO, JOE HIN and ALBERT LEVAN. 1956. The chromosome number of man. *Hereditas*, 42: 1–6.

195. TOYNBEE, ARNOLD JOSEPH. 1947. *A Study of History* (Abridged by D. C. Somervell). xiii + 617 pp. N.Y.: Oxford Univ. Press.

196. TSCHERMAK, E. 1900. Ueber künstliche Kreuzung bei *Pisum sativum*. *Ber. deutsch. Bot. Ges.*, 18: 232–239.

197. TURNER, E. S. 1950. *Roads to Ruin: the Shocking History of Social Reform*. 256 pp. London: Michael Joseph.

198. VOLTERRA, VITO. 1926. Variazioni e fluttuazioni del numero d'individui in specie animali conviventi. *Mem. R. Accad. Naz. dei Lincei*. Ser. VI, vol. 2.

199. ———— 1931. *Leçons sur la Théorie Mathématique de la Lutte pour la Vie*. 214 pp. Paris: Gauthier-Villars.

200. VOS, ANTOON DE, RICHARD H. MANVILLE and RICHARD G. VAN GELDER. 1956. Introduced mammals and their influence on native biota. *Zoologica*, 41: 163–194.

201. DE VRIES, HUGO. 1900. Das Spaltungsgesetz der Bastarde. *Ber. deutsch. Bot. ges.*, 18: 83–90.

202. ———— 1900. Sur la loi de disjonction des hybrides. *Compt. Rend. de l'Acad. des Sci.* (Paris), 130: 845–847.

203. WEINBERG, W. 1908. Über den Nachweis der Vererbung beim Menschen. *Jahresh. Verein vaterl. Naturkunde. Wurtemberg*, 64: 369–382.

204. WEST, GEOFFREY. 1938. *Charles Darwin.* xiv + 359 pp. New Haven: Yale Univ. Press

205. WHEWELL, WILLIAM. 1837. *History of the Inductive Sciences, from the Earliest to the Present Time.* 3 vols. London: J. W. Parker.

206. WHITE, ANDREW DICKSON. 1896. *A History of the Warfare of Science with Theology in Christendom.* 2 vols. N.Y.: Appleton. 1900.

207. WHITEHEAD, ALFRED NORTH. 1925. *Science and the Modern World.* viii + 184 pp. N.Y.: The New American Library (MD162). 1948.

208. WHORF, BENJAMIN LEE. 1956. *Language, Thought, and Reality.* xi + 278 pp. N.Y.: Wiley.

209. Wiener, Norbert. 1948. *Cybernetics.* 194 pp. New York: Wiley.

209a. WILLIAMS, GLANVILLE. 1957. *The Sanctity of Life and the Criminal Law.* xi + 350 + xi pp. N.Y.: Knopf.

210. WILLIAMS, ROGER J. 1946. *The Human Frontier.* viii + 314 pp. N.Y.: Harcourt, Brace.

211. ———— 1953. *Free and Unequal.* xiii + 177 pp. Austin, Texas: Univ. of Texas Press.

212. ———— 1956. *Biochemical Individuality.* xiii + 214 pp. N.Y.: Wiley.

213. ———— 1957. Standard human beings versus standard values. *Science,* **126:** 453–454.

214. ZIRKLE, CONWAY. 1949. *Death of a Science in Russia.* xiv + 319 pp. Philadelphia: Univ. of Pennsylvania Press.

Index